Fourier Analysis on Polytopes and the Geometry of Numbers

STUDENT MATHEMATICAL LIBRARY
Volume 107

Fourier Analysis on Polytopes and the Geometry of Numbers

Part I:
A Friendly Introduction

Sinai Robins

AMERICAN
MATHEMATICAL
SOCIETY
Providence, Rhode Island

EDITORIAL COMMITTEE

2020 *Mathematics Subject Classification.* Primary 51M20, 11P21, 32A50, 11H06, 11H16, 11H31, 52B20.

For additional information and updates on this book, visit
www.ams.org/bookpages/stml-107

Library of Congress Cataloging-in-Publication Data

Names: Robins, Sinai, author.
Title: Fourier analysis on polytopes and the geometry of numbers / Sinai Robins.
Description: Providence, Rhode Island : American Mathematical Society, 2024. | Series: Student mathematical library, 1520-9121 ; volume 107 | Includes bibliographical references and index. | Contents: Part I. A friendly introduction –
Identifiers: LCCN 2023053408 | ISBN 9781470470333 (pt. 1 ; paperback) | 9781470476632 (pt. 1 ; ebook)
Subjects: LCSH: Fourier analysis. | Polytopes. | Geometry of numbers. | AMS: Geometry – Real and complex geometry – Polyhedra and polytopes; regular figures, division of spaces. | Number theory – Additive number theory; partitions – Lattice points in specified regions. | Several complex variables and analytic spaces – Holomorphic functions of several complex variables – Harmonic analysis of several complex variables. | Number theory – Geometry of numbers – Lattices and convex bodies. | Number theory – Geometry of numbers – Nonconvex bodies. | Number theory – Geometry of numbers – Lattice packing and covering. | Convex and discrete geometry – Polytopes and polyhedra – Lattice polytopes (including relations with commutative algebra and algebraic geometry).
Classification: LCC QA403.5 .R63 2024 | DDC 516/.158–dc23/eng/20231213
LC record available at https://lccn.loc.gov/2023053408

Dedicated to the memory of my mom

Contents

Acknowledgments

The famous saying "no man is an island" is doubly true in mathematics, and indeed I have had the good fortune to know and learn from many interesting people, concerning the contents of this book. Special thanks goes to Ricardo Diaz, my first collaborator along these topics. Importantly, the encouragement of Paulo Ney de Souza led to the initial ideas of my IMPA book [212], which in turn gave rise later to this much expanded version. I would like to thank the following people, from the bottom of my heart, for their valuable input and interesting discussions about some of these topics over the years: Ian Alevy, Artur André, Christine Bachoc, Tamar Bar, Imre Bárány, Alexander Barvinok, Matthias Beck, Dori Bejleri, Luca Brandolini, Michel Brion, Sunil Chetty, Henry Cohn, Leonardo Colzani, Amalia Culiuc, Pierre Deligne, Jesús A. De Loera, Holley Friedlander, Michel Faleiros, Brett Frankel, Lenny Fukshansky, Sergei Gelfand, Nick Gravin, Tom Hagedorn, Christian Hasse, Martin Henk, Didier Henrion, Roberto Hirata Junior, Jeffrey Hoffstein, Judy Holdener, Alex Iosevich, Michael Joswig, Gil Kalai, Marvin Knopp, Mihalis Kolountzakis, Matthias Köppe, Greg Kuperberg, Jean Bernard Lasserre, Nhat Le Quang, Rafael Zuolo Coppini Lima, Sameer Iyer, Fabrício Caluza Machado, Romanos Malikiosis, Máté Matolci, Tyrrell McAllister, Nathan McNew, Paul Melvin, Victor Moll, Mel Nathanson, James Pommersheim, Jim Propp, Thales Paiva, Jill Pipher, Geremias Polanco, Jorge Luis Ramírez Alfonsín, Ethan Reiner, Bruce Reznick, Tiago Royer, Nicolas Salter, Gervásio Santos, Richard Schwartz, Dima Shiryaev,

Joseph Silverman, Richard Stanley, Irena Swanson, Stephanie Treneer, Christophe Vignat, Sergei Tabachnikov, Karen Taylor, Giancarlo Travaglini, Mckenzie West, Ian Whitehead, Kevin Woods, Ren Yi, Günter Ziegler, Chuanming Zong.

Preface

Joseph Fourier

What is a Fourier transform? Why is it so useful? How can we apply Fourier transforms and Fourier series—which were originally used by Fourier to study heat diffusion—in order to better understand topics in discrete and combinatorial geometry, number theory, and sampling theory?

To begin, there are some useful analogies: imagine that you are drinking a milkshake (lactose-free), and you want to know the ingredients of your tasty drink. You would need to filter the shake into some

of its most basic components. This decomposition into its basic ingredients may be thought of as a sort of "Fourier transform of the milkshake".
Once we understand each of the ingredients, we will also be able to re-
structure these ingredients in new ways, to form many other types of
tasty goodies. To move the analogy back into mathematical language,
the milkshake represents a function, and each of its basic ingredients
represents a basis element, namely a sine or a cosine. We may also think
of a basic ingredient more compactly as a complex exponential $e^{2\pi i n x}$ for
some $n \in \mathbb{Z}$. Composing these basic ingredients together in a new way
represents a Fourier series.

Mathematically, one of the most basic kinds of milkshakes is the
indicator function of the unit interval and to break it down into its basic components, mathematicians, engineers, computer scientists, and
physicists have used the sinc function (since the 1800s)

$$\text{sinc}(z) := \frac{\sin(\pi z)}{\pi z}$$

with great success because it happens to be the Fourier transform of the
unit interval $[-\frac{1}{2}, \frac{1}{2}]$:

$$\int_{-\frac{1}{2}}^{\frac{1}{2}} e^{-2\pi i z x} dx = \text{sinc}(z),$$

as we will compute in Chapter 2, Section 2. Somewhat surprisingly,
comparatively little energy has been given to some of its higher dimensional extensions, namely those extensions that arise naturally as Fourier
transforms of polytopes.

One motivation for this book is to better understand how this 1-
dimensional function—which has proved to be extremely powerful in
applications—extends to higher dimensions. Namely, we will build various mathematical structures that are motivated by the question:

What is the Fourier transform of a polytope?

Of course, we will ask "how can we apply it"? An alternate title for this
book might have been:

We are taking Poisson summation

and Fourier transforms of polytopes for a long ride...

In many applied scientific areas—specifically radio astronomy, computational tomography, magnetic resonance imaging, and X-ray crystallography—a frequent theme is the reconstruction of a function from knowledge of its Fourier transform. Somewhat surprisingly, in various applications we only require partial/sparse knowledge of its Fourier transform in order to reconstruct the required function, which may represent an image or a signal. There are also current research developments of the material developed here, in particular the learning of deep neural networks.

One of the goals of this book is to allow the general mathematical reader to quickly approach the forefront of modern research in this expanding area, and even tackle some of its unsolved problems. There is a rapidly increasing amount of research focused in these directions in recent years, and it is therefore time to put some of these new findings in one place, making them much more accessible to a general scientific reader.

The approach we take here is to gain insight into how the Fourier transform of a polytope can be used to solve various specific problems in discrete geometry, combinatorics, optimization, approximation theory, and the Shannon–Whittaker sampling theory in higher dimensions:

(1) Give wonderful formulas for the Fourier transform of a polytope (Brion's theorem) and hence for the volume of a polytope

(2) Study tilings of Euclidean space by translations of polytopes

(3) Compute discrete volumes of polytopes, which are combinatorial approximations to the continuous volume

(4) Introduce and develop the geometry of numbers via Poisson summation

(5) Study sphere packings and get bounds on their optimal densities via Poisson summation

(6) Finally, we study the question: what is an angle in higher dimensions?

Sinai Robins

July 2023

IME, University of São Paulo

Introduction

Siméon Denis Poisson

Historically, sinc functions were used by Claude Shannon when he published his seminal work on sampling theory and information theory. Hardy, Kotelnikov, and Whittaker all published some of the same ideas on sampling theory earlier, though Shannon further developed these ideas in the context of information theory.

One of the goals here is to allow the reader to approach the forefront of modern research in this expanding area, and even tackle some of its unsolved problems. There is a rapidly increasing amount of research focused in these directions in recent years, and it is therefore time to put some of these new findings in one place, making them much more accessible to a general scientific reader.

In many applied scientific areas, in particular radio astronomy, computational tomography, magnetic resonance imaging, and X-ray crystallography, a frequent theme is the reconstruction of a function from knowledge of its Fourier transform. Somewhat surprisingly, in various applications we only require partial/sparse knowledge of its Fourier transform in order to reconstruct the required function, which may represent an image or a signal.

The fact that the sinc function is indeed the Fourier transform of the 1-dimensional line segment $[-\frac{1}{2}, \frac{1}{2}]$, which is a 1-dimensional polytope, gives us a first hint that there is a deeper link between the geometry of a polytope and the analysis of its Fourier transform.

Indeed, one reason that sampling and information theory works so well is precisely because the Fourier transform of the unit interval has this nice form, and even more so because of the existence of the Poisson summation formula.

The level of the current book is aimed at **advanced undergraduates** and **beginning graduate students** in various fields, in particular mathematics, computer science, electrical engineering, and physics, but I have included some goodies here and there for researchers as well. Indeed, one of the goals of this book is to allow the reader to begin with classical techniques, and then rapidly reach the forefront of research in this area.

1. Initial ideas

Let us see at least one direction that quickly motivates the study of Fourier transforms. In particular, we often begin with simple-sounding problems that arise naturally in combinatorial enumeration, discrete and computational geometry, and number theory.

Throughout, an **integer point** is any vector $v := (v_1, \ldots, v_d)$ in $\mathbb{R}^d$, all of whose coordinates v_j are integers. In other words, v belongs to the integer lattice $\mathbb{Z}^d$. A **rational point** is a point m whose coordinates are rational numbers; in other words, $m \in \mathbb{Q}^d$. We define the **Fourier**

transform of a function $f(x)$:

$$(0.1) \qquad \hat{f}(\xi) := \int_{\mathbb{R}^d} f(x) e^{-2\pi i \langle \xi, x \rangle} dx,$$

defined for all $\xi \in \mathbb{R}^d$ for which the latter integral converges, and where we use the standard inner product $\langle a, b \rangle := a_1 b_1 + \cdots + a_d b_d$. We will also use the notation $\mathcal{F}(f)$ for the Fourier transform of f, which is useful in some typographical contexts, for example when considering the inverse Fourier transform $\mathcal{F}^{-1}(f)$.

We introduce one of the main objects of study in this book, the **Fourier transform of a polytope** $\mathcal{P}$, defined by:

$$(0.2) \qquad \hat{1}_{\mathcal{P}}(\xi) := \int_{\mathbb{R}^d} 1_{\mathcal{P}}(x) e^{-2\pi i \langle \xi, x \rangle} dx = \int_{\mathcal{P}} e^{-2\pi i \langle \xi, x \rangle} dx,$$

where the function $1_{\mathcal{P}}(x)$ is the **indicator function** of $\mathcal{P}$, defined by

$$1_{\mathcal{P}}(x) := \begin{cases} 1 & \text{if } x \in \mathcal{P} \\ 0 & \text{if not.} \end{cases}$$

Thus, the words "Fourier transform of a polytope $\mathcal{P}$" will always mean the Fourier transform of the indicator function of $\mathcal{P}$.

For some applications to discrete geometry, we notice the trivial but very useful identity:

$$\hat{1}_{\mathcal{P}}(0) = \int_{\mathcal{P}} dx := \text{vol}(\mathcal{P}).$$

We therefore see another important motivation for this book: the Fourier transform of a polytope is a very **natural extension of volume**. Computing the volume of a polytope $\mathcal{P}$ captures a bit of information about $\mathcal{P}$, but we also lose a lot of information.

On the other hand, the Fourier transform of a polytope $\hat{1}_{\mathcal{P}}(\xi)$ uniquely determines $\mathcal{P}$, so we do not lose any information at all. Another way of saying this is that the Fourier transform of a polytope is a **complete invariant**. In other words, it is a fact of life that

$$\hat{1}_{\mathcal{P}}(\xi) = \hat{1}_{\mathcal{Q}}(\xi) \text{ for all } \xi \in \mathbb{R}^d \iff \mathcal{P} = \mathcal{Q}.$$

2. The Poisson summation formula

The **Poisson summation formula**, named after Siméon Denis Poisson, tells us that for any "sufficiently nice" function $f : \mathbb{R}^d \to \mathbb{C}$ we have:

$$(0.3) \qquad\qquad \sum_{n \in \mathbb{Z}^d} f(n) = \sum_{\xi \in \mathbb{Z}^d} \hat{f}(\xi).$$

In particular, if we were to naively set $f(n) := 1_{\mathcal{P}}(n)$, the indicator function of a polytope $\mathcal{P}$, then we would get

$$(0.4) \qquad\qquad \sum_{n \in \mathbb{Z}^d} 1_{\mathcal{P}}(n) = \sum_{\xi \in \mathbb{Z}^d} \hat{1}_{\mathcal{P}}(\xi),$$

which is technically false for functions, due to the fact that the indicator function $1_{\mathcal{P}}$ is discontinuous on $\mathbb{R}^d$.

However, this technically false statement is very useful! We make this claim because it helps us build intuition for the more rigorous statements that are true, and which we study in later chapters.

Combinatorially, there are brilliant identities (notably the Brion identities) that emerge between the Fourier and Laplace transforms of a given polytope, and its facets and vertex tangent cones.

In statistics, the moment-generating function of any probability distribution is given by a Fourier transform of the indicator function of the distribution, hence Fourier transforms arise very naturally in statistical applications. At this point, a natural glaring question naturally comes up:

(0.5) How do we **compute** the Fourier transform of a polytope $\hat{1}_{\mathcal{P}}(\xi)$?

Brion's continuous theorem (see Theorem 7.12) gives us one useful way to compute the FT of a polytope, which is very efficient in the case of a simple polytope. But it is an open question whether there are other efficient formulas for the FT of more general polytopes.

There are many applications of the theory that we will build up. We often find it instructive to give an informal proof first because it brings the intuitive ideas to the foreground, allowing the reader to gain an overview of the steps. Later on, we revisit the same intuitive proof again, making all of the steps rigorous.

The Poisson summation formula is one of our main stars, and some of its variations have relatively easy proofs. But it constitutes a very first step for many of our explorations.

How to use this book. Because of the large number of exercises, with solutions to many of them in the back, this book can also be used effectively for self-study. If an exercise is marked with a ♣ symbol, it means that we have mentioned this exercise in the body of the text for that particular chapter.

We proceed by developing an intuitive understanding first, using many examples and analogies, and this intuition then points us to a rigorous path for the details of the ensuing proofs.

Prerequisites. A word about some of the required background for this book: **linear algebra** is always extremely useful, and this cannot be overstated. A couple of calculus courses are required as well, with some real analysis. In particular, familiarity with infinite series is assumed. We endeavor, however, to make things as self-contained as possible.

We give new proofs for the main theorems in this theory, including Theorems 4.5, 7.12, and 7.15. Corollary 7.25 is one of the new results that appear in this book, which may also prove useful in extending the study of zero sets of the Fourier transform. These new Fourier-type proofs help streamline the theory, unifying sporadic results in the literature. This unifying thread will hopefully help the reader put the various results—from antiquity to modernity—into context.

We will also assume some familiarity with the basic definitions of polytopes and their faces, although at places we will remind the reader of some of these definitions. There are many excellent texts that introduce the student to the classical language of polytopes, in particular the two classics: Günter Ziegler's *Lectures on Polytopes* [**265**], and Branko Grünbaum's *Convex Polytopes* [**101**]. For an easy introduction to the interactions between polytopes and lattice point enumeration, the reader is invited to consult *Computing the continuous discretely: integer point enumeration in polytopes*, by Beck and Robins [**25**]. But the contents of the latter book are not necessary for the study of the current book.

Most importantly, we hope that the reader has fun with the material, and that they may use the seeds that we have planted here to grow their own forests.

Chapter 1

Motivational problem: Tiling a rectangle with rectangles

"Ripping up carpet is easy—*tiling* is the issue."
– Douglas Wilson

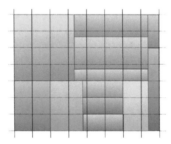

Figure 1.1. A rectangle tiled by nice rectangles.

1. Intuition

To warm up, we begin with a simple tiling problem in the plane. A rectangle will be called **nice** if at least one of its sides is an integer. We prove a now classical fact about tiling a rectangle with nice rectangles, namely Theorem 1.1, and we focus on the **method** of the straightforward proof.

This proof brings to the foreground an important idea: by simply taking a Fourier transform of a body B, we immediately get interesting geometric consequences for B. In particular, we will see throughout this book various ways in which the Fourier transform of a geometric body is a natural extension of its volume, sometimes in a continuous way, and sometimes in a discrete way. So in order to study relationships between volumes of bodies, it is very natural and useful to play with their Fourier transforms.

2. Nice rectangles

The tilings that we focus on in this small chapter are tilings that are composed of smaller rectangles, all of which have their sides parallel to the axes, and all of which are nice. There are at least fourteen different known proofs [**258**] of Theorem 1.1. Here we give the proof that uses very basic Fourier tools, from first principles, motivating the chapters that follow. The idea for this proof goes back to Nicolaas Govert De Bruijn [**64**].

Theorem 1.1 (De Bruijn). *Suppose we tile a fixed rectangle $\mathcal{R}$ with smaller, nice rectangles. Then $\mathcal{R}$ is a nice rectangle.*

Proof. Suppose that the rectangle $\mathcal{R}$ is tiled with smaller rectangles $\mathcal{R}_1$, ..., $\mathcal{R}_N$, as in Figure 1.1. Due to our tiling hypothesis, we have

(1.1)
$$1_{\mathcal{R}}(x) = \sum_{k=1}^{N} 1_{\mathcal{R}_k}(x)$$

(1.2) $+ \sum (\pm \text{ indicator functions of lower-dimensional polytopes}),$

where the notation $1_S(x)$ always means we are using indicator functions. To ease the reader into the computations, we begin by computing from first principles the Fourier transform of any rectangle $\mathcal{R} := [a,b] \times [c,d]$:

$$(1.3) \quad \hat{1}_{\mathcal{R}}(\xi) := \int_{\mathbb{R}^2} 1_{\mathcal{R}}(x) e^{-2\pi i \langle \xi, x \rangle} dx = \int_{\mathcal{R}} e^{-2\pi i \langle \xi, x \rangle} dx$$

$$(1.4) \qquad = \int_a^b \int_c^d e^{-2\pi i (\xi_1 x_1 + \xi_2 x_2)} dx_2 dx_1$$

$$(1.5) \qquad = \int_a^b e^{-2\pi i \xi_1 x_1} dx_1 \int_c^d e^{-2\pi i \xi_2 x_2} dx_2$$

$$(1.6) \qquad = \frac{e^{-2\pi i \xi_1 b} - e^{-2\pi i \xi_1 a}}{-2\pi i \xi_1} \cdot \frac{e^{-2\pi i \xi_2 d} - e^{-2\pi i \xi_2 c}}{-2\pi i \xi_2}$$

$$(1.7) \qquad = \frac{1}{(-2\pi i)^2} \frac{e^{-2\pi i (\xi_1 a + \xi_2 c)}}{\xi_1 \xi_2} \left(e^{-2\pi i \xi_1 (b-a)} - 1 \right) \left(e^{-2\pi i \xi_2 (d-c)} - 1 \right),$$

valid for all $(\xi_1, \xi_2) \in \mathbb{R}^2$ except for the union of the two lines $\xi_1 = 0$ and $\xi_2 = 0$. Now we may formally take the Fourier transform of both sides of (1.1). In other words, we simply multiply both sides of (1.1) by the exponential function $e^{-2\pi i \langle \xi, x \rangle}$ and then integrate both sides over $\mathbb{R}^2$ to get

$$(1.8) \qquad \hat{1}_{\mathcal{R}}(\xi) = \sum_{k=1}^N \hat{1}_{\mathcal{R}_k}(\xi).$$

In (1.8) we have used the fact that a 2-dimensional integral over a 1-dimensional line segment always vanishes, due to the fact that a line segment has measure 0 relative to the 2-dimensional measure of the 2-dimensional transform.

Considering the latter formula for the Fourier transform of a rectangle, we make the following leap of faith:

Claim 1.2. *Suppose that $\mathcal{R}$ is a rectangle whose sides are parallel to the axes. Then*

$$(1.9) \qquad \mathcal{R} \text{ is a nice rectangle} \iff \hat{1}_{\mathcal{R}}\left(\begin{pmatrix} 1 \\ 1 \end{pmatrix} \right) = 0.$$

Proof of the claim. Looking at equality (1.7), we see that

$$(1.10) \qquad \hat{1}_{\mathcal{R}}(\xi) = 0 \iff (e^{-2\pi i \xi_1 (b-a)} - 1)(e^{-2\pi i \xi_2 (d-c)} - 1) = 0,$$

which is equivalent to the statement:

$$e^{-2\pi i \xi_1 (b-a)} = 1 \text{ or } e^{-2\pi i \xi_2 (d-c)} = 1 \quad \text{(or both).}$$

But we know from Euler that

(1.11) $$e^{2\pi i\theta} = 1 \iff \theta \in \mathbb{Z},$$

which is a nice elementary exercise (Exercise (1)) that is very important. So we have

(1.12) $$\hat{1}_{\mathcal{R}}(\xi) = 0 \iff \xi_1(b - a) \in \mathbb{Z} \text{ or } \xi_2(d - c) \in \mathbb{Z}.$$

Now, if $\mathcal{R}$ is a nice rectangle, then one of its sides is an integer, say $b - a \in \mathbb{Z}$ without loss of generality. Therefore $\xi_1(b - a) \in \mathbb{Z}$ for $\xi_1 = 1$, and by (1.12), we see that $\hat{1}_{\mathcal{R}}\left(\left(\begin{smallmatrix}1\\1\end{smallmatrix}\right)\right) = 0$. Conversely, if we assume that $\hat{1}_{\mathcal{R}}\left(\left(\begin{smallmatrix}1\\1\end{smallmatrix}\right)\right) = 0$, then by (1.12) we have either $1 \cdot (b-a) \in \mathbb{Z}$ or $1 \cdot (d-c) \in \mathbb{Z}$ (or both), proving the claim.

To finish the proof of the theorem by hypothesis, each little rectangle $\mathcal{R}_k$ is a nice rectangle, so by the claim above it satisfies $\hat{1}_{\mathcal{R}_k}\left(\left(\begin{smallmatrix}1\\1\end{smallmatrix}\right)\right) = 0$. Returning to (1.8), we see that therefore

$$0 = \sum_{k=1}^{N} \hat{1}_{\mathcal{R}_k}(\xi) = \hat{1}_{\mathcal{R}}(\xi)$$

for $\xi = \left(\begin{smallmatrix}1\\1\end{smallmatrix}\right)$, and using claim (1.9) again (the converse part of it), we conclude that $\mathcal{R}$ must be nice. □

The proof of Theorem 1.1 was simple and elegant, motivating the use of Fourier transforms of polytopes in the ensuing chapters. The claim, namely equation (1.9), offers an intriguing springboard for deeper investigations—it tells us that we can convert a geometric statement about tiling into a purely analytic statement about the vanishing of a certain integral transform. Later, when we learn about Theorem 4.6, we will see that this small initial success of (1.9) is part of a larger theory. This is the beginning of a beautiful friendship.

3. Conventions and some definitions

We mention some conventions that we use throughout the book. First, we note that whenever we are given a complex-valued function $f :$ $\mathbb{R}^d \to \mathbb{C}$, we may write f in terms of its real and imaginary parts: $f(x) :=$

$u(x) + iv(x)$. The **integral of such an** f is defined by

$$(1.13) \qquad \int_{\mathbb{R}^d} f(x)dx := \int_{\mathbb{R}^d} u(x)dx + i \int_{\mathbb{R}^d} v(x)dx$$

so that all of our Fourier transforms are really reduced to the usual integration of real-valued functions on Euclidean space (see Exercise (4)). This is good news for the reader because even though we see complex numbers in the integrand, elementary calculus suffices.

Let $S \subset \mathbb{R}^d$ be a set. For our purposes, we may call S a **measurable** set if the integral $\int_S dx$ exists, and in this case we define

$$\text{measure}(S) := \int_S dx.$$

Equivalently, we may call S measurable if the indicator function 1_S is an integrable function by definition of the (Lebesgue) integral.

Throughout this book **all of our sets are assumed to be measurable**. It is a fact that every open set, every closed set, and every compact set is measurable [**217**]. A set S is said to have **measure zero** if

$$\int_S dx = 0.$$

In $\mathbb{R}$, for example, we may alternatively define a set S of measure 0 as follows. Given any $\varepsilon > 0$, there exists a countable collection of open intervals I_n that cover all of S, and whose total length satisfies $\sum_{n=1}^{\infty} |I_n| < \varepsilon$. But we will assume the reader knows the definition(s) of an integral (either the Riemann integral or the Lebesgue integral), circumventing discussions about σ-algebras of sets, so that the background required of the reader is kept to a minimum.

The point we want to make here is that most things are in fact easier than the reader may have previously thought.

We say that a statement $A(x)$ concerning points $x \in \mathbb{R}^d$ **holds for almost every** $x \in \mathbb{R}^d$ (we also use the words **almost everywhere**) if the set of $x \in \mathbb{R}^d$ for which $A(x)$ is false is a set of measure 0. For example, we have the following fact from real analysis:

$$\int_{\mathbb{R}^d} |f(x) - g(x)| \, dx = 0 \iff f = g \text{ almost everywhere,}$$

which means that $f(x) = g(x)$ for almost every $x \in \mathbb{R}^d$.

We also mention our convention/notation for some definitions. Whenever we want to define a new object called N, in terms of some combination of previously known mathematical objects called K, we will use the standard notation

$$N := K.$$

For any set $A \subset \mathbb{R}^d$, we define the **closure** of A as the the smallest (w.r.t containment) closed set that contains A, written as $\operatorname{clos} A$. We define the **interior** of A as the set of all points $x \in A$ such that there exists a ball of some positive radius ε, centered at x, with $B_\varepsilon(x) \subset A$. We define the **boundary** of A, written as ∂A, by

$$\partial A := \operatorname{clos} A \setminus \operatorname{int} A.$$

An important concept is that of the support of a function $f : \mathbb{R}^d \to \mathbb{C}$, defined by

(1.14) $$\operatorname{support}(f) := \operatorname{clos}\{x \in \mathbb{R}^d \mid f(x) \neq 0\}.$$

With this definition, we have for example:

$$\operatorname{support}(1_{[0,1]}) = \operatorname{support}(1_{(0,1)}) = [0,1].$$

We will also say that a function f is **compactly supported** if the support of f is a compact set C. In particular this means that f vanishes outside of C.

Notes

(1) This small chapter was motivated by the lovely article written by Stan Wagon [**258**], which gives fourteen different proofs of Theorem 1.1. The article [**258**] is important because it shows—in a concrete manner—how tools from one field can leak into another field, and may therefore lead to important discoveries in the future.

(2) In a related direction, we might wonder which polygons, and more generally which polytopes, tile Euclidean space by translations with a lattice. It turns out (Theorem 4.6) that this question is equivalent to the statement that the Fourier transform of $\mathcal{P}$ vanishes on a (dual) lattice.

(3) In the context of the Hilbert space of functions $L^2([0,1])$, Exercise (3) is one step towards showing that the set of exponentials $\{e_n(x)\}_{n \in \mathbb{Z}}$ form an orthonormal basis for $L^2([0,1])$. Namely,

the identity (1.15) shows that these basis elements are orthogonal to each other—their inner product

$$\langle e_a, e_b \rangle := \int_0^1 e_a(x)\overline{e_b(x)}dx$$

vanishes for integers $a \neq b$. Thus, the identity (1.15) is often called the orthogonality relations for exponentials over $L^2([0,1])$. To show that they *span* the space of functions in $L^2([0,1])$ is a bit harder, but see [251] for details.

(4) Theorem 1.1 is due to De Bruijn, but it has an interesting precursor. Namely, according to [258], Dehn proved, using a different approach, that if a rectangle is tiled with the same hypothesis of Theorem 1.1, then one of the sides is rational.

(5) The question in Exercise (16) for $\mathbb{Z}$ was originally asked by Paul Erdős in 1951, and has an affirmative answer. This question also has higher-dimensional analogues:

Suppose we give a partition of the integer lattice $\mathbb{Z}^d$ into a finite, disjoint union of translated sublattices. Is it always true that at least two of these sublattices are translates of each other?

The answer is known to be false for $d \geq 3$, but is still unsolved for $d = 2$ (see [84], [44]).

Exercises

"The game is afoot."
   – Sherlock Holmes in "The Adventure of the Abbey Grange"
by Arthur Conan Doyle

(1) ♣ Show that if $z \in \mathbb{C}$, then $e^{2\pi i z} = 1$ if and only if $z \in \mathbb{Z}$.

Notes. This exercise is our first hint that number theory, concerned initially with $\mathbb{Z}$, is intimately tied up with the exponential function.

(2) Show that $|e^z| \leq e^{|z|}$, for all complex numbers $z \in \mathbb{C}$.

(3) ♣ Here we prove the **orthogonality relations for the exponential functions** defined by $e_n(x) := e^{2\pi i n x}$ for each integer n. Recall that

the complex conjugate of any complex number $x + iy$ is defined by

$$\overline{x + iy} := x - iy,$$

so that $\overline{e^{i\theta}} := e^{-i\theta}$ for all real θ. Prove that for all integers a, b:

(1.15) $$\int_0^1 e_a(x)\overline{e_b(x)}dx = \begin{cases} 1 & \text{if } a = b \\ 0 & \text{if not.} \end{cases}$$

(4) Here the reader may gain some practice with the definitions of integrals that use complex-valued integrands $f(x) := u(x) + iv(x)$. We recall for the reader the following definition:

(1.16) $$\int_{\mathbb{R}^d} f(x)dx := \int_{\mathbb{R}^d} (u(x) + iv(x))\, dx$$

$$:= \int_{\mathbb{R}^d} u(x)dx + i\int_{\mathbb{R}^d} v(x)dx,$$

a linear combination of two real-valued integrals. Recalling that by definition,

$$\hat{1}_{[0,1]}(\xi) := \int_{[0,1]} e^{-2\pi i \xi x}dx$$

follows directly from definition (1.16) and from Euler's identity $e^{i\theta} = \cos\theta + i\sin\theta$ that for any nonzero $\xi \in \mathbb{R}$ we have

$$\int_{[0,1]} e^{-2\pi i \xi x}dx = \frac{e^{-2\pi i \xi} - 1}{-2\pi i \xi}.$$

Notes. Another way of thinking about this exercise is that it extends the "Fundamental theorem of calculus" to complex-valued functions in a rather easy way. The anti-derivative of the integrand $f(x) := e^{-2\pi i \xi x}$ is $F(x) := \frac{e^{-2\pi i \xi x}}{-2\pi i \xi}$, and we are saying that it is ok to use it in place of the usual anti-derivative in calculus 1—it is consistent with definition (1.16). In the future, we generally do not have to break up complex integrals into their real and imaginary parts because we can make use of the fact that anti-derivatives of complex-valued functions are often simple, such as the one in this example.

We also note that this is *not* calculus with a complex variable, because the **domains of our integrands**, as well as the measures we are using throughout this book, are defined over real Euclidean space $\mathbb{R}^d$. This means we are still using basic calculus.

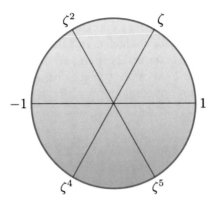

Figure 1.2. The 6th roots of unity, with $\zeta := e^{\frac{2\pi i}{6}}$. Geometrically, Exercise (5) tells us that their center of mass is the origin.

(5) ♣ We recall that the Nth roots of unity are by definition the set of N complex solutions to $z^N = 1$, and are given by the set $\{e^{2\pi ik/N} \mid k = 0, 1, 2, \ldots, N-1\}$ of points on the unit circle. Prove that the sum of all of the Nth roots of unity vanishes. Precisely fix any positive integer $N \geq 2$, and show that

$$\sum_{k=0}^{N-1} e^{\frac{2\pi ik}{N}} = 0.$$

(6) Prove that, given positive integers M, N, we have

$$\frac{1}{N}\sum_{k=0}^{N-1} e^{\frac{2\pi ikM}{N}} = \begin{cases} 1 & \text{if } N \mid M \\ 0 & \text{if not.} \end{cases}$$

Notes. This result is sometimes referred to as **"the harmonic detector"** for detecting when a rational number $\frac{M}{N}$ is an integer; that is, it assigns a value of 1 to the sum if $\frac{M}{N} \in \mathbb{Z}$, and it assigns a value of 0 to the sum if $\frac{M}{N} \notin \mathbb{Z}$.

(7) ♣ Here we prove the **orthogonality relations for roots of unity**. Namely, fix any two nonnegative integers a, b, and prove that

(1.17) $$\frac{1}{N}\sum_{k=0}^{N-1} e^{\frac{2\pi ika}{N}} e^{-\frac{2\pi ikb}{N}} = \begin{cases} 1 & \text{if } a \equiv b \mod N \\ 0 & \text{if not.} \end{cases}$$

Notes. In a later chapter on Euclidean lattices (Chapter 5), we will see that the identity (1.17) is a special case of the more general orthogonality relations for characters on lattices. From this perspective, this exercise gives the orthogonality relations on the finite cyclic group $\mathbb{Z}/N\mathbb{Z}$. There are more general orthogonality relations for characters of group representations, which play an important role in number theory.

(8) Show that for any positive integer n, we have

$$n = \prod_{k=1}^{n-1} (1 - \zeta^k),$$

where $\zeta := e^{2\pi i/n}$.

(9) An Nth root of unity is called a **primitive root of unity** if it is not a kth root of unity for some smaller positive integer $k < N$. Show that the primitive Nth roots of unity are precisely the numbers $e^{2\pi i k/N}$ for which $\gcd(k, N) = 1$.

(10) The Möbius μ-function is defined by:

$$\mu(n) := \begin{cases} (-1)^k & \text{if } n > 1 \text{ is a product of } k \text{ distinct primes} \\ 0 & \text{if } n \text{ is divisible by a square} \\ 1 & \text{if } n = 1. \end{cases}$$

Prove that the sum of all of the primitive Nth roots of unity is equal to the Möbius μ-function, evaluated at N:

(1.18)
$$\sum_{\substack{1 \le k < N \\ \gcd(k,N)=1}} e^{\frac{2\pi i k}{N}} = \mu(N).$$

Notes. See problem (25) as a way of intertwining the Möbius μ-function with Poisson summation.

(11) ♣ We follow the Weierstrassian approach to defining the complex exponential e^z for all complex $z \in \mathbb{C}$:

(1.19)
$$e^z := \sum_{n=0}^{\infty} \frac{1}{n!} z^n,$$

which converges absolutely for all $z \in \mathbb{C}$. We also have the (Weierstrassian) definitions of $\cos z$ and $\sin z$:

$$\cos z := \sum_{n=0}^{\infty} \frac{1}{(2n)!}(-1)^n z^{2n}, \quad \sin z := \sum_{n=1}^{\infty} \frac{1}{(2n-1)!}(-1)^{n-1} z^{2n-1},$$

both converging absolutely again for all $z \in \mathbb{C}$. Using these three Taylor series in z, prove that Euler's formula has the extension:

$$e^{iz} = \cos z + i \sin z,$$

valid for all $z \in \mathbb{C}$.

Notes. Beginning with such a power series approach to many of the standard functions, Karl Weierstrass developed a rigorous and beautiful theory of real and complex functions.

(12) Here the reader needs to know a little bit about the quotient of two groups (this is one of the few exercises that assumes group theory). We prove that the group of "real numbers mod 1" under addition, is isomorphic to the unit circle, and under multiplication of complex numbers. Therefore we can define $h : \mathbb{R} \to S^1$ by $h(x) := e^{2\pi i x}$.
   (a) We recall the definition of the kernel of a map, namely $ker(h) := \{x \in \mathbb{R} \mid h(x) = 1\}$. Show that $ker(h) = \mathbb{Z}$.
   (b) Using the first isomorphism theorem for groups, show that $\mathbb{R}/\mathbb{Z}$ is isomorphic to the unit circle S^1.

(13) Using gymnastics with roots of unity, we recall a very classical solution to the problem of finding the roots of a cubic polynomial.
   (a) Let $\omega := e^{2\pi i/3}$ and show that we have the polynomial identity:

$$(x + a + b)(x + \omega a + \omega^2 b)(x + \omega^2 a + \omega b) = x^3 - 3abx + a^3 + b^3.$$

   (b) Using the latter identity, solve the cubic polynomial $x^3 - px + q = 0$ by substituting $p = 3ab$ and $q = a^3 + b^3$.

(14) Thinking of the function $\sin(\pi z)$ as a function of a complex variable $z \in \mathbb{C}$, show that its zeros are precisely the integers $\mathbb{Z}$.

(15) Here we give another equivalent condition for a rectangle in Theorem 1.1 to be a nice rectangle using the same definitions as before.
   Let us call $\xi \in \mathbb{Z}^2$ a **generic** integer point if ξ is not orthogonal to any of the edges of $\mathcal{R}$. In other words, a generic integer vector satisfies $\langle \xi, p \rangle \neq 0$ for all $p \in \mathcal{R}$, and in particular $p = 0$ is not

generic, nor is any point p on the x-axis or the y-axis. Then

$$\mathcal{R} \text{ is a nice rectangle } \iff \hat{1}_{\mathcal{R}}(\xi) = 0, \text{ for all generic points } \xi \in \mathbb{Z}^2.$$

(16) In 1951 Erdős asked: "Can the set $\mathbb{Z}_{>0}$ of all positive integers be partitioned (that is, written as a disjoint union) into a finite number of arithmetic progressions, such that no two of the arithmetic progressions will have the same common difference?"

      Suppose that we have

(1.20) $\mathbb{Z} = \{a_1 n + b_1 \mid n \in \mathbb{Z}\} \cup \cdots \cup \{a_N n + b_N \mid n \in \mathbb{Z}\},$

for some positive integers $a_1 \leq a_2 \leq \cdots \leq a_N$, and $N \geq 2$, and where the arithmetic progressions are pairwise disjoint.

      Prove that in any such partitioning of the integers, we must have $a_N = a_{N-1}$. In other words, show that the largest common difference must appear at least twice.

Notes. For example, if we write

$$\mathbb{Z} = \{4n + 1 \mid n \in \mathbb{Z}\} \cup \{2n \mid n \in \mathbb{Z}\} \cup \{4n + 3 \mid n \in \mathbb{Z}\},$$

a disjoint union of 3 arithmetic progressions, then we see that the largest common difference of 4 appears twice. Erdős noticed that such a phenomenon must always occur.

(17) Continuing with the ideas of Exercise (16), suppose we are given a disjoint union of arithmetic progressions such as (1.20) above.

    (a) Prove that:

(1.21) $1 = \dfrac{1}{a_1} + \cdots + \dfrac{1}{a_N}.$

    (b) Prove that $\gcd(a_i, a_j) > 1$ for all indices i, j.

Chapter 2

Examples nourish the theory

"To many, mathematics is a collection of theorems. For me, mathematics is a collection of examples; a theorem is a statement about a collection of examples and the purpose of proving theorems is to classify and explain the examples..."

– John B. Conway

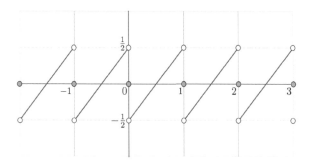

Figure 2.1. The first periodic Bernoulli polynomial $P_1(x)$, sometimes called the sawtooth function, which turns out to be one of the building blocks of integer point enumeration in polytopes.

1. Intuition

One way to think about the Fourier transform of a polytope $\mathcal{P} \subset \mathbb{R}^d$ is that it simultaneously captures all of the moments of $\mathcal{P}$, thereby uniquely defining $\mathcal{P}$. Here we begin concretely by computing some Fourier transforms of various polytopes in dimensions 1 and 2, as well as the Fourier transforms of some simple families of polytopes in dimension d as well.

The 2-dimensional computations will get the reader more comfortable with the basics. In later chapters, once we learn a little more theory, we will return to these families of polytopes and compute some of their Fourier transforms in general.

We also see, from small examples, that the Bernoulli polynomials immediately enter into the picture, forming natural building blocks. In this chapter we compute Fourier transforms without thinking too much about convergence issues, to let the reader run with the ideas. But commencing with the next chapter, we will be more rigorous when using Poisson summation, and with convergence issues.

2. Dimension 1—the classical sinc function

We begin by computing the classical 1-dimensional example of the Fourier transform of the symmetrized unit interval $\mathcal{P} := [-\frac{1}{2}, \frac{1}{2}]$:

$$\hat{1}_{\mathcal{P}}(\xi) := \int_{\mathbb{R}} 1_{\mathcal{P}}(x)\, e^{-2\pi i x \xi} dx$$

$$= \int_{[-\frac{1}{2}, \frac{1}{2}]} e^{-2\pi i x \xi} dx.$$

For all $\xi \neq 0$, we have

$$\int_{[-\frac{1}{2}, \frac{1}{2}]} e^{-2\pi i x \xi} dx$$

$$(2.1) \qquad = \frac{e^{-2\pi i \left(\frac{1}{2}\right)\xi} - e^{-2\pi i \left(\frac{-1}{2}\xi\right)}}{-2\pi i \xi}$$

$$(2.2) \qquad = \frac{\cos(-\pi\xi) + i\sin(-\pi\xi) - (\cos(\pi\xi) + i\sin(\pi\xi))}{-2\pi i \xi}$$

$$(2.3) \qquad = \frac{\sin(\pi\xi)}{\pi\xi}.$$

Noticing that $\xi = 0$ is a removable singularity, we define the continuous **sinc-function** by

$$(2.4) \qquad \operatorname{sinc}(x) := \begin{cases} \frac{\sin(\pi x)}{\pi x}, & \text{if } x \neq 0 \\ 1 & \text{if } x = 0, \end{cases}$$

which is in fact infinitely smooth, via Lemma 2.3 below.

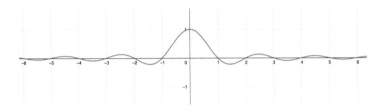

Figure 2.2. The function $\operatorname{sinc}(x)$, which is Fourier transform of the 1-dimensional polytope $\mathcal{P} = [-\frac{1}{2}, \frac{1}{2}]$.

3. The Fourier transform of $\mathcal{P}$ as a complete invariant

The main goal of this section is to state Lemma 2.4, which tells us that all of the information about a polytope is contained in its Fourier transform. To that end, we introduce the inverse Fourier transform, often called the **Fourier inversion formula**. We would like to see the fundamental fact that under certain conditions, the Fourier transform is invertible. First, we call a function $f : \mathbb{R}^d \to \mathbb{C}$ **absolutely integrable** if $\int_{\mathbb{R}^d} |f(x)| dx < \infty$, and we write this as $f \in L^1(\mathbb{R}^d)$.

Theorem 2.1. *Given a function f such that both $f \in L^1(\mathbb{R}^d)$ and $\hat{f} \in L^1(\mathbb{R}^d)$, we have*

$$(2.5) \qquad f(x) = \int_{\mathbb{R}^d} \hat{f}(\xi) e^{2\pi i \langle \xi, x \rangle} d\xi$$

for all $x \in \mathbb{R}^d$, except possibly on a set of measure 0. $\qquad\square$

(See [**79**] for a proof.) We will also use the notation $\mathcal{F}(f) := \hat{f}$. Equation (2.5) tells us that the inverse Fourier transform $\mathcal{F}^{-1}$ exists, and is almost equal to $\mathcal{F}$ itself. A moment's thought reveals that we may rewrite (2.5) in the following useful form:

$$(2.6) \qquad (\mathcal{F} \circ \mathcal{F}) f(x) = f(-x).$$

Example 2.2. A famous and historically somewhat tricky integral formula for the sinc function is the following fact:

$$\text{(2.7)} \qquad \int_{-\infty}^{\infty} \text{sinc}(x)dx := \int_{-\infty}^{\infty} \frac{\sin(\pi x)}{\pi x} dx = 1,$$

also known as the Dirichlet integral. The careful reader might notice that the latter integrand is not absolutely convergent, which means that $\int_{-\infty}^{\infty} \left| \frac{\sin(\pi x)}{\pi x} \right| dx = \infty$ (Exercise (23)). So we have to specify what we really mean by identity (2.7). The rigorous claim is

$$\lim_{N \to \infty} \int_0^N \frac{\sin(\pi x)}{\pi x} dx = \frac{1}{2}.$$

Let us see an intuitive derivation of (2.7), where we will be fast and loose for the moment. Using (2.2), we have seen above that the Fourier transform of the indicator function of the interval $\mathcal{P} := [-\frac{1}{2}, \frac{1}{2}]$ is

$$\text{(2.8)} \qquad \mathcal{F}(1_{\mathcal{P}})(\xi) = \frac{\sin(\pi \xi)}{\pi \xi},$$

so that

$$\text{(2.9)} \qquad \mathcal{F}\left(\frac{\sin(\pi \xi)}{\pi \xi} \right) = (\mathcal{F} \circ \mathcal{F})(1_{\mathcal{P}})(\xi) = 1_{\mathcal{P}}(-\xi).$$

Using the definition of the Fourier transform, the latter identity is:

$$\text{(2.10)} \qquad \int_{\mathbb{R}} \frac{\sin(\pi x)}{\pi x} e^{-2\pi i \xi x} dx = 1_{\mathcal{P}}(\xi),$$

and now evaluating both sides at $\xi = 0$ gives us (2.7). Although this derivation appears very convincing, it would not make it past the rigor police (see also Note (6)). Why not? It is because we applied the Fourier inversion formula to a function that was **not** in $L^1(\mathbb{R})$, namely the sinc function. So we owe it to ourselves to pursue a rigorous approach by showing that

$$\text{(2.11)} \qquad \lim_{N \to \infty} \int_{-N}^N \frac{\sin(\pi \xi)}{\pi \xi} e^{-2\pi i \langle \xi, x \rangle} d\xi = 1_{[-\frac{1}{2}, \frac{1}{2}]}(x),$$

whose validity would give us a variation on Fourier inversion, for a function that is not in $L^1(\mathbb{R})$, namely $\hat{1}_{[-\frac{1}{2}, \frac{1}{2}]}(\xi) = \text{sinc}(\xi)$. This is tricky business, but such an endeavor is taken up in Exercise (36). $\qquad \square$

We can extend Example 2.2 in a natural way to all Fourier pairs of functions $\{f(x), \hat{f}(\xi)\}$, provided that we may apply Fourier inversion, as follows. Simply let $x = 0$ in (2.5), to get

$$(2.12) \qquad\qquad f(0) = \int_{\mathbb{R}^d} \hat{f}(x)dx.$$

Summarizing, Example 2.2 is just identity (2.12) with $f(x) := 1_{[-\frac{1}{2},\frac{1}{2}]}(x)$.

Another nice and very useful fact about the Fourier transform of a polytope is that it is an entire function, meaning that it is differentiable everywhere. This differentiability is already observable in the sinc function above, defined in (2.4).

Lemma 2.3. *Let $\mathcal{P} \subset \mathbb{R}^d$ be a d-dimensional polytope. Then $\hat{1}_{\mathcal{P}}(\xi)$ is an entire function of $\xi \in \mathbb{C}^d$.*

Proof. Because $\mathcal{P}$ is compact, we can safely differentiate under the integral sign (this is a special case of Lebesgue's dominated convergence theorem), and we do so for each variable separately. Namely, for the coordinate variable ξ_1, we have

$$\frac{\partial}{\partial \xi_1} \int_{\mathcal{P}} e^{-2\pi i \langle \xi, x \rangle} dx = \int_{\mathcal{P}} \frac{\partial}{\partial \xi_1} e^{-2\pi i \langle \xi, x \rangle} dx = -2\pi i \int_{\mathcal{P}} x_1 e^{-2\pi i \langle \xi, x \rangle} dx.$$

Since the complex derivative of $\hat{1}_{\mathcal{P}}(\xi)$ now exists in the complex variable ξ_1, the function $\hat{1}_{\mathcal{P}}(\xi)$ is analytic in ξ_1. Using the same reasoning it is also analytic in each of the variables $\xi_2, \xi_3, \ldots, \xi_d$. $\qquad\square$

We also have the very fortuitous fact that the Fourier transform of any polytope $\mathcal{P} \subset \mathbb{R}^d$ is a complete invariant in the following sense. We recall that by definition a polytope is in particular a closed set.

Lemma 2.4. *Let $\mathcal{P} \subset \mathbb{R}^d$ be a polytope. Then $\hat{1}_{\mathcal{P}}(\xi)$ uniquely determines $\mathcal{P}$. In other words, given any two d-dimensional polytopes $P, Q \subset \mathbb{R}^d$, we have*

$$\hat{1}_{\mathcal{P}}(\xi) = \hat{1}_Q(\xi) \text{ for all } \xi \in \mathbb{R}^d \iff \mathcal{P} = Q.$$

Proof (outline). If $\mathcal{P} = Q$, it is clear that $\hat{1}_{\mathcal{P}}(\xi) = \hat{1}_Q(\xi)$ for all $\xi \in \mathbb{R}^d$. Conversely, suppose that $\hat{1}_{\mathcal{P}}(\xi) = \hat{1}_Q(\xi)$ for all $\xi \in \mathbb{R}^d$. Using Fourier inversion, namely Theorem 2.1, we may take the Fourier transform of both sides of the latter equation to get $1_{\mathcal{P}}(-\xi) = 1_Q(-\xi)$ for all $\xi \in \mathbb{R}^d$. $\qquad\square$

The reason that the proof above is only an outline—at this point—is due to the fact that we have applied the Fourier inversion formula (2.5) to $\hat{1}_{\mathcal{P}}$, which is not an absolutely integrable function (as we will see in Corollary 3.16 in even greater generality).

We will revisit Lemma 2.4 in Chapter 3, as well as Theorem 3.18 for a rigorous proof. In fact, much more is true—see Note (2). There is also a nice version of the Fourier inversion formula, due to Podkorytov and Minh, which is related [195]. The reason we have put Lemma 2.4 so early in the text is because it offers an extremely strong motivation for the study of Fourier transforms of polytopes, showing that they are complete invariants.

A fascinating consequence of Lemma 2.4 is that when we take the Fourier transform of a polytope, then **all of the combinatorial and geometric information** of $\mathcal{P}$ is "somehow" contained in the formula of its Fourier transform. So we may begin to create a complete dictionary between the geometry and combinatorics of a polytope in the space domain, and its Fourier transform in the frequency domain.

4. Bernoulli polynomials

We introduce the Bernoulli polynomials, which turn out to be a sort of "glue" between discrete geometry, number theory, and Fourier analysis, as we will see throughout the book. Historically, Jacob Bernoulli was considering the formulas

$$1 + 2 + \cdots + n = \frac{n(n+1)}{2},$$

$$1^2 + 2^2 + \cdots + n^2 = \frac{n(n+1)(2n+1)}{6},$$

$$1^3 + 2^3 + \cdots + n^3 = \frac{n^2(n+1)^2}{4},$$

and so on. Bernoulli was wondering if there is a general formula for these sums, of the type

$1^d + 2^d + \cdots + n^d =$ Some polynomial of degree d+1, in the variable n?

With hindsight giving us slightly better vision, the modern approach to the latter polynomials begins with the following generating function:

$$(2.13) \qquad \frac{te^{xt}}{e^t - 1} = \sum_{k=0}^{\infty} B_k(x)\frac{t^k}{k!}.$$

It follows from equation (2.13) that each coefficient $B_k(x)$ is a polynomial in x of degree k (Exercise (4)). These polynomials $B_k(x)$ are called **Bernoulli polynomials**, and Bernoulli was able to show that in general

$$\sum_{k=0}^{n-1} k^{d-1} = \frac{B_d(n) - B_d(0)}{d},$$

for all integers $d \geq 1$ and $n \geq 2$ (Exercise (8)). The reader can develop their skills by proving some of the surprising and important properties of Bernoulli polynomials in Exercises (4)–(18).

Example 2.5. The first few Bernoulli polynomials are:

(2.14) $\qquad B_0(x) = 1$

(2.15) $\qquad B_1(x) = x - \dfrac{1}{2}$

(2.16) $\qquad B_2(x) = x^2 - x + \dfrac{1}{6}$

(2.17) $\qquad B_3(x) = x^3 - \dfrac{3}{2}x^2 + \dfrac{1}{2}x$

(2.18) $\qquad B_4(x) = x^4 - 2x^3 + x^2 - \dfrac{1}{30}$

(2.19) $\qquad B_5(x) = x^5 - \dfrac{5}{2}x^4 + \dfrac{5}{3}x^3 - \dfrac{1}{6}x$

(2.20) $\qquad B_6(x) = x^6 - 3x^5 + \dfrac{5}{2}x^4 - \dfrac{1}{2}x^2 + \dfrac{1}{42}$

$\square$

It turns out that it is very useful to periodize the Bernoulli polynomials in the following sense. We first define

$$\{x\} := x - \lfloor x \rfloor,$$

the fractional part of x. Now we define the nth **periodic Bernoulli polynomial**

(2.21) $\qquad\qquad\qquad P_n(x) := B_n(\{x\})$

for $n \geq 2$. Since $P_n(x)$ is periodic on $\mathbb{R}$ with period 1 it has a Fourier series, and it turns out that

(2.22) $\qquad\qquad P_n(x) = -\frac{n!}{(2\pi i)^n} \sum_{k \in \mathbb{Z} - \{0\}} \frac{e^{2\pi i k x}}{k^n},$

valid for $x \in \mathbb{R}$ (Exercise (9)). When $n = 1$ we have the first Bernoulli polynomial

$$P_1(x) := \begin{cases} x - \lfloor x \rfloor - \frac{1}{2} & \text{if } x \notin \mathbb{Z}, \\ 0 & \text{if } x \in \mathbb{Z}, \end{cases}$$

which is very special (see Figure 2.1). For one thing, $P_1(x)$ is the only periodic Bernoulli polynomial that is not continuous everywhere, and we note that its Fourier series does not converge absolutely, although it is quite appealing:

$$(2.23) \qquad P_1(x) = -\frac{1}{2\pi i} \sum_{k \in \mathbb{Z} - \{0\}} \frac{e^{2\pi i k x}}{k},$$

valid for all $x \notin \mathbb{Z}$. But how are we supposed to sum up a conditionally convergent series such as (2.23)? A common way to define it rigorously is to prove that

$$\lim_{N \to \infty} \sum_{k=1}^{N} \frac{e^{2\pi i k x}}{k} \text{ exists.}$$

As we can see, special care must be taken with $P_1(x)$, and Exercise (34) provides a rigorous proof of the convergence of (2.23). The **Bernoulli numbers** are defined to be the constant terms of the Bernoulli polynomials:

$$B_k := B_k(0).$$

Perusing Example 2.5 we see that the first few Bernoulli numbers are:

$$B_0 = 1, \ B_1 = -\frac{1}{2}, \ B_2 = \frac{1}{6}, \ B_3 = 0, \ B_4 = -\frac{1}{30}, \ B_5 = 0, \ B_6 = \frac{1}{42}.$$

It follows quickly from equation (2.13) that for odd $k \geq 3$, $B_k = 0$ (Exercise (15)). Using the generating function (2.13), the Bernoulli numbers are defined via

$$(2.24) \qquad \frac{t}{e^t - 1} = \sum_{k=0}^{\infty} B_k \frac{t^k}{k!}.$$

An interesting identity that allows us to compute the Bernoulli numbers recursively is:

$$\sum_{k=0}^{n} \binom{n+1}{k} B_k = 0,$$

valid for all $n \geq 1$ (Exercise (17)). Some of the most natural and beautiful Fourier series arise naturally from the periodized Bernoulli polynomials.

Recalling the statement of Poisson summation (0.3) from the introduction, we now give a fast and loose application in dimension $d = 1$. The following intuitive application of the Poisson summation formula already suggests an initial connection between periodized Bernoulli polynomials and Fourier transforms of polytopes.

Example 2.6 (Intuitive Poisson summation). In this example we allow ourselves to be completely intuitive and unrigorous at this moment, but often such arguments are useful in pointing us to their rigorous counterparts. Consider the 1-dimensional polytope $\mathcal{P} := [a, b]$ and restrict attention to the case of $a, b \notin \mathbb{Z}$. If we could use the Poisson summation formula

$$\sum_{n \in \mathbb{Z}^d} f(n) = \sum_{\xi \in \mathbb{Z}^d} \hat{f}(\xi)$$

applied to the function $f(x) := 1_{\mathcal{P}}(x)$, then we would get

$$\sum_{n \in \mathbb{Z}} 1_{\mathcal{P}}(n) \text{ “} = \text{ ” } \sum_{\xi \in \mathbb{Z}} \hat{1}_{\mathcal{P}}(\xi)$$

$$\text{“} = \text{ ” } \hat{1}_{\mathcal{P}}(0) + \sum_{\xi \in \mathbb{Z} - \{0\}} \frac{e^{-2\pi i \xi b} - e^{-2\pi i \xi a}}{-2\pi i \xi}$$

$$\text{“} = \text{ ” } (b - a) - \frac{1}{2\pi i} \sum_{\xi \in \mathbb{Z} - \{0\}} \frac{e^{-2\pi i \xi b}}{\xi} + \frac{1}{2\pi i} \sum_{\xi \in \mathbb{Z} - \{0\}} \frac{e^{-2\pi i \xi a}}{\xi}$$

$$\text{“} = \text{ ” } (b - a) + \frac{1}{2\pi i} \sum_{\xi \in \mathbb{Z} - \{0\}} \frac{e^{2\pi i \xi b}}{\xi} - \frac{1}{2\pi i} \sum_{\xi \in \mathbb{Z} - \{0\}} \frac{e^{2\pi i \xi a}}{\xi}$$

$$\text{“} = \text{ ” } (b - a) - \left(\{b\} - \frac{1}{2} \right) + \left(\{a\} - \frac{1}{2} \right)$$

$$\text{“} = \text{ ” } b - \{b\} - (a - \{a\})$$

$$= \lfloor b \rfloor - \lfloor a \rfloor.$$

We have used quotation marks around the latter string of equalities because the sums are formally divergent. But we already know how to evaluate the left-hand side of Poisson summation above, namely $\sum_{n \in \mathbb{Z}} 1_{\mathcal{P}}(n) = \#\{\mathbb{Z} \cap \mathcal{P}\} = \lfloor b \rfloor - \lfloor a \rfloor$. So we have confirmed that Poisson summation has given us the correct formula here, in spite of the lack of rigor at this point. We also see rather quickly why the first periodic Bernoulli polynomial $P_1(x)$ appears so naturally in integer point enumeration in polytopes from this perspective.

Why is the intuitive argument above not rigorous yet? In order to plug a function f into Poisson summation and consider convergence at each point of the domain, f and its Fourier transform $\hat{f}$ must both satisfy some growth conditions at infinity—at the very least ensuring proper convergence of both sides of the Poisson summation formula. We will see such conditions later, in Chapter 3, Theorem 3.41. After we learn how to use Poisson summation, we will return to this example, which will become rigorous in Section 4.   □

We recall that a series $\sum_{n\in\mathbb{Z}} a_n$ is said to **converge absolutely** if $\sum_{n\in\mathbb{Z}} |a_n|$ converges. It is easy to see that the series in (2.23) for $P_1(x)$ does not converge absolutely. Such convergent series that do not converge absolutely are called **conditionally convergent**.

To prove rigorously that the conditionally convergent series (2.23) does in fact converge, see Exercises (30), (31), (33), and (34), which include the Abel summation formula and the Dirichlet convergence test.

5. The cube and its Fourier transform

Perhaps the easiest way to extend the Fourier transform of the unit interval is to consider the d-dimensional unit cube

$$\square := \left[-\frac{1}{2}, \frac{1}{2}\right]^d.$$

What is its Fourier transform? When we compute a Fourier transform of a function f, we will say that $\{f, \hat{f}\}$ is a **Fourier pair**. We have seen that $\left\{1_{[-\frac{1}{2},\frac{1}{2}]}(x), \mathrm{sinc}(\xi)\right\}$ is a Fourier pair in dimension 1.

Example 2.7. Due to the fact that the cube is the direct product of line segments, it follows that the ensuing integral can be separated into a product of integrals, and so it is the product of 1-dimensional transforms:

$$
\hat{1}_{\square}(\xi) = \int_{\mathbb{R}^d} 1_{\square}(x) e^{-2\pi i \langle x, \xi \rangle} dx \tag{2.25}
$$

$$
= \int_{\square} e^{-2\pi i (x_1 \xi_1 + \cdots + x_d \xi_d)} dx \tag{2.26}
$$

$$
= \prod_{k=1}^{d} \int_{-\frac{1}{2}}^{\frac{1}{2}} e^{-2\pi i x_k \xi_k} dx_k \tag{2.27}
$$

$$
= \prod_{k=1}^{d} \frac{\sin(\pi \xi_k)}{\pi \xi_k}, \tag{2.28}
$$

valid for all $\xi \in \mathbb{R}^d$ such that none of their coordinates vanishes. So here we have the Fourier pair

$$\left\{ 1_\square(x), \prod_{k=1}^{d} \frac{\sin(\pi\xi_k)}{\pi\xi_k} \right\}.$$

In general, though, polytopes are not a direct product of lower-dimensional polytopes, so we will need to develop more tools to compute their Fourier transforms. □

6. The standard simplex and its Fourier transform

Another basic building block for polytopes is the **standard simplex**, defined by

$$(2.29) \qquad \triangle := \left\{ x \in \mathbb{R}^d \mid x_1 + \cdots + x_d \le 1, \text{ and all } x_k \ge 0 \right\}.$$

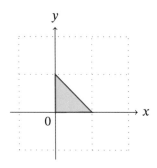

Figure 2.3. The standard simplex in $\mathbb{R}^2$.

Example 2.8. Just for fun, let us compute the Fourier transform of $\triangle$ for $d = 2$, via brute force. We may use the following parametrization (called a hyperplane description) for this standard triangle:

$$\triangle = \left\{ (x, y) \mid x + y \le 1, \text{ and } x \ge 0, y \ge 0 \right\}.$$

Hence, we have:

$$\hat{1}_\triangle(\xi_1, \xi_2) := \int_\triangle e^{-2\pi i\left(x\xi_1 + y\xi_2\right)} dx dy$$

$$= \int_0^1 \int_{y=0}^{y=1-x} e^{-2\pi i\left(x\xi_1 + y\xi_2\right)} dy dx$$

$$= \int_0^1 e^{-2\pi i x\xi_1} \left[\frac{e^{-2\pi i y\xi_2}}{-2\pi i\xi_2} \Big|_{y=0}^{y=1-x} \right] dx$$

$$= \frac{1}{-2\pi i\xi_2} \int_0^1 e^{-2\pi i x\xi_1} \left(e^{-2\pi i(1-x)\xi_2} - 1 \right) dx$$

$$= \frac{1}{-2\pi i\xi_2} \int_0^1 \left(e^{-2\pi i x(\xi_1 - \xi_2)} e^{-2\pi i\xi_2} - e^{-2\pi i x\xi_1} \right) dx$$

$$= \frac{1}{(-2\pi i)^2} \frac{e^{-2\pi i\xi_2}}{\xi_2(\xi_1 - \xi_2)} (e^{-2\pi i(\xi_1 - \xi_2)} - 1)$$

$$- \frac{1}{(-2\pi i)^2} \frac{e^{-2\pi i\xi_1} - 1}{\xi_1\xi_2}$$

$$= \frac{1}{(-2\pi i)^2} \left[\frac{e^{-2\pi i\xi_1} - e^{-2\pi i\xi_2}}{\xi_2(\xi_1 - \xi_2)} - \frac{e^{-2\pi i\xi_1} - 1}{\xi_1\xi_2} \right].$$

We may simplify further by noticing the rational function identity

$$\frac{e^{-2\pi i\xi_1}}{\xi_2(\xi_1 - \xi_2)} - \frac{e^{-2\pi i\xi_1}}{\xi_1\xi_2} = \frac{e^{-2\pi i\xi_1}}{\xi_1(\xi_1 - \xi_2)},$$

giving us the symmetric function of (ξ_1, ξ_2):

$$(2.30) \quad \hat{1}_\triangle(\xi_1, \xi_2) = \frac{1}{(-2\pi i)^2} \left[\frac{e^{-2\pi i\xi_1}}{\xi_1(\xi_1 - \xi_2)} + \frac{e^{-2\pi i\xi_2}}{\xi_2(\xi_2 - \xi_1)} + \frac{1}{\xi_1\xi_2} \right]. \qquad \square$$

7. Convex sets and polytopes

We need the concept of a **convex set** $X \subset \mathbb{R}^d$, defined by the property that the line segment joining any two points of X lies entirely in X. In other words, given any two points $x, y \in X$, we have the containment

$$(2.31) \qquad \{\lambda x + (1 - \lambda)y \mid 0 \le \lambda \le 1\} \subseteq X.$$

Given any finite set of points $S := \{v_1, v_2, \ldots, v_N\} \subset \mathbb{R}^d$, we can also form the set of all **convex linear combinations** of S by defining
(2.32)
$$\text{conv}(S) := \left\{ \lambda_1 v_1 + \lambda_2 v_2 + \cdots + \lambda_N v_N \mid \sum_{k=1}^{N} \lambda_k = 1, \text{ where all } \lambda_k \geq 0 \right\}.$$
The standard fact that $\text{conv}(S)$ satisfies the convexity property defined by (2.31) is left for the pleasure of the reader to prove. Given any set $U \subset \mathbb{R}^d$ (which is not restricted to be finite or bounded), we define the **convex hull** of U as the set of convex linear combinations taken over all finite subsets of U and denoted by $\text{conv}(U)$.

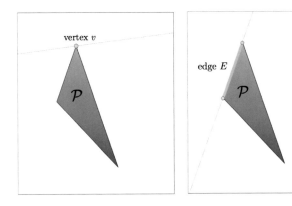

Figure 2.4. Left: A triangle $\mathcal{P}$ with a vertex $v \in \mathcal{P}$ and one of its supporting lines. Right: An edge $E \subset \mathcal{P}$ with its supporting line.

We define a **polytope** as the convex hull of any finite set of points in $\mathbb{R}^d$. This definition of a polytope is called its **vertex description**. We define a k-**simplex** Δ as the convex hull of a finite set of vectors $\{v_1, v_2, \ldots, v_{k+1}\}$:
$$\Delta := \text{conv}\{v_1, v_2, \ldots, v_{k+1}\},$$
where $0 \leq k \leq d$, and $v_2 - v_1, v_3 - v_1, \ldots, v_{k+1} - v_1$ are linearly independent vectors in $\mathbb{R}^d$. The points $v_1, v_2, \ldots, v_{k+1}$ are called the vertices of Δ, and this object is one of the basic building blocks of polytopes, especially when triangulating a polytope.

The simplex Δ is a k-dimensional polytope sitting in $\mathbb{R}^d$. When $k = d$ the dimension of Δ equals the dimension of the ambient space $\mathbb{R}^d$—see Figure 2.6. We have already computed the Fourier transform of a particular 2-simplex in (2.30).

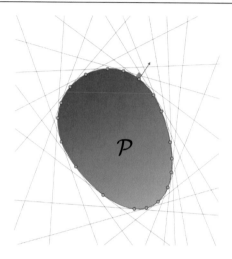

Figure 2.5. Here the convex body $\mathcal{P}$ is not a polygon—it has infinitely many vertices, some of which are shown here with their supporting lines.

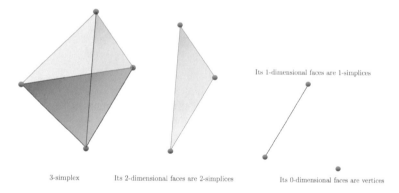

3-simplex   Its 2-dimensional faces are 2-simplices   Its 1-dimensional faces are 1-simplices

Its 0-dimensional faces are vertices

Figure 2.6. A 3-simplex and its faces, which are lower-dimensional simplices as well.

How do we define a face of a polytope $\mathcal{P}$ more precisely? To begin, a **hyperplane** is defined by

$$H := \{x \in \mathbb{R}^d \mid \langle x, n \rangle = b\}$$

for any fixed vector $n \in \mathbb{R}^d$ and any $b \in \mathbb{R}$. A hyperplane is called a **supporting hyperplane for** $\mathcal{P}$ if $\mathcal{P}$ lies on one side of H, in the precise sense that

$$\mathcal{P} \subset \{x \in \mathbb{R}^d \mid \langle x, n \rangle \leq b\} \text{ or } \mathcal{P} \subset \{x \in \mathbb{R}^d \mid \langle x, n \rangle \geq b\}.$$

We can now define a face of $\mathcal{P}$ of any dimension: $F \subseteq \mathcal{P}$ is a **face of** $\mathcal{P}$ if $F = H \cap \mathcal{P}$ for some supporting hyperplane H of $\mathcal{P}$. As a consequence of the latter definition, the empty set is also a face of $\mathcal{P}$, because we may pick a hyperplane very far from $\mathcal{P}$, which does not intersect $\mathcal{P}$. As a separate definition, we define $\mathcal{P}$ to be a face of $\mathcal{P}$ itself.

A **vertex** of $\mathcal{P}$ is defined to be a 0-dimensional face of $\mathcal{P}$. An **edge** of $\mathcal{P}$ is a 1-dimensional face of $\mathcal{P}$. A **facet** of $\mathcal{P}$ is a $(d-1)$-dimensional face of $\mathcal{P}$. Figure 2.4 shows the supporting hyperplanes for a triangle, which are lines in dimension 2. Figure 2.5 shows some supporting lines for a convex set in $\mathbb{R}^2$, which is not a polygon.

8. Any triangle and its Fourier transform

We are now ready to compute the Fourier transform of any 2-simplex in $\mathbb{R}^2$. In order to handle a general triangle, let Δ be any triangle in the plane with vertices

$$v_1 := \begin{pmatrix} a_1 \\ b_1 \end{pmatrix}, v_2 := \begin{pmatrix} a_2 \\ b_2 \end{pmatrix}, v_3 := \begin{pmatrix} a_3 \\ b_3 \end{pmatrix}.$$

Can we reduce the computation of $\hat{1}_\Delta$ to our already known formula for $\hat{1}_\triangle$ given by (2.30)? We first notice (after a quick cup of coffee) that we can map any triangle in the plane to the standard triangle by using a linear transformation followed by a translation:

$$(2.33) \qquad\qquad \Delta = M(\triangle) + v_3,$$

where M is the 2×2 matrix whose columns are $v_1 - v_3$ and $v_2 - v_3$. We are now ready to compute the Fourier transform of a general triangle Δ:

$$\hat{1}_\Delta(\xi) = \int_\Delta e^{-2\pi i \langle \xi, x \rangle} dx = \int_{M(\triangle) + v_3} e^{-2\pi i \langle \xi, x \rangle} dx.$$

Making the substitution $x := My + v_3$ with $y \in \triangle$ we have the differential $dx = |\det M| dy$, and so

$$\int_{M(\triangle)+v_3} e^{-2\pi i \langle \xi, x \rangle} dx$$

$$= |\det M| \int_\triangle e^{-2\pi i \langle \xi, My + v_3 \rangle} dy$$

$$= |\det M| e^{-2\pi i \langle \xi, v_3 \rangle} \int_\triangle e^{-2\pi i \langle M^T \xi, y \rangle} dy$$

$$= |\det M| e^{-2\pi i \langle \xi, v_3 \rangle} \hat{1}_\triangle (M^T \xi)$$

$$= |\det M| e^{-2\pi i \langle \xi, v_3 \rangle} \hat{1}_\triangle \left(\langle v_1 - v_3, \xi \rangle, \langle v_2 - v_3, \xi \rangle \right)$$

$$= |\det M| e^{-2\pi i \langle \xi, v_3 \rangle} \frac{1}{(-2\pi i)^2} \left[\frac{e^{-2\pi i z_1}}{z_1(z_1 - z_2)} + \frac{e^{-2\pi i z_2}}{z_2(z_2 - z_1)} + \frac{1}{z_1 z_2} \right],$$

where we have used our formula (2.30) for the FT of the standard triangle with $z_1 := \langle v_1 - v_3, \xi \rangle$ and $z_2 := \langle v_2 - v_3, \xi \rangle$, thereby bootstrapping our way to the general case. Substituting these values into the latter expression, we finally arrive at the FT of our general triangle $\triangle$:

(2.34)

$$\hat{1}_\triangle(\xi) = c \frac{e^{-2\pi i \langle v_1, \xi \rangle}}{\langle v_1 - v_3, \xi \rangle \langle v_1 - v_2, \xi \rangle} + c \frac{e^{-2\pi i \langle v_2, \xi \rangle}}{\langle v_2 - v_3, \xi \rangle \langle v_2 - v_1, \xi \rangle} + c \frac{e^{-2\pi i \langle v_3, \xi \rangle}}{\langle v_3 - v_1, \xi \rangle \langle v_3 - v_2, \xi \rangle},$$

where $c := \frac{|\det M|}{(-2\pi i)^2}$.

We can notice in equation (2.34) many of the same patterns that had already occurred in Example 2.14. Namely, the Fourier transform of a triangle has denominators that are products of linear forms in ξ, and it is a finite linear combination of rational functions multiplied by complex exponentials.

Also, in the particular case of equation (2.34), $\hat{1}_\triangle(\xi)$ is a symmetric function of v_1, v_2, v_3, as we might have expected.

Using exactly the same ideas that were used in equation (2.34), it is possible to prove—by induction on the dimension—that the Fourier transform of a general d-dimensional simplex $\triangle \subset \mathbb{R}^d$ is:

(2.35) $$\hat{1}_\triangle(\xi) = (\text{vol } \triangle) d! \sum_{j=1}^{N} \frac{e^{-2\pi i \langle v_j, \xi \rangle}}{\prod_{k=1}^{d} \langle v_j - v_k, \xi \rangle} [k \neq j],$$

where the vertex set of $\mathcal{P}$ is $\{v_1, \dots, v_N\}$ (Exercise (29)), and in fact the same formula persists for all complex $\xi \in \mathbb{C}^d$ such that the products of linear forms in the denominators do not vanish.

However, looking back at the computation leading to (2.34) and the corresponding computation which would give (2.35), the curious reader might be thinking:

                    "There must be an easier way!"

But never fear—indeed there is. So even though at this point the computation of $\hat{1}_\triangle(\xi)$ may be a bit laborious (but still interesting), computing the Fourier transform of a general simplex will become quite easy once we will revisit it in a later chapter (see Theorem 7.12).

9. Stretching and translating

The perspicacious reader may have noticed that in order to arrive at formula (2.34) for the FT of a general triangle, we exploited the fact that the Fourier transform interacted peacefully with the linear transformation M and with the translation by the vector v. Is this true in general?

Indeed it is, and we record these thoughts in Lemmas 2.9 and 2.10, which will become our bread and butter for future computations. In general, given any invertible linear transformation $M : \mathbb{R}^d \to \mathbb{R}^d$ and any function $f : \mathbb{R}^d \to \mathbb{C}$ whose FT (Fourier transform) exists, we have the following useful interaction between Fourier transforms and linear transformations.

Lemma 2.9 (Stretch).

$$(2.36) \qquad \widehat{(f \circ M)}(\xi) = \frac{1}{|\det M|} \hat{f}\left(M^{-T}\xi\right)$$

Proof. By definition we have $\widehat{(f \circ M)}(\xi) := \int_{\mathbb{R}^d} f(Mx)e^{-2\pi i \langle \xi, x \rangle} dx$. We perform the change of variable $y := Mx$, implying that $dy = |\det M| dx$, so that:

$$\begin{aligned}
\widehat{(f \circ M)}(\xi) &= \frac{1}{|\det M|} \int_{\mathbb{R}^d} f(y)e^{-2\pi i \langle \xi, M^{-1}y \rangle} dy \\
&= \frac{1}{|\det M|} \int_{\mathbb{R}^d} f(y)e^{-2\pi i \langle M^{-T}\xi, y \rangle} dy \\
&= \frac{1}{|\det M|} \hat{f}\left(M^{-T}\xi\right).
\end{aligned}$$

$\square$

What about translations? They are even simpler.

Lemma 2.10 (Translate). *For any translation $T(x) := x + v$ where $v \in \mathbb{R}^d$ is a fixed vector, we have*

$$(2.37) \qquad \widehat{(f \circ T)}(\xi) = e^{2\pi i \langle \xi, v \rangle} \hat{f}(\xi).$$

Proof. Again, by definition we have

$$\widehat{(f \circ T)}(\xi) := \int_{\mathbb{R}^d} f(Tx)e^{-2\pi i \langle \xi, x \rangle} dx,$$

so that performing the simple change of variable $y = Tx := x + v$ we have $dy = dx$. The latter integral becomes

$$(\widehat{f \circ T})(\xi) = \int_{\mathbb{R}^d} f(y)e^{-2\pi i\langle \xi, y - v\rangle} dy$$

$$= e^{2\pi i\langle \xi, v\rangle} \int_{\mathbb{R}^d} f(y)e^{-2\pi i\langle \xi, y\rangle} dy$$

$$:= e^{2\pi i\langle \xi, v\rangle} \hat{f}(\xi).$$

□

In general, any function $\phi : \mathbb{R}^d \to \mathbb{C}$ of the form

(2.38) $\phi(x) = Mx + v,$

where M is a fixed linear transformation and $v \in \mathbb{R}^d$ is a fixed vector is called an **affine transformation**. For example, we have already seen in (2.33) that the right triangle ◺ was mapped to the more general triangle Δ by an affine transformation. So the latter two lemmas allow us to compose Fourier transforms very easily with affine transformations.

Example 2.11. The simplest example of stretch Lemma 2.9 is obtained in $\mathbb{R}$, where the matrix $M = r$, a positive real number. So we have $M^{-T} = \frac{1}{r}$. Considering $f(rx)$ as a function of $x \in \mathbb{R}$, we have by (2.37):

(2.39) $\widehat{f(rx)} := (\widehat{f \circ M})(\xi) = \frac{1}{r}\hat{f}\left(\frac{1}{r}\xi\right).$

As an interesting sub-example, let us take $f(x) := 1_{\left[-\frac{c}{2}, \frac{c}{2}\right]}(x)$ for a fixed constant $c > 0$. What is the easy way to use the stretch lemma to compute $\hat{f}(\xi)$? First, we have to make a slight conversion: $1_{\left[-\frac{c}{2}, \frac{c}{2}\right]}(x) = 1_{\left[-\frac{1}{2}, \frac{1}{2}\right]}(\frac{1}{c}x)$. Using the FT of the unit interval—equation (2.3)—together with (2.39) we have:

(2.40) $\hat{1}_{\left[-\frac{c}{2}, \frac{c}{2}\right]}(\xi) = c\, \hat{1}_{\left[-\frac{1}{2}, \frac{1}{2}\right]}(c\xi) = c\, \text{sinc}(c\xi) = \dfrac{\sin(c\pi\xi)}{\pi\xi}.$ □

Example 2.12. Consider any set $B \subset \mathbb{R}^d$, for which 1_B is integrable. Let us translate B by a fixed vector $v \in \mathbb{R}^d$, and compute $\hat{1}_{B+v}(\xi)$.

First, we notice that because $1_{B+v}(\xi) = 1_B(\xi - v)$ the translated lemma applies, but with a minus sign. That is, we can use $T(x) := x - v$ and $f := 1_B$ to get:

(2.41) $\hat{1}_{B+v}(\xi) = (\widehat{1_B \circ T})(\xi) = e^{-2\pi i\langle \xi, v\rangle} \hat{1}_B(\xi).$ □

10. The parallelepiped and its Fourier transform

Now that we know how to compose the FT with affine transformations (translations and linear transformations), we can easily find the FT of any parallelepiped in $\mathbb{R}^d$ by using our formula for the Fourier transform of the unit cube $\square := \left[-\frac{1}{2}, \frac{1}{2}\right]^d$, which we derived in Example 2.7:

$$(2.42) \qquad \hat{1}_{\square}(\xi) = \prod_{k=1}^{d} \frac{\sin(\pi \xi_k)}{\pi \xi_k},$$

for all $\xi \in \mathbb{R}^d$ such that all the coordinates of ξ do not vanish. First, we translate the cube $\square$ by the vector $(\frac{1}{2}, \cdots, \frac{1}{2})$ to obtain

$$C := \square + \left(\frac{1}{2}, \cdots, \frac{1}{2}\right) = [0, 1]^d.$$

It is straightforward to compute its FT as well (Exercise (2)), by using Lemma 2.10, the "translated" lemma:

$$(2.43) \qquad \hat{1}_C(\xi) = \frac{1}{(2\pi i)^d} \prod_{k=1}^{d} \frac{1 - e^{-2\pi i \xi_k}}{\xi_k}.$$

Next, we define a d-dimensional **parallelepiped** $\mathcal{P} \subset \mathbb{R}^d$ as an affine image of the unit cube. In other words, any parallelepiped has the description

$$\mathcal{P} = M(C) + v$$

for some linear transformation M and some translation vector v. Geometrically, the cube is stretched and translated into a parallelepiped.

For the sake of concreteness, we will first set $v := 0$ and compute the Fourier transform of $\mathcal{P} := M(C)$, where we now give M as a $d \times d$ invertible matrix whose columns are $w_1, w_2, \ldots, w_d$. Because the cube C may be written as a convex linear combination of the basis vectors e_j, we see that $\mathcal{P}$ may be written as a convex linear combination of $Me_j = w_j$. In other words, we see that the (closed) parallelepiped $\mathcal{P}$ has the equivalent vertex description:

$$\mathcal{P} = \left\{ \sum_{k=1}^{d} \lambda_k w_k \mid \text{all } \lambda_k \in [0, 1] \right\}.$$

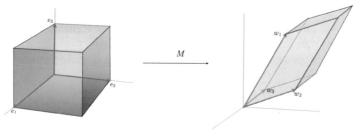

The unit cube $\square := [0, 1]^3$

A parallelepiped, obtained as a linear transformation of $\square$,

via the matrix $M := \begin{pmatrix} | & | & | \\ w_1 & w_2 & w_3 \\ | & | & | \end{pmatrix}$

Figure 2.7. Mapping the unit cube to a parallelepiped.

To review the basics, let us compute the FT of our parallelepiped $\mathcal{P}$ from first principles:

$$(2.44) \qquad \hat{1}_{\mathcal{P}}(\xi) := \int_{\mathcal{P}} e^{-2\pi i \langle \xi, x \rangle} dx = \int_{M(C)} e^{-2\pi i \langle \xi, x \rangle} dx$$

$$(2.45) \qquad = |\det M| \int_C e^{-2\pi i \langle \xi, My \rangle} dy$$

$$(2.46) \qquad = |\det M| \int_C e^{-2\pi i \langle M^T \xi, y \rangle} dy := |\det M| \, \hat{1}_C \left(M^T \xi \right)$$

$$(2.47) \qquad = \frac{|\det M|}{(2\pi i)^d} \prod_{k=1}^{d} \frac{1 - e^{-2\pi i \langle w_k, \xi \rangle}}{\langle w_k, \xi \rangle}.$$

where in the third equality we used the substitution $x := My$ with $y \in C$, yielding $dx = |\det M| dy$. In the last equality we used our known formula (2.43) for the FT of the cube C together with the elementary linear algebra fact that the kth coordinate of $M^T \xi$ is given by $\langle w_k, \xi \rangle$.

Finally, for a general parallelepiped we have $Q := \mathcal{P} + v$ so that by definition

$$Q = \left\{ v + \sum_{k=1}^{d} \lambda_k w_k \mid \text{all } \lambda_k \in [0, 1] \right\}.$$

Noting that $1_{\mathcal{P}+v}(\xi) = 1_{\mathcal{P}}(\xi - v)$, we compute the Fourier transform of Q by using the "translate lemma" (Lemma 2.10) together with formula

(2.47) for the Fourier transform of $\mathcal{P}$:

$$(2.48) \qquad \hat{1}_Q(\xi) = e^{-2\pi i \langle \xi, v \rangle} \frac{|\det M|}{(2\pi i)^d} \prod_{k=1}^{d} \frac{1 - e^{-2\pi i \langle w_k, \xi \rangle}}{\langle w_k, \xi \rangle},$$

for all $\xi \in \mathbb{R}^d$ except for those ξ that are orthogonal to one of the w_k (which are edge vectors for Q).

Example 2.13. A straightforward computation shows that if we let $v := -\frac{w_1 + \cdots + w_d}{2}$ then $Q := \{v + \sum_{k=1}^{d} \lambda_k w_k \mid \text{all } \lambda_k \in [0,1]\}$ is symmetric about the origin, in the sense that $x \in Q \iff -x \in Q$ (Exercise (25)). In other words, the center of mass of this new Q is now the origin. Geometrically, we have translated the previous parallelepiped by using half its "body diagonal". For such a parallelepiped Q, centered at the origin, formula (2.48) gives the more pleasing expression:

$$(2.49) \qquad \hat{1}_Q(\xi) = e^{2\pi i \langle \xi, \frac{w_1 + \cdots + w_d}{2} \rangle} \frac{|\det M|}{(2\pi i)^d} \prod_{k=1}^{d} \frac{1 - e^{-2\pi i \langle w_k, \xi \rangle}}{\langle w_k, \xi \rangle}$$

$$(2.50) \qquad = \frac{|\det M|}{(2\pi i)^d} \prod_{k=1}^{d} \frac{e^{\pi i \langle w_k, \xi \rangle} - e^{-\pi i \langle w_k, \xi \rangle}}{\langle w_k, \xi \rangle}$$

$$(2.51) \qquad = \frac{|\det M|}{(2\pi i)^d} \prod_{k=1}^{d} \frac{(2i)\sin(\pi \langle w_k, \xi \rangle)}{\langle w_k, \xi \rangle}$$

$$(2.52) \qquad = |\det M| \prod_{k=1}^{d} \frac{\sin(\pi \langle w_k, \xi \rangle)}{\pi \langle w_k, \xi \rangle}.$$

To summarize, for a parallelepiped that is symmetric about the origin, we have the Fourier pair

$$\left\{ 1_Q(x), \quad |\det M| \prod_{k=1}^{d} \frac{\sin(\pi \langle w_k, \xi \rangle)}{\pi \langle w_k, \xi \rangle} \right\}.$$

We could have also computed the latter FT by beginning with our known Fourier transform (2.42) of the cube □, composing the FT with the same linear transformation M of (2.44), and using the 'stretch' lemma, so everything is consistent.   □

11. The cross-polytope

Another natural convex body in $\mathbb{R}^2$ is the cross-polytope

$$(2.53) \qquad \Diamond_2 := \{(x_1, x_2) \in \mathbb{R}^2 \mid |x_1| + |x_2| \le 1\}.$$

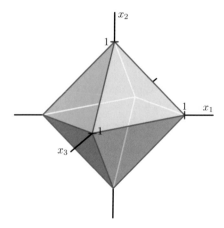

Figure 2.8. The cross-polytope $\Diamond$ in $\mathbb{R}^3$ (courtesy of David Austin).

In dimension d the **cross-polytope** $\Diamond_d$ can be defined similarly by its **hyperplane description**

$$(2.54) \qquad \Diamond_d := \{(x_1, x_2, \ldots, x_d) \in \mathbb{R}^d \mid |x_1| + |x_2| + \cdots + |x_d| \leq 1\}.$$

The cross-polytope is also, by definition, the unit ball in the L_1-norm on Euclidean space, and from this perspective a very natural object. In $\mathbb{R}^3$, the cross-polytope $\Diamond_3$ is often called an **octahedron**.

In this section we only work out the 2-dimensional case of the Fourier transfrom of the crosspolytope. In Chapter 7 we will work out the Fourier transform of any d-dimensional cross-polytope $\hat{1}_{\Diamond_d}$ because we will have more tools at our disposal.

Nevertheless, it is instructive to compute $\hat{1}_{\Diamond_2}$ via brute-force for $d = 2$ here, in order to gain some facility with the computation of Fourier transforms.

Example 2.14. Using the definition of the Fourier transform, we first compute the FT of the 2-dimensional cross polytope:

$$(2.55) \qquad \hat{1}_{\Diamond_2}(\xi) := \int_{\Diamond_2} e^{-2\pi i \langle \xi, x \rangle} dx.$$

In $\mathbb{R}^2$, we may write $\Diamond_2$ as a union of the following 4 triangles:

$$\Delta_1 := \text{conv}(\begin{pmatrix} 0 \\ 0 \end{pmatrix}, \begin{pmatrix} 1 \\ 0 \end{pmatrix}, \begin{pmatrix} 0 \\ 1 \end{pmatrix}),$$

$$\Delta_2 := \text{conv}(\begin{pmatrix} 0 \\ 0 \end{pmatrix}, \begin{pmatrix} -1 \\ 0 \end{pmatrix}, \begin{pmatrix} 0 \\ 1 \end{pmatrix}),$$

$$\Delta_3 := \text{conv}(\begin{pmatrix} 0 \\ 0 \end{pmatrix}, \begin{pmatrix} -1 \\ 0 \end{pmatrix}, \begin{pmatrix} 0 \\ -1 \end{pmatrix}),$$

$$\Delta_4 := \text{conv}(\begin{pmatrix} 0 \\ 0 \end{pmatrix}, \begin{pmatrix} 1 \\ 0 \end{pmatrix}, \begin{pmatrix} 0 \\ -1 \end{pmatrix}).$$

Since these four triangles only intersect in lower-dimensional subsets of $\mathbb{R}^2$, the 2-dimensional integral vanishes on such lower dimensional subsets and we have:

$$(2.56) \qquad \hat{1}_{\Diamond_2}(\xi) = \hat{1}_{\Delta_1}(\xi) + \hat{1}_{\Delta_2}(\xi) + \hat{1}_{\Delta_3}(\xi) + \hat{1}_{\Delta_4}(\xi).$$

Recalling from equation (2.30) of Example 2.8 that the Fourier transform of the standard simplex Δ_1 is

$$(2.57) \qquad \hat{1}_{\Delta_1}(\xi) = \left(\frac{1}{2\pi i}\right)^2 \left(\frac{1}{\xi_1 \xi_2} + \frac{e^{-2\pi i \xi_1}}{(-\xi_1 + \xi_2)\xi_1} + \frac{e^{-2\pi i \xi_2}}{(\xi_1 - \xi_2)\xi_2}\right),$$

we can compute $\hat{1}_{\Delta_2}(\xi)$ by reflecting Δ_2 about the x_2-axis (the Jacobian of this transformation is 1) and using the already-computed transform (2.57) of Δ_1:

$$\hat{1}_{\Delta_2}(\xi_1, \xi_2) := \int_{\Delta_2} e^{-2\pi i(x_1 \xi_1 + x_2 \xi_2)} dx$$

$$= \int_{\Delta_1} e^{-2\pi i(-x_1 \xi_1 + x_2 \xi_2)} dx$$

$$= \int_{\Delta_1} e^{-2\pi i(x_1(-\xi_1) + x_2 \xi_2)} dx$$

$$= \hat{1}_{\Delta_1}(-\xi_1, \xi_2)).$$

Similarly, we have

$$\hat{1}_{\Delta_3}(\xi_1, \xi_2) = \hat{1}_{\Delta_1}(-\xi_1, -\xi_2), \text{ and } \hat{1}_{\Delta_4}(\xi_1, \xi_2) = \hat{1}_{\Delta_1}(\xi_1, -\xi_2).$$

Thus we may continue the computation from equation (2.56), putting all the pieces back together:

(2.58)

$$\hat{1}_{\Diamond_2}(\xi)$$

(2.59)

$$= \hat{1}_{\Delta_1}(\xi_1, \xi_2) + \hat{1}_{\Delta_1}(-\xi_1, \xi_2) + \hat{1}_{\Delta_1}(-\xi_1, -\xi_2) + \hat{1}_{\Delta_1}(\xi_1, -\xi_2)$$

(2.60)

$$= \left(\frac{1}{2\pi i}\right)^2 \left(\frac{1}{\xi_1\xi_2} + \frac{-e^{2\pi i\xi_1}}{(-\xi_1 + \xi_2)\xi_1} + \frac{-e^{2\pi i\xi_2}}{(\xi_1 - \xi_2)\xi_2}\right)$$

(2.61)

$$+ \left(\frac{1}{2\pi i}\right)^2 \left(\frac{-1}{\xi_1\xi_2} + \frac{e^{-2\pi i\xi_1}}{(\xi_1 + \xi_2)\xi_1} + \frac{e^{2\pi i\xi_2}}{(\xi_1 + \xi_2)\xi_2}\right)$$

(2.62)

$$+ \left(\frac{1}{2\pi i}\right)^2 \left(\frac{1}{\xi_1\xi_2} + \frac{e^{-2\pi i\xi_1}}{(\xi_1 - \xi_2)\xi_1} + \frac{e^{-2\pi i\xi_2}}{(-\xi_1 + \xi_2)\xi_2}\right)$$

(2.63)

$$+ \left(\frac{1}{2\pi i}\right)^2 \left(\frac{-1}{\xi_1\xi_2} + \frac{e^{2\pi i\xi_1}}{(\xi_1 + \xi_2)\xi_1} + \frac{e^{-2\pi i\xi_2}}{(\xi_1 + \xi_2)\xi_2}\right)$$

(2.64)

$$= -\frac{1}{2\pi^2} \left(\frac{\cos(2\pi\xi_1)}{(\xi_1 - \xi_2)\xi_1} + \frac{\cos(2\pi\xi_2)}{(-\xi_1 + \xi_2)\xi_2} + \frac{\cos(2\pi\xi_1)}{(\xi_1 + \xi_2)\xi_1} + \frac{\cos(2\pi\xi_2)}{(\xi_1 + \xi_2)\xi_2}\right)$$

(2.65)

$$= -\frac{1}{\pi^2} \left(\frac{\cos(2\pi\xi_1) - \cos(2\pi\xi_2)}{(\xi_1 + \xi_2)(\xi_1 - \xi_2)}\right).$$

$\square$

It is time to mention another important relationship between the cross-polytope $\Diamond$ and the cube $\mathcal{P} := [-1, 1]^d$. To see this relationship, we define—for any polytope $\mathcal{P} \subset \mathbb{R}^d$—its **polar polytope**:

(2.66) $$\mathcal{P}^o := \{x \in \mathbb{R}^d \mid \langle x, y \rangle \leq 1, \text{ for all } y \in \mathcal{P}\}.$$

It is an easy fact (Exercise (26)) that in $\mathbb{R}^d$, the cross-polytope $\Diamond_d$ and the cube $\mathcal{P} := [-1, 1]^d$ are polars of each other, as in Figure 2.9.

In many applications it turns out the the volume of the cross-polytope plays an important role. So we compute it here for a generalized

Figure 2.9. Left: A page from Kepler's book, *Harmonices Mundi* (1619), showing the author's interest in various polar polytopes, over 400 years ago. Right: The cube and the cross-polytope as polars of each other.

cross-polytope defined by the image of $\Diamond_d$ under any invertible linear transformation M whose kth column is defined by v_k:

(2.67) $$Q := M(\Diamond_d) = \mathrm{conv}(\pm v_1, \pm v_2, \ldots, \pm v_d).$$

Lemma 2.15. *With the notation above, we have*

(1)
$$\mathrm{vol}\,\Diamond_d = \frac{2^d}{d!}$$

(2)
$$\mathrm{vol}\,Q = |\det M|\frac{2^d}{d!}.$$

(3) *In particular, if $v_k := \alpha_k e_k$, then we have*

$$\mathrm{vol}\,Q = \alpha_1 \alpha_2 \cdots \alpha_d \frac{2^d}{d!}.$$

Proof. To prove part (1) we can simply triangulate the crosspolytope into 2^d isometric simplices by using the coordinate planes. Each such

simplex has volume $\frac{1}{d!}$, so we are done. For part (2), we have:
(2.68)
$$\text{vol}\,Q := \int_{M(\Diamond_d)} dx = |\det M| \int_{\Diamond_d} dy = |\det M|\,\text{vol}\,\Diamond_d = |\det M|\frac{2^d}{d!},$$

where we used the change of variable $x := My$ and its ensuing Jacobian transformation $dx = |\det M|dy$. The last equality above follows from part (1). Part (3) follows trivially from part (2) using the determinant of a diagonal matrix. $\qquad\square$

12. Observations and questions

Now we can make several observations about all of the formulas that we found so far, for the Fourier transforms of various polytopes. For the 2-dimensional cross-polytope we found that

$$(2.69) \qquad \hat{1}_{\Diamond_2}(\xi) = -\frac{1}{\pi^2}\left(\frac{\cos(2\pi\xi_1) - \cos(2\pi\xi_2)}{(\xi_1 + \xi_2)(\xi_1 - \xi_2)}\right).$$

(1) It is real-valued for all $\xi \in \mathbb{R}^2$, and this is due to the fact that $\Diamond_2$ is symmetric about the origin (see Section 6).

Question 2.16. Is it true that *any* symmetric property of a polytope $\mathcal{P}$ is somehow mirrored by a corresponding symmetric property of its Fourier transform?

Although this question is not well defined at the moment (it depends on how we define "symmetric property") it does sound exciting, and we can morph it into a few well-defined questions later.

(2) The only apparent singularities of the FT in (2.69) (though they are in fact removable singularities) are the two lines $\xi_1 - \xi_2 = 0$ and $\xi_1 + \xi_2 = 0$, and these two lines are *perpendicular* to the facets of $\Diamond_2$, which is not a coincidence.

(3) It is always true that the Fourier transform of a polytope is an entire function by Lemma 2.3, so that the singularities in the denominator $(\xi_1 + \xi_2)(\xi_1 - \xi_2)$ of (2.69) must be removable singularities!

(4) The denominators of all of the FTs so far are always products of **linear forms** in ξ.

Question 2.17 (Rhetorical). Is it true that the Fourier transform of any polytope is always a finite sum of rational functions times an exponential where the denominators of the rational functions are always products of linear forms?

Answer: (Spoiler alert.) Yes! It is too early to prove this here, but we will do it in the course of proving Theorem 7.15.

(5) We may retrieve the volume of $\Diamond_2$ by letting ξ_1 and ξ_2 tend to zero (Exercise (21)), as always. In doing so, we obtain

$$\lim_{\xi \to 0} \hat{1}_{\Diamond_2}(\xi) = 2 = \text{Area}(\Diamond_2).$$

Notes

(1) Another way to compute $1_\Diamond(\xi)$ for the 2-dimensional cross-polytope $\Diamond$ is by starting with the square $[-\frac{1}{2}, \frac{1}{2}]^2$ and applying a rotation of the plane by $\pi/4$, followed by a simple dilation. Because we know that linear transformations interact in a very elegant way with the FT, this method gives an alternate approach for the Example 2.14 in $\mathbb{R}^2$.

However, this method no longer works for the cross-polytope in dimensions $d \geq 3$, where it is not (yet) known if there is a simple way to go from the FT of the cube to the FT of the cross-polytope.

More generally, one may ask:

Question 2.18. Is there a nice relationship between the FT of a polytope $\mathcal{P}$ and the FT of its polar?

(2) With regards to Lemma 2.4, much more is true. If the Fourier transforms of any two compact sets $A, B \subset \mathbb{R}^d$ agree on any convergent sequence (with a finite limit point), then $A = B$. The reason is that $\hat{1}_A(\xi)$ and $\hat{1}_B(\xi)$ are both entire functions of $\xi \in \mathbb{C}^d$, so the proof follows from the identity theorem in complex variables.

(3) We note that $P_1(x)$ is defined to be equal to 0 at the integers because its Fourier series naturally converges to the mean of the discontinuity of the function at each integer.

(4) It has been known since the work of Riemann that the Bernoulli numbers occur as special values of the Riemann zeta function (see Exercise (4)). Similarly, the Hurwitz zeta function, defined for each fixed $x > 0$ by

$$\zeta(s, x) := \sum_{n=0}^{\infty} \frac{1}{(n+x)^s},$$

has a meromorphic continuation to all of $\mathbb{C}$ and its special values at the negative integers are essentially the Bernoulli polynomials: $\zeta(-n, x) = -\frac{1}{n+1} B_{n+1}(x)$ for each $n \in \mathbb{Z}_{\geq 1}$.

(5) There are sometimes very unusual (yet useful) formulations for the Fourier transform of certain functions. Ramanujan ([**201**, eq. (2)]) discovered the following remarkable formula for the Fourier transform of the Gamma function:

$$(2.70) \qquad \int_{\mathbb{R}} |\Gamma(a + iy)|^2 e^{-2\pi i \xi y} dy = \frac{\sqrt{\pi}\Gamma(a)\Gamma(a + \frac{1}{2})}{\cosh(\pi\xi)^{2a}},$$

valid for $a > 0$.

For example, with $a := \frac{1}{2}$ in the language of this chapter we have the Fourier pair $\{|\Gamma(\frac{1}{2} + iy)|^2, \frac{\pi}{\cosh(\pi\xi)}\}$. But from the Γ-function identity (2.75) (extended to a complex variable s), it quickly follows that $|\Gamma(\frac{1}{2} + iy)|^2 = \frac{\pi}{\cosh(\pi y)}$. So this special case of $a := \frac{1}{2}$ allows us to conclude the interesting fact that $f(y) := \frac{1}{\cosh(\pi x)}$ is a fixed point of the Fourier transform.

(6) I borrowed this joke from [**189**], a nice and informal introduction to Fourier analysis.

Exercises

"Problems worthy of attack prove their worth by fighting back."
   – Paul Erdős

(1) ♣ Show that the Fourier transform of the closed interval $[a, b]$ is

$$\hat{1}_{[a,b]}(\xi) = \frac{e^{-2\pi i \xi a} - e^{-2\pi i \xi b}}{2\pi i \xi}$$

for $\xi \neq 0$.

(2) Show that the Fourier transform of the unit cube $C := [0, 1]^d \subset \mathbb{R}^d$ is:

$$(2.71) \qquad \hat{1}_C(\xi) = \frac{1}{(2\pi i)^d} \prod_{k=1}^{d} \frac{1 - e^{-2\pi i \xi_k}}{\xi_k},$$

valid for all $\xi \in \mathbb{R}^d$ except for the union of hyperplanes defined by

$$H := \{x \in \mathbb{R}^d \mid \xi_1 = 0 \text{ or } \xi_2 = 0 \ldots \text{ or } \xi_d = 0\}.$$

(3) Suppose we are given two polynomials $p(x)$ and $q(x)$ of degree d. If there are $d + 1$ distinct points $\{z_1, \ldots, z_{d+1}\}$ in the complex plane such that $p(z_k) = q(z_k)$ for $k = 1, \ldots, d + 1$, show that the two polynomials are identical. (Hint: consider $(p - q)(z_k)$.)

(4) To gain some facility with generating functions, show by a brute force computation with Taylor series that the coefficients on the right-hand side of equation (2.13), which are called $B_n(x)$, by definition, must in fact be polynomials in x.

In fact, our direct computations will show that for all $n \geq 1$, we have

$$B_n(x) = \sum_{k=0}^{n} \binom{n}{k} B_{n-k}\, x^k,$$

where B_j is the jth Bernoulli number.

(5) ♣ Show that for all $n \geq 1$, we have

$$B_n(1 - x) = (-1)^n B_n(x).$$

(6) ♣ Show that for all $n \geq 1$, we have

$$B_n(x + 1) - B_n(x) = nx^{n-1}.$$

(7) ♣ Show that for all $n \geq 1$, we have

$$\frac{d}{dx} B_n(x) = n B_{n-1}(x).$$

(8) ♣ Prove that

$$\sum_{k=0}^{n-1} k^{d-1} = \frac{B_d(n) - B_d}{d}$$

for all integers $d \geq 1$ and $n \geq 2$.

(9) ♣ Show that the periodic Bernoulli polynomials $P_n(x) := B_n(\{x\})$ for all $n \geq 2$ have the following Fourier series:

(2.72)
$$P_n(x) = -\frac{n!}{(2\pi i)^n} \sum_{k \neq 0} \frac{e^{2\pi i k x}}{k^n},$$

valid for all $x \in \mathbb{R}$. For $n \geq 2$ these series are absolutely convergent. We note that from the definition above $B_n(x) = P_n(x)$ when $x \in (0, 1)$.

(10) Show that the greatest integer function $\lfloor x \rfloor$ (often called the "floor function") enjoys the property:

$$\sum_{k=0}^{N-1} \left\lfloor x + \frac{k}{N} \right\rfloor = \lfloor Nx \rfloor,$$

for all $x \in \mathbb{R}$ and all positive integers N.

(11) Show that the Bernoulli polynomials enjoy the following identity, proved by Joseph Ludwig Raabe in 1851:

$$B_n(Nx) = N^{n-1} \sum_{k=0}^{N-1} B_n\left(x + \frac{k}{N}\right),$$

for all $x \in \mathbb{R}$, all positive integers N, and for each $n \geq 1$.

Notes. Such formulas—in these last two exercises—are also called "multiplication Theorems" and they hold for many other functions, including the gamma function, the dilogarithm, the Hurwitz zeta function, the cotangent, and many more.

(12) ♣ Here we give a different method for defining the Bernoulli polynomials, based on the following three properties that they enjoy:
   (a) $B_0(x) = 1$.
   (b) For all $n \geq 1$, $\frac{d}{dx}B_n(x) = nB_{n-1}(x)$.
   (c) For all $n \geq 1$, we have $\int_0^1 B_n(x)dx = 0$.
   Show that the latter three properties imply the original defining property of the Bernoulli polynomials (2.13).

(13) Here is a more explicit, useful recursion for computing the Bernoulli polynomials. Show that

$$\sum_{k=0}^{n-1} \binom{n}{k}B_k(x) = nx^{n-1}$$

for all $n \geq 2$.

(14) Use the previous exercise together with equations (2.14)–(2.20) of the first six Bernoulli polynomials that appear in equation (2.20) to compute $B_7(x)$.

(15) Show that for odd $k \geq 3$, we have $B_k = 0$.

(16) Show that the even Bernoulli numbers alternate in sign. More precisely, show that

$$(-1)^{n+1}B_{2n} \geq 0$$

for each positive integer n.

(17) Show that the Bernoulli numbers enjoy the recursive property

$$\sum_{k=0}^{n} \binom{n+1}{k}B_k = 0$$

for all $n \geq 1$.

(18) Show that the Bernoulli numbers enjoy the following asymptotics:

$$B_{2n} \sim 2\frac{(2n)!}{(2\pi)^{2n}}$$

as $n \to \infty$. Here we are using the usual notation for asymptotic functions, namely that $f(n) \sim g(n)$ as $n \to \infty$ if $\lim_{n\to\infty} \frac{f(n)}{g(n)} \to 1$.

(19) ♣ Show that the following integrals converge and have the closed forms:

(2.73)
$$\int_{-\infty}^{\infty} \cos(x^2)dx = \sqrt{\frac{\pi}{2}},$$

(2.74)
$$\int_{-\infty}^{\infty} \sin(x^2)dx = \sqrt{\frac{\pi}{2}}.$$

Notes. These integrals are called Fresnel integrals, and they are related to the Cornu spiral, which was created by Marie Alfred Cornu. Cornu used the spiral as a tool for computing diffraction patterns that arise naturally in optics.

(20) Prove the following gamma function identity using the sinc function:

(2.75)
$$\frac{\sin(\pi x)}{\pi x} = \frac{1}{\Gamma(1 + x)\Gamma(1 - x)}$$

for all $x \notin \mathbb{Z}$.

Notes. This identity is often called Euler's reflection formula. $\Gamma(x)$ $:= \int_0^{\infty} e^{-t}t^{x-1}dt$ is by definition the gamma function, where the integral converges for all $x > 0$ (see Section 8 for more on the Γ function).

(21) ♣ Using the formula for the Fourier transform of the 2-dimensional cross-polytope ◊ derived in the text, namely

$$\hat{1}_{\Diamond}(\xi) = -\frac{1}{\pi^2}\left(\frac{\cos(2\pi\xi_1) - \cos(2\pi\xi_2)}{\xi_1^2 - \xi_2^2}\right),$$

find the area of ◊ by letting $\xi \to 0$ in the latter formula.

(22) Some elementary but very useful bounds for trig functions are developed here.
   (a) Prove that
$$\frac{2}{\pi} < \frac{\sin x}{x} \leq 1,$$

where the left inequality holds for $0 < x < \frac{\pi}{2}$ and the right inequality holds for $x \in \mathbb{R}$.

(b) Prove that
$$\frac{2x}{\pi} \le |1 - e^{ix}| \le |x|,$$
where the left inequality holds for $|x| \le \pi$, and the right inequality holds for $x \in \mathbb{R}$.

(c) Prove that
$$\frac{2x^2}{\pi^2} \le |1 - \cos x| \le \frac{x^2}{2},$$
where the left inequality holds for $|x| \le \pi$ and the right inequality holds for $x \in \mathbb{R}$.

(23) ♣ Show that $\int_{-\infty}^{\infty} \left|\frac{\sin(\pi x)}{\pi x}\right| dx = \infty$.

Notes. Once we have the inverse Fourier transform and its consequences at our disposal, this exercise will become trivial and much more general (Corollary 3.16), but it is still instructive to prove it from first principles here.

(24) There are (at least) two different ways of periodizing a given function $f : \mathbb{R} \to \mathbb{C}$ with respect to $\mathbb{Z}$. First, we can define $F_1(x) := f(\{x\})$ so that F_1 is periodic on $\mathbb{R}$ with period 1. Second, we may also define $F_2(x) := \sum_{n \in \mathbb{Z}} f(x + n)$, which is also a periodic function on $\mathbb{R}$ with period 1.

Find an absolutely integrable (meaning that $\int_{\mathbb{R}} |f(x)| dx$ converges) function f for which these two functions are not equal: $F_1 \ne F_2$.

Notes. In Chapter 3, we will see that the latter function $F_2(x) := \sum_{n \in \mathbb{Z}} f(x + n)$ captures a lot more information about f, and often captures all of f as well.

(25) Given linearly independent vectors $w_1, \dots, w_d \in \mathbb{R}^d$, let
$$v := -\frac{w_1 + \cdots + w_d}{2}$$
and define $Q := \{v + \sum_{k=1}^{d} \lambda_k w_k \mid \text{all } \lambda_k \in [0, 1]\}$, a parallelepiped. Show that Q is symmetric about the origin in the precise sense that $x \in Q \iff -x \in Q$.

(26) ♣ Show that the d-dimensional cross-polytope $\Diamond$ and the cube $\square :=$ $[-1, 1]^d$ are polar to each other.

(27) (a) Suppose $C \subset \mathbb{R}^3$ is a convex polytope with 5 vertices. Prove that at least one of the vertices of C has degree 4.

(b) Construct a convex polytope $\mathcal{P} \subset \mathbb{R}^3$ with 5 vertices, such that all of its vertices have degree 4.

(28) Prove the following 2-dimensional integral formula:

$$(2.76) \qquad \int_{\substack{\lambda_1,\lambda_2 \geq 0 \\ \lambda_1+\lambda_2 \leq 1}} e^{a\lambda_1} e^{b\lambda_2} d\lambda_1 d\lambda_2 = \frac{be^a - ae^b}{ab(a-b)} + \frac{1}{ab},$$

valid for all $a, b \in \mathbb{C}$ such that $ab(a-b) \neq 0$.

(29) Using the ideas of Example 2.34, prove (by induction on the dimension) that the Fourier transform of a general d-dimensional simplex $\Delta \subset \mathbb{R}^d$ is given by:

$$(2.77) \qquad \hat{1}_\Delta(\xi) = (\text{vol } \Delta)d! \sum_{j=1}^N \frac{e^{-2\pi i \langle v_j, \xi \rangle}}{\prod_{1 \leq k \leq d} \langle v_j - v_k, \xi \rangle} [k \neq j],$$

for all $\xi \in \mathbb{R}^d$, where the vertex set of $\mathcal{P}$ is $\{v_1, \ldots, v_N\}$.

(30) (**Abel summation by parts**) ♣ Here we prove the straightforward but very useful technique of Niels Abel. Suppose we are given two sequences $\{a_n\}_{n=1}^\infty$, and $\{b_n\}_{n=1}^\infty$. We define the finite partial sums $B_n := \sum_{k=1}^n b_k$. Then we have

$$(2.78) \qquad \sum_{k=1}^n a_k b_k = a_n B_n + \sum_{k=1}^{n-1} B_k(a_k - a_{k+1}),$$

for all $n \geq 2$.

Notes. Using the forward difference operator, it is easy to recognize identity (2.78) as a discrete version of integration by parts.

(31) (**Dirichlet's convergence test**) ♣ Suppose we are given a real sequence $\{a_n\}_{n=1}^\infty$, and a complex sequence $\{b_n\}_{n=1}^\infty$, such that
  (a) $\{a_n\}$ is monotonically decreasing to 0, and
  (b) $|\sum_{k=1}^n b_k| \leq M$, for some positive constant M, and all $n \geq 1$.
  Then $\sum_{k=1}^\infty a_k b_k$ converges.

(32) Prove that for all $x \in \mathbb{R} \setminus \mathbb{Z}$ we have the following important identity, called the "Dirichlet kernel", named after Dirichlet:

$$(2.79) \qquad \sum_{k=-n}^n e^{2\pi i k x} = \frac{\sin(\pi x(2n+1))}{\sin(\pi x)}.$$

Notes. An equivalent way to write (2.79) is clearly:

$$1 + 2 \sum_{k=1}^n \cos(2\pi k x) = \frac{\sin(\pi x(2n+1))}{\sin(\pi x)}.$$

(33) Prove that we have the bound on the following exponential sum:

(2.80)
$$\left| \sum_{k=1}^{n} e^{2\pi i k x} \right| \le \frac{1}{|\sin(\pi x)|},$$

for any fixed $x \in \mathbb{R} - \mathbb{Z}$ and for all $n \in \mathbb{Z}_{>0}$.

(34) ♣ Prove that $\sum_{m=1}^{\infty} \frac{e^{2\pi i m a}}{m}$ converges, given any fixed $a \in \mathbb{R} - \mathbb{Z}$.

Notes. We see that, although $\sum_{m=1}^{\infty} \frac{e^{2\pi i m a}}{m}$ does not converge absolutely, Abel's summation formula (2.78) gives us

$$\sum_{k=1}^{n} \frac{e^{2\pi i k a}}{k} = \frac{1}{n} \sum_{r=1}^{n} e^{2\pi i r a} + \sum_{k=1}^{n-1} \left(\sum_{r=1}^{k} e^{2\pi i r a} \right) \frac{1}{k(k+1)},$$

and the latter series **does converge absolutely** as $n \to +\infty$. So we see that Abel summation transforms one series (that barely converges at all) into another series that converges more rapidly.

(35) ♣ Here we will prove that

(2.81)
$$\int_{-\infty}^{\infty} \frac{\sin(\pi t)}{\pi t} dt = 1$$

in the sense that $\int_{0}^{\infty} \frac{\sin t}{t} dt = \frac{\pi}{2}$. The integral (2.81) is sometimes called "the Dirichlet integral". Comparing this Dirichlet integral with Exercise (23), we see that there is something subtle going on here. We will end up proving something slightly more general here:

$$\int_{0}^{\infty} e^{-st} \frac{\sin t}{t} dt = \frac{\pi}{2} - \tan^{-1} s,$$

for all $s > 0$.

(a) Define

(2.82)
$$F(s) := \int_{0}^{\infty} e^{-st} \frac{\sin t}{t} dt$$

for each $s > 0$. Justify differentiation under the integral sign and show that

$$\frac{dF}{ds} = -\int_{0}^{\infty} e^{-st} \sin t \, dt.$$

(b) Show that $\int_{0}^{\infty} e^{-st} \sin t \, dt = \frac{1}{1+s^2}$.

(c) Show that $F(s) = C - \tan^{-1} s$, and then show that the constant $C = \frac{\pi}{2}$.

(d) Prove that F is a continuous function of $s \in \mathbb{R}_{>0}$, and finally prove that

$$\lim_{s \to 0} F(s) = \frac{\pi}{2},$$

which is the desired result (Here you might want to integrate by parts first, and then use the dominated convergence theorem).

Notes. There are many proofs of this famous identity (2.81), and although the method of contour integration is arguably the most straightforward, here we are only assuming knowledge of some real analysis. The expression in (2.82) is also known as the Laplace transform of the sinc function, and it is a variation of the Fourier transform that we will revisit when studying similar transforms of cones in Section 8.

(36) ♣ Here we give a rigorous proof of the tricky fact that for all $x \in \mathbb{R}$, we have

$$\lim_{N \to \infty} \int_{-N}^{N} \frac{\sin(\pi\xi)}{\pi\xi} e^{-2\pi i \xi x} d\xi = 1_{[-\frac{1}{2}, \frac{1}{2}]}(x),$$

following an approach taken by Bochner [40]. We begin by noticing that this integral can be easily reduced to a real-valued integral:

$$\int_{-N}^{N} \frac{\sin(\pi\xi)}{\pi\xi} e^{-2\pi i \xi x} d\xi = \int_{-N}^{N} \frac{\sin(\pi\xi)}{\pi\xi} \cos(2\pi\xi x) d\xi,$$

because for each $x \in \mathbb{R}$, $\int_{-N}^{N} \frac{\sin(\pi\xi)}{\pi\xi} \sin(2\pi\xi x) d\xi = 0$, owing to the oddness of the integrand.

(a) Using the result from Exercise (35), prove that

$$\lim_{N \to \infty} \int_{-N}^{N} \frac{\sin(\pi\alpha t)}{\pi t} dt = \begin{cases} 1 & \text{if } \alpha > 0, \\ 0 & \text{if } \alpha = 0, \\ -1 & \text{if } \alpha < 0. \end{cases}$$

(b) Finish up by using $2 \sin t \cos(\alpha t) = \sin(1 - \alpha)t + \sin(1 + \alpha)t$, thereby showing that the desired integral

$$\lim_{N \to \infty} \int_{-N}^{N} \frac{\sin(\pi t)}{\pi t} \cos(2\pi t x) dt$$

reduces to part (36a).

Chapter 3

The basics of Fourier analysis

"If a function is periodic, then we should try to expand it into its Fourier series, and wonderful things will begin to happen..."
– Erich Hecke

Figure 3.1. The unit cube $\square := [0,1]^3$ in $\mathbb{R}^3$, which tiles the space by translations. Which other polytopes tile by translations? How can we make mathematical use of such tilings? In particular, can we give an explicit basis of exponentials for functions defined on $\square$?

1. Intuition

Because we will use tools from Fourier analysis throughout, we introduce them here as an outline of the field with the goal of *applying* them to the discrete geometry of polytopes, lattices, and their interactions. We will sometimes introduce a concept by using an intuitive argument, which we call "fast and loose", but after such an intuitive argument we state the precise version of the corresponding theorem. In this chapter we will sometimes point to the literature for some of the proofs.

Our goal is to use the necessary tools of Fourier analysis in order to tackle problems in the enumerative combinatorics of polytopes, in number theory, in discrete geometry, and in some other fields. One important idea is that the Poisson summation formula allows us to **discretize integrals**, in a sense that will be made precise in later chapters.

One pattern that the reader may have already noticed—among all of the examples of Fourier transforms of polytopes computed thus far—is that each of them is a linear combination of a very special kind of rational function of ξ multiplied by a complex exponential that involves a vertex of the polytope:

$$(3.1) \qquad \hat{1}_{\mathcal{P}}(\xi) = \sum_{k=1}^{M} \frac{1}{\prod_{j=1}^{d} \langle \omega_{j,k}(v_k), \xi \rangle} \, e^{2\pi i \langle v_k, \xi \rangle},$$

where the vertices of $\mathcal{P}$ are $v_1, \ldots, v_N$, and where $M \geq N$. We observed that in all of our examples thus far the denominators are in fact products of linear forms, as in (3.1). We will be able to see some of the more precise geometric structure for these products of linear forms, which come from the edges of the polytope, once we learn more about Fourier–Laplace transforms of cones.

It is rather astounding that every single fact about a given polytope $\mathcal{P}$ is somehow hiding inside these **rational-exponential** functions given by (3.1) due to the fact that the Fourier transform $\hat{1}_{\mathcal{P}}$ is a complete invariant (Lemma 2.4).

Finally, it is worth mentioning that not every fact in this chapter is necessary for the comprehension of the rest of the book. The reader is advised to learn just some of this chapter, and as she/he reads the rest of the book periodically revisit this chaper.

2. Introducing the Fourier transform on $L^1(\mathbb{R}^d)$

In the spirit of bringing the reader very quickly up to speed regarding the applications of Fourier analytic tools, we outline the basics of the field and prove some of them. Nowadays, there are many good texts on Fourier analysis and the reader is encouraged to peruse some of these books (see Note (1)).

Unless otherwise stated, all of our functions will have the form $f :$ $\mathbb{R}^d \to \mathbb{C}$. One of the most useful tools for us is the Poisson summation formula. We provide several versions of Poisson summation, each of which uses a different set of sufficient conditions.

As we will see, the Fourier transform is a very friendly creature, allowing us to travel back and forth between the "space domain" and the "frequency domain" to obtain many useful results. The readers who are already familiar with basics of Fourier analysis may skip this chapter without impeding their understanding of the rest of the book. Although we enjoy thinking about the warm and cozy Hilbert spaces $L^2(\mathbb{R}^d)$ and $L^2([0,1]^d)$, there are exotic Fourier series that are pointwise divergent and yet represent continuous functions, a whole field onto itself. We won't go there. However, the very basic convergence issues are still important for us as well, and we will study them because we want to get the reader up and running.

The function space that immediately comes up very naturally is the the space of **absolutely integrable functions** on $\mathbb{R}^d$:

$$L^1(\mathbb{R}^d) := \left\{ f : \mathbb{R}^d \to \mathbb{C} \mid \int_{\mathbb{R}^d} |f(x)| dx < \infty \right\}.$$

Secondly, the space of **square-integrable functions** on $\mathbb{R}^d$ is defined by:

$$L^2(\mathbb{R}^d) := \left\{ f : \mathbb{R}^d \to \mathbb{C} \mid \int_{\mathbb{R}^d} |f(x)|^2 dx < \infty \right\}.$$

The usual theory of Fourier transforms progresses by first defining the Fourier transform for functions belonging to $L^1(\mathbb{R}^d)$, which is quite a natural condition, and then later extending the Fourier transform to the $L^2(\mathbb{R}^d)$ space by taking appropriate limits. We initially restrict attention to functions $f \in L^1(\mathbb{R}^d)$.

There are many fascinating facts about all of these functions spaces. For practice, let us ask:

Question 3.1 (Rhetorical). Given two functions $f, g \in L^2(\mathbb{R}^d)$, is their product always in $L^1(\mathbb{R}^d)$?

Well, we have the **Cauchy–Schwartz inequality** for the Hilbert space $L^2(\mathbb{R}^d)$:

$$(3.2) \quad \int_{\mathbb{R}^d} |f(x)g(x)| dx \leq \left(\int_{\mathbb{R}^d} |f(x)|^2 dx \right)^{\frac{1}{2}} \left(\int_{\mathbb{R}^d} |g(x)|^2 dx \right)^{\frac{1}{2}} < \infty,$$

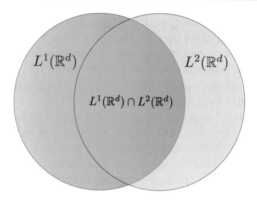

Figure 3.2. Neither of the function spaces $L^1(\mathbb{R}^d)$ and $L^2(\mathbb{R}^d)$ is contained in the other, as in Example 3.7.

the latter inequality holding by the assumption $f, g \in L^2(\mathbb{R}^d)$. So the product $f(x)g(x)$ is indeed in $L^1(\mathbb{R}^d)$, answering Question 3.1 in the affirmative. This is the first sign that there is an interesting dance between L^1 functions and L^2 functions. In fact, this metaphorical dance between $L^1(\mathbb{R}^d)$ and $L^2(\mathbb{R}^d)$ is simply too useful to ignore so we will study some of the interactions between these two spaces from first principles (see Section 17, for example).

The utility of the Cauchy–Schwarz inequality should never be underestimated, and holds in greater generality.

Lemma 3.2. *Let V be an inner product space, with the inner product $\langle x, y \rangle$. Then the following Cauchy–Schwarz inequality holds:*

$$|\langle x, y \rangle| \le \|x\|\|y\|$$

for all $x, y \in V$. Moreover, equality holds $\iff$ x and y are linearly dependent. In addition, the function

$$\|x\| := \sqrt{\langle x, x \rangle}$$

is a norm on V.   □

For a proof see [**79**, Proposition 3.2]. Appendix 3.3 has some related material. We conclude from Lemma 3.2 that every inner product space is also a normed vector space. The converse is false, though, in the sense that there are normed vector spaces whose norm does not arise from any inner product. One fascinating example of such a space is $L^1(\mathbb{R}^d)$, which is not a Hilbert space, as we now easily show by exhibiting a counterexample to the Cauchy–Schwarz inequality.

Example 3.3. We claim that the Cauchy–Schwarz inequality is false in $L^1(\mathbb{R})$. If the Cauchy–Schwarz inequality was true here, then (3.2) would be valid for all functions $f, g \in L^1(\mathbb{R})$. But as a counterexample, let

$$f(x) := 1_{(0,1)}(x)\frac{1}{\sqrt{x}}.$$

It is easy to see that $f \in L^1(\mathbb{R})$:

$$\int_{\mathbb{R}} 1_{(0,1)}(x)\frac{1}{\sqrt{x}}dx = \int_0^1 \frac{1}{\sqrt{x}}dx = \frac{1}{2}.$$

But $\int_{\mathbb{R}} f(x) \cdot f(x)dx = \int_0^1 \frac{1}{x}dx$ diverges so that we do not have a Cauchy–Schwarz inequality in $L^1(\mathbb{R})$ because here both the left-hand side and the right-hand side of such an inequality do not converge. $\qquad\square$

We say that f is **bounded on a set** $S \subset \mathbb{R}^d$ by a constant $M > 0$, if $|f(x)| < M$ for all $x \in S$. In the opposite direction of Example 3.3, if two functions f, g are bounded on $\mathbb{R}^d$ and absolutely integrable on $\mathbb{R}^d$, then we do have a Cauchy–Schwartz inequality for the pair f, g, and we let the reader enjoy its verification.

We will see that despite the fact that $L^1(\mathbb{R}^d)$ is not a Hilbert space it does have a very beautiful structure; namely that it is a Banach algebra (Lemma 3.46).

3. The triangle inequality for integrals

An easy but extremely important inequality is the **triangle inequality for integrals**, as follows.

Theorem 3.4. *For any* $f \in L^1(\mathbb{R}^d)$ *and any subset* $S \subset \mathbb{R}^d$, *we have:*

$$(3.3) \qquad \left|\int_S f(x)dx\right| \leq \int_S |f(x)|dx.$$

Proof. Letting $z := \int_S f(x)dx \in \mathbb{C}$, we may write $|z| = \alpha z$ for a (unique) complex α on the unit circle. We let u be the real part of $\alpha f := u + iv$ so that $u \leq \sqrt{u^2 + v^2} = |\alpha f| = |f|$. Altogether, we have:
(3.4)

$$\left|\int_S f(x)dx\right| = \alpha \int_S f(x)dx = \int_S \alpha f(x)dx = \int_S u(x)dx \leq \int_S |f(x)|dx.$$

In the third equality we used the fact that $\int_S \alpha f(x)dx$ is real, which follows from the first two equalities: $\int_S \alpha f(x)dx = \left|\int_S f(x)dx\right|$. $\qquad\square$

Although Theorem 3.4 seems innocently trivial, it is sometimes quite powerful.

Corollary 3.5. *If f is bounded on a set $S \subset \mathbb{R}^d$ by a constant $M > 0$, then:*

$$(3.5) \qquad \left| \int_S f(x)dx \right| \leq \text{vol}(S) \cdot M.$$

Proof.

$$\left| \int_S f(x)dx \right| \leq \int_S |f(x)|dx \leq \int_S Mdx = \text{vol}(S) \cdot M,$$

where the first inequality uses the triangle inequality for integrals, namely Theorem (3.4), and the second inequality uses the boundedness assumption on f. $\qquad \square$

What about the equality case in Theorem 3.4? Luckily there is a very satisfying answer, which turns out to be so useful that it merits its own corollary. We will keep using the same notation as in the proof of Theorem 3.4.

Corollary 3.6 (Equality conditions for the triangle inequality). *Let $f \in L^1(\mathbb{R}^d)$ fix any subset $S \subset \mathbb{R}^d$ and suppose that we have the following equality for the nonzero integral $\int_S f(x)dx$:*

$$(3.6) \qquad \left| \int_S f(x)dx \right| = \int_S |f(x)|dx.$$

We define the constant $\alpha := \frac{|\int_S f(x)dx|}{\int_S f(x)dx}$. Then we have

$$|f(x)| = \alpha f(x),$$

for almost all $x \in \mathbb{R}^d$.

Proof. Returning to the proof of Theorem 3.4, in particular equation (3.4), our equality assumption in (3.6) now implies:

$$(3.7) \qquad \int_S (|f(x)| - u(x))dx = 0.$$

We also have $|f(x)| - u(x) \geq 0$, so by (3.7) we now have $|f(x)| - u(x) = 0$ almost everywhere. Now we recall that u is the real part of αf. So we have $|f(x)| = \mathcal{R}(\alpha f(x))$ almost everywhere. Since $|f(x)| = |\alpha f(x)|$ we see that $\mathcal{R}(\alpha f(x)) = |\alpha f(x)|$ almost everywhere. In other words, $\alpha f(x) = |\alpha f(x)| = |f(x)|$ almost everywhere. $\qquad \square$

Next, we will show that

$$L^1(\mathbb{R}^d) \not\subset L^2(\mathbb{R}^d), \text{ and } L^2(\mathbb{R}^d) \not\subset L^1(\mathbb{R}^d),$$

confirming the validity of set intersections in Figure 3.2. We will do it for $d = 1$, but the idea works for any dimension.

Example 3.7. Let us define

$$f(x) := \begin{cases} x^{-\frac{2}{3}} & \text{if } 0 < x < 1, \\ 0 & \text{otherwise.} \end{cases}$$

Then $f \in L^1(\mathbb{R})$ because $\int_{\mathbb{R}} |f(x)| dx := \int_0^1 |x^{-\frac{2}{3}}| dx = 3x^{\frac{1}{3}}\big|_0^1 = 3$. But $f \notin L^2(\mathbb{R})$ because $\int_{\mathbb{R}} |f(x)|^2 dx = \int_0^1 |x^{-\frac{4}{3}}| dx = -3x^{-\frac{1}{3}}\big|_0^1 = \infty$. So $L^1(\mathbb{R}) \not\subset L^2(\mathbb{R})$.

On the other hand, if we consider

$$g(x) := \begin{cases} x^{-\frac{2}{3}} & \text{if } x > 1, \\ 0 & \text{otherwise,} \end{cases}$$

then $g \in L^2(\mathbb{R})$ because $\int_{\mathbb{R}} |g(x)|^2 dx = \int_1^\infty |x^{-\frac{4}{3}}| dx = -3x^{-\frac{1}{3}}\big|_1^\infty = 3$. But $g \notin L^1(\mathbb{R})$ because $\int_{\mathbb{R}} |g(x)| dx = \int_1^\infty x^{-\frac{2}{3}} dx = 3x^{\frac{1}{3}}\big|_1^\infty = \infty$. So $L^2(\mathbb{R}) \not\subset L^1(\mathbb{R})$. $\qquad\square$

We have defined the Fourier transform before, and we remind the reader that for any function $f \in L^1(\mathbb{R}^d)$, the **Fourier transform** of f is

$$(3.8) \qquad \hat{f}(\xi) := \int_{\mathbb{R}^d} f(x) e^{-2\pi i \langle x, \xi \rangle} dx.$$

Where does this definition really come from? One motivation comes from the inner product for functions (in $L^2(\mathbb{R}^d)$), where we project a function f onto each exponential function:

$$\langle f, e^{2\pi i \langle x, \xi \rangle} \rangle := \int_{\mathbb{R}^d} f(x) e^{-2\pi i \langle x, \xi \rangle} dx.$$

Another motivation comes from the proof of the Poisson summation formula—equation (3.56), which shows a crucial connection between the Fourier transform of f and the Fourier coefficients of the periodized function $\sum_{n \in \mathbb{Z}^d} f(x + n)$.

One of the first things we might notice is:

Claim 3.8. *The Fourier transform is a bounded linear operator.*

The Fourier transform is a linear operator by the linearity of the integral: $\widehat{(f + g)} = \hat{f} + \hat{g}$; and it is a bounded operator due to the elementary estimate in Lemma 3.9.

A natural question is: Where does the Fourier transform take a function $f \in L^1(\mathbb{R}^d)$? An immediate partial answer is that for any $f \in L^1(\mathbb{R}^d)$, we have

$$\hat{f} \in B(\mathbb{R}^d),$$

where

$$B(\mathbb{R}^d) := \{f : \mathbb{R}^d \to \mathbb{C} \mid \exists M > 0 \text{ such that } |f(x)| < M, \forall x \in \mathbb{R}^d\}$$

is the space of bounded functions on $\mathbb{R}^d$. Here the constant M depends only on f. To see this, consider:

$$(3.9) \qquad |\hat{f}(\xi)| := \left| \int_{\mathbb{R}^d} f(x) e^{-2\pi i \langle x, \xi \rangle} dx \right|$$

$$\leq \int_{\mathbb{R}^d} \left| f(x) e^{-2\pi i \langle x, \xi \rangle} \right| dx$$

$$(3.10) \qquad = \int_{\mathbb{R}^d} |f(x)| \, dx := \|f\|_{L^1(\mathbb{R}^d)},$$

where we used Theorem 3.4, the triangle inequality for integrals, together with the fact that $\left| e^{-2\pi i \langle x, \xi \rangle} \right| = 1$. So we have just proved the following fact.

Lemma 3.9. *Given $f \in L^1(\mathbb{R}^d)$, its Fourier transform is uniformly bounded, with the following bound:*

$$(3.11) \qquad |\hat{f}(\xi)| \leq \|f\|_{L^1(\mathbb{R}^d)},$$

for all $\xi \in \mathbb{R}^d$. □

Example 3.10. Let us bound the Fourier transform of an indicator function 1_S for any bounded set $S \subset \mathbb{R}^d$:

$$|\hat{1}_S(\xi)| := \left| \int_S e^{-2\pi i \langle x, \xi \rangle} dx \right| \leq \int_S \left| e^{-2\pi i \langle x, \xi \rangle} \right| dx = \int_S dx = \text{measure}(S).$$

In particular, for any polytope $\mathcal{P} \subset \mathbb{R}^d$,

$$|\hat{1}_{\mathcal{P}}(\xi)| \leq \text{vol } \mathcal{P}, \text{ for all } \xi \in \mathbb{R}^d.$$

We already know that $\hat{1}_{\mathcal{P}}(0) = \text{vol } \mathcal{P}$, so it is natural to ask whether the maximum allowed value of vol $\mathcal{P}$ can also be achieved by a nonzero $\xi \in \mathbb{R}^d$; or perhaps it may be the case that we always have the strict inequality $|\hat{1}_{\mathcal{P}}(\xi)| < \text{vol } \mathcal{P}$, for all nonzero $\xi \in \mathbb{R}^d$? (See Exercise (26)). □

But a lot more is true for absolutely integrable functions.

Lemma 3.11. *If $f \in L^1(\mathbb{R}^d)$, then $\hat{f}$ is uniformly continuous on $\mathbb{R}^d$.*

Proof. We fix any $\xi \in \mathbb{R}^d$, and $h \in \mathbb{R}^d$, and we compute:

$$\hat{f}(\xi + h) - \hat{f}(\xi) := \int_{\mathbb{R}^d} f(x)\left(e^{-2\pi i \langle x, \xi + h \rangle} - e^{-2\pi i \langle x, \xi \rangle}\right) dx$$

$$= \int_{\mathbb{R}^d} f(x) e^{-2\pi i \langle x, \xi \rangle}\left(e^{-2\pi i \langle x, h \rangle} - 1\right) dx,$$

so by the triangle inequality for integrals, we have

$$(3.12) \qquad |\hat{f}(\xi + h) - \hat{f}(\xi)| \le \int_{\mathbb{R}^d} |f(x)||e^{-2\pi i \langle x, h \rangle} - 1| dx.$$

Letting $g_h(x) := f(x)\left(e^{-2\pi i \langle x, h \rangle} - 1\right)$, we see that

$$|g_h(x)| \le 2|f(x)|, \text{ and } \lim_{h \to 0} |g_h(x)| = 0$$

using $|e^{-2\pi i \langle x, h \rangle} - 1| \le 2$. We may now use the dominated convergence theorem because the functions g_h are dominated by the absolutely integrable function $2f$. So we get:

$$\lim_{h \to 0} \int_{\mathbb{R}^d} |f(x)||e^{-2\pi i \langle x, h \rangle} - 1| dx = \int_{\mathbb{R}^d} \lim_{h \to 0} |f(x)||e^{-2\pi i \langle x, h \rangle} - 1| dx = 0.$$

Because the latter limit is independent of ξ, (3.12) tells us that

$$|\hat{f}(\xi + h) - f(\xi)| \to 0,$$

as $h \to 0$ uniformly in $\xi \in \mathbb{R}^d$. $\qquad\square$

It turns out that sometimes we need to measure distance between functions in a manner different than just pointwise convergence. We therefore introduce convergence in the L^2 norm. We say that a sequence of functions $f_n : \mathbb{R}^d \to \mathbb{C}$ converges to a function f **in the L^2 norm** if

$$(3.13) \qquad \int_{\mathbb{R}^d} |f_n(x) - f(x)|^2 dx \to 0, \text{ as } n \to \infty,$$

for which we also use the notation $\lim_{n\to\infty} \|f_n - f\|_2 = 0$. It is very useful to define the $L^p(\mathbb{R}^d)$ spaces for each $1 \le p < \infty$:

$$(3.14) \qquad L^p(\mathbb{R}^d) := \{f : \mathbb{R}^d \to \mathbb{C} \mid \int_{\mathbb{R}^d} |f(x)|^p dx < \infty\},$$

which naturally extend the L^1 and L^2 spaces. In fact, for functions $f \in L^p(\mathbb{R}^d)$, the function

$$(3.15) \qquad \|f\|_{L^p(\mathbb{R}^d)} := \left(\int_{\mathbb{R}^d} |f(x)|^p dx \right)^{\frac{1}{p}}$$

is a norm (see Exercise (44)). It is also a fact that for $p \neq 2$ this norm does not arise from an inner product. But for $p = 2$ this norm *does* arise from an inner product via Lemma 3.2. It is well known that among all of the $L^p(\mathbb{R}^d)$ spaces, the only one that is a Hilbert space is $L^2(\mathbb{R}^d)$. For the curious reader, the other $L^p(\mathbb{R}^d)$ spaces for $p \neq 2$ also possess some additional structure, namely that they are Banach spaces (and Banach algebras as well), after identifying two functions that are equal almost everywhere (see [79] for details). The development of L^p spaces is very important for Fourier analysis; for the sake of simplicity of exposition, here we will mostly work with $p = 1$ and $p = 2$.

Similar to (3.13), we define **convergence in the L^p norm** for $1 \leq p < \infty$ by

$$(3.16) \qquad \int_{\mathbb{R}^d} |f_n(x) - f(x)|^p \, dx \to 0, \text{ as } n \to \infty,$$

for which we also use the notation

$$\lim_{n \to \infty} \|f_n - f\|_p = 0.$$

For a review of some of these various forms of convergence, see Appendix A.

4. The Riemann–Lebesgue lemma

The celebrated **Riemann–Lebesgue lemma** gives us the basic decay property of the Fourier transform $\hat{f}(\xi)$ as $|\xi| \to \infty$. To prove it, we will use the fact that we can approximate any function $f \in L^1(\mathbb{R}^d)$ with arbitrary precision by using "step functions" in $\mathbb{R}^d$. More precisely, let a **box in** $\mathbb{R}^d$ be defined by $\mathcal{P} := [a_1, b_1] \times \cdots \times [a_d, b_d]$, and consider the indicator function $1_{\mathcal{P}}$ of this box. If we consider the set of all finite sums taken over all such indicator functions (varying over all boxes) with arbitrary real coefficients, then this set turns out to be dense in $L^1(\mathbb{R}^d)$ in the L^1 norm. We record this fact as a lemma.

Lemma 3.12. *If $f \in L^1(\mathbb{R}^d)$, then there is a finite sum of indicator functions of boxes that approaches f, in the L^1 norm.*   □

Lemma 3.13 (Riemann–Lebesgue lemma). *If $f \in L^1(\mathbb{R}^d)$, then:*

$$\lim_{|\xi| \to \infty} \hat{f}(\xi) = 0.$$

Proof. We first show the result in the case that f is the indicator function of a box. We already know via Exercise (1) that if $\mathcal{P} := [a_1, b_1] \times \cdots \times [a_d, b_d]$, then

$$(3.17) \qquad \hat{1}_{\mathcal{P}}(\xi) = \prod_{k=1}^{d} \frac{e^{-2\pi i \xi_k a_k} - e^{-2\pi i \xi_k b_k}}{2\pi i \xi_k}$$

for all $\xi \in \mathbb{R}^d$ with nonvanishing coordinates. As $|\xi| \to \infty$ through a sequence of ξs with nonvanishing coordinates, we see that while the numerator of (3.17) stays bounded, the denominator satisfies

$$\prod_{k=1}^{d} |\xi_k| \to \infty.$$

Hence, we have proved the lemma for indicator functions of boxes. Since $f \in L^1(\mathbb{R}^d)$, we know by Lemma 3.12 that there exists a sequence of functions $g_n \in L^1(\mathbb{R}^d)$, such that $\|f - g_n\|_1 \to 0$ as $n \to \infty$. Also, by (3.17) we know that this sequence already satisfies $\lim_{|\xi| \to \infty} \hat{g}_n(\xi) = 0$. Using the elementary inequality (3.11), we get:

$$|\hat{f}(\xi) - \hat{g}_n(\xi)| = |\widehat{(f - g_n)}(\xi)| \le \|f - g_n\|_1 \to 0,$$

as $n \to \infty$. Therefore $\lim_{|\xi| \to \infty} \hat{f}(\xi) = 0$. □

With all of the above properties, it is now natural to consider the space of all uniformly continuous functions on $\mathbb{R}^d$ that go to 0 at infinity:

$$C_0(\mathbb{R}^d) := \{f : \mathbb{R}^d \to \mathbb{C} \mid f \text{ is uniformly continuous on } \mathbb{R}^d,$$
$$\text{and } \lim_{|x| \to \infty} |f| = 0\}.$$

So, although the Fourier transform does not map the space $L^1(\mathbb{R}^d)$ into itself, all of the above results may be summarized as follows.

Lemma 3.14. *If $f \in L^1(\mathbb{R}^d)$, then $\hat{f} \in C_0(\mathbb{R}^d)$.*

Proof. The boundedness of $\hat{f}$ follows from the inequality

$$|\hat{f}(\xi)| \le \|f\|_1$$

which is equation (3.11), the uniform continuity follows from Lemma 3.11, and the decay to zero at infinity follows from Lemma 3.13. □

5. The inverse Fourier transform

We mentioned briefly in Theorem 2.1 and Example 2.2 that we may invert the Fourier Transform and we gave an inuitive description there. Now we state things more formally.

Theorem 3.15 (The inverse Fourier transform). *If $f \in L^1(\mathbb{R}^d)$ and $\hat{f} \in L^1(\mathbb{R}^d)$, then*

$$(3.18) \qquad f(x) = \int_{\mathbb{R}^d} \hat{f}(\xi) e^{2\pi i \langle \xi, x \rangle} d\xi$$

for almost all $x \in \mathbb{R}^d$. If we further assume that f is continuous, then (3.18) holds for all $x \in \mathbb{R}^d$. □

The reader is invited to see [**79**] for a proof. Usually, the proofs of Theorem 3.15 proceed by introducing a Gaussian approximate identity inside the integrand of the inversion formula, then recognizing the integrand as a convolution with an approximate identity, and finally removing the approximate identity by invoking a limit, such as (3.115) at each point of continuity of f.

The inverse Fourier transform is sometimes called "Fourier inversion". Let us see an interesting application, showing in particular that the Fourier transform of a polytope is *not* absolutely integrable.

Corollary 3.16. *Let $C \subset \mathbb{R}^d$ be a finite union of convex, compact sets, of positive measure. Then we have:*

$$\hat{1}_C \notin L^1(\mathbb{R}^d).$$

Proof. Suppose to the contrary that $\hat{1}_C \in L^1(\mathbb{R}^d)$. Because we also have $1_C \in L^1(\mathbb{R}^d)$ (trivially true), we may apply Fourier inversion, namely formula (3.18):

$$(3.19) \qquad \mathcal{F}\left(\hat{1}_C\right)(x) = 1_C(-x)$$

for almost all $x \in \mathbb{R}^d$. But by Lemma 3.11 we may also conclude that $\mathcal{F}\left(\hat{1}_C\right)$ is a continuous function on all of $\mathbb{R}^d$. This means that it is possible to modify 1_C on a set of measure 0 to obtain a function $f(x)$ that is continuous everywhere. But this is easily seen to be impossible, as follows.

Since 1_C is already continuous on all of the interior of C and on the complement of its closure, the only points of discontinuity where we can redefine 1_C to become the continuous function $f(x)$ is on ∂C, the boundary of C. Pick a point $z \in \partial C$ (there exists such a nontrivial point by the assumption of the structure of C). So there is a sequence $x_n \to z$ with $x_n \in \text{int } C$, and there is also a sequence $y_n \to z$ with $y_n \in C^c$. By definition $f(y_n) = 1_C(y_n) = 0$ for all n, and by the continuity of f we also have $f(z) = 0$. On the other hand, $f(x_n) = 1_C(x_n) = 1$ for all n, and by the continuity of f we also have $f(z) = 1$, a contradiction. $\qquad \square$

If C is a convex set, for example, then we see that $\hat{1}_C$ is not absolutely integrable and we did not have to make any messy computations to see it. Of course, one of the most basic consequences of Fourier inversion is the uniqueness of transforms, as follows.

Corollary 3.17. *Suppose that $f, g \in L^1(\mathbb{R}^d)$ and that $\hat{f}(\xi) = \hat{g}(\xi)$ for all $\xi \in \mathbb{R}^d$. Then $f = g$ almost everywhere.*

Proof. Letting $h := f - g$, we clearly have $h \in L^1(\mathbb{R}^d)$. It follows that $\hat{h}(\xi) = (\hat{f} - \hat{g})(\xi) = 0$ for all $x \in \mathbb{R}^d$. In particular $\hat{h} \in L^1(\mathbb{R}^d)$, so that we may apply Fourier inversion:

$$h(x) = \int_{\mathbb{R}^d} \hat{h}(\xi) e^{2\pi i \langle x, \xi \rangle} dx = \int_{\mathbb{R}^d} 0 \, dx = 0,$$

almost everywhere. $\qquad \square$

Now we can revisit our intuitive Lemma 2.4 and give a rigorous proof of a more general statement (see also Note (2) in Chapter 2).

Theorem 3.18. *Let $\mathcal{P} \subset \mathbb{R}^d$ be a compact set. Then the function $\hat{1}_{\mathcal{P}}$ uniquely determines $\mathcal{P}$. As such, given any two d-dimensional compact sets $\mathcal{P}, Q \subset \mathbb{R}^d$, we have*

(3.20) $\qquad \hat{1}_{\mathcal{P}}(\xi) = \hat{1}_Q(\xi)$ *for all* $\xi \in \mathbb{R}^d \iff \mathcal{P} = Q.$

In particular, for any polytope $\mathcal{P}$, its Fourier transform $\hat{1}_{\mathcal{P}}$ uniquely determines the polytope.

Proof. Suppose that $\hat{1}_{\mathcal{P}}(\xi) = \hat{1}_Q(\xi)$ for all $\xi \in \mathbb{R}^d$. We apply Corollary 3.17 to the L^1 functions $1_{\mathcal{P}}$ and 1_Q to conclude that $1_{\mathcal{P}}(x) = 1_Q(x)$ for almost all $x \in \mathbb{R}^d$. In other words, $1_{\mathcal{P}} - 1_Q = 0$ almost everywhere.

The latter statement implies that $1_{\mathcal{P}} - 1_Q$ vanishes at each of its points of continuity. But $1_{\mathcal{P}}$ is continuous on the whole interior of $\mathcal{P}$, and the same goes for 1_Q (they are both identically 1 there). Therefore $1_{\mathcal{P}}(x) = 1_Q(x) = 1$ for all x in the interior of $\mathcal{P}$ and for all x in the interior of Q. Also, $1_{\mathcal{P}}(x) = 1_Q(x) = 0$ for each $x \notin \mathcal{P}$ and for each $x \notin Q$. Therefore $1_{\mathcal{P}} = 1_Q$, and hence $\mathcal{P} = Q$. $\qquad \square$

Example 3.19. What would happen if we assume less and replace $\mathbb{R}^d$ by a lattice, say $\mathbb{Z}^d$? Is it possible for the following phenomenon to occur?

$$(3.21) \qquad \hat{1}_{\mathcal{P}}(\xi) = \hat{1}_{\mathcal{Q}}(\xi) \text{ for all } \xi \in \mathbb{Z}^d \not\Rightarrow \mathcal{P} = \mathcal{Q}?$$

Indeed, this scenario can happen, but we need to learn about extremal bodies first (see Section 5 and Example 4.11). $\qquad\qquad\square$

6. The torus $\mathbb{R}^d/\mathbb{Z}^d$

Suppose a function $f : \mathbb{R} \to \mathbb{C}$ is **periodic on the real line** with period 1: $f(x + 1) = f(x)$ for all $x \in \mathbb{R}$. Then we may think of f as "living" on the unit circle via the map $x \to e^{2\pi i x}$, which wraps the real line onto the unit circle. In this setting we may also think of the circle as the quotient group $\mathbb{R}/\mathbb{Z}$. As we promised, knowledge of group theory will not be assumed of the reader, but it will be developed a little bit in the concrete context of lattices—see Section 4 as well.

We may also traverse these ideas in the other direction: commencing with any function g whose domain is just $[0, 1)$, we can always extend g by periodicity to the whole real line by defining $G(x) := \{x\}$, the fractional part of x, for all $x \in \mathbb{R}$. Then $G(x) = g(x)$ for all $x \in \mathbb{T}$, G is periodic on $\mathbb{R}$, and therefore we may think of g as living on the circle $\mathbb{T}$.

More generally, we may think of a **periodic function** $f : \mathbb{R}^d \to \mathbb{C}$ as living on the cube $\square := [0, 1]^d$ if we insist that f is periodic in the following sense:

$$f(x) = f(x + e_k), \text{ for all } x \in \square, \text{ and all } 1 \leq k \leq d.$$

In this case the 1-dimensional circle is replaced by the d-dimensional torus

$$\mathbb{T}^d := \mathbb{R}^d/\mathbb{Z}^d,$$

which we may also think of as the unit cube $[0, 1]^d$, but with opposite facets "glued together". Here we define another infinite-dimensional vector space, namely:

$$(3.22) \qquad L^2(\mathbb{T}^d) := \left\{ f : \mathbb{T}^d \to \mathbb{C} \mid \int_{[0,1]^d} |f(x)|^2 dx < \infty \right\}.$$

We notice that the domains of the integrals in $L^2(\mathbb{T}^d)$ are cubes, and hence always compact. So we may therefore expect nicer phenomena to occur in this space.

We also have the space of absolutely integrable functions on the torus:

$$(3.23) \qquad L^1(\mathbb{T}^d) := \left\{ f : \mathbb{T}^d \to \mathbb{C} \mid \int_{[0,1]^d} |f(x)|dx < \infty \right\},$$

which plays a simpler role than the analogous $L^1(\mathbb{R}^d)$ space we had before. Finally, we also define the useful space of k-differentiable functions on the torus:

$$(3.24) \qquad C^k(\mathbb{T}^d) := \{ f : \mathbb{T}^d \to \mathbb{C} \mid f \text{ has } k \text{ continuous derivatives} \}.$$

As a special case, we will simply denote the space of all continuous functions on the torus by $C(\mathbb{T}^d)$. We emphasize that by definition, all of the latter function spaces $C^k(\mathbb{T}^d), L^1(\mathbb{T}^d), L^2(\mathbb{T}^d)$, consist of *periodic functions* on the cube $[0,1]^d$.

Similar to the inner product on $L^2(\mathbb{R}^d)$, we also have in this new context a natural inner product for the space of square-integrable functions $f \in L^2(\mathbb{T}^d)$, defined by:

$$(3.25) \qquad \langle f, g \rangle := \int_{[0,1]^d} f(x)\overline{g(x)}dx,$$

making $L^2(\mathbb{T}^d)$ a Hilbert space. For each $n \in \mathbb{Z}^d$, we define

$$e_n : \mathbb{R}^d \to \mathbb{C}$$

by

$$(3.26) \qquad e_n(x) := e^{2\pi i \langle n, x \rangle}.$$

This countable collection of exponentials turns out to form a complete orthonormal basis for $L^2(\mathbb{T}^d)$. The orthogonality is the first step, which we prove next. For the proof that the exponentials span $L^2(\mathbb{T}^d)$ and are complete, we refer the reader to [79].

Theorem 3.20 (Orthogonality relations for the exponentials $e_n(x)$ on the torus).

$$(3.27) \qquad \int_{[0,1]^d} e_n(x)\overline{e_m(x)}dx = \begin{cases} 1 & \text{if } n = m \\ 0 & \text{if not.} \end{cases}$$

Proof. Because of the geometry of the cube we can proceed in this case by separating the variables. If $n \neq m$ then there is at least one index k for which $n_k \neq m_k$. We compute:

$$\int_{[0,1]^d} e_n(x)\overline{e_m(x)}dx$$

$$= \int_{[0,1]^d} e^{2\pi i \langle n-m,x \rangle} dx$$

$$= \int_0^1 e^{2\pi i (n_k-m_k)x_k} dx \int_{[0,1]^{d-1}} \prod_{j \neq k} e^{2\pi i (n_j-m_j)x_j} dx$$

$$= \int_0^1 e^{2\pi i (n_k-m_k)x_k} dx \int_{[0,1]^{d-1}} \prod_{j \neq k} e^{2\pi i (n_j-m_j)x_j} dx$$

$$= \left(\frac{e^{2\pi i (n_k-m_k)} - 1}{2\pi i (n_k - m_k)} \right) \int_{[0,1]^{d-1}} \prod_{j \neq k} e^{2\pi i (n_j-m_j)x_j} dx = 0,$$

because $n_k - m_k$ is a nonzero integer. $\square$

Because $L^2(\mathbb{T}^d)$ is also an inner product space, it still enjoys the Cauchy–Schwartz inequality. Intuitively, the space $L^2(\mathbb{T}^d)$ should be a cozier little space than $L^1(\mathbb{T}^d)$. This intuition can be made more rigorous by the following lemma despite the fact that $L^2(\mathbb{R}^d) \not\subset L^1(\mathbb{R}^d)$. More generally, given any compact and convex set $\mathcal{P} \subset \mathbb{R}^d$ and any $p \geq 1$, we define

$$(3.28) \qquad L^p(\mathcal{P}) := \{f : \mathcal{P} \to \mathbb{C} \mid \int_{\mathcal{P}} |f(x)|^p dx < \infty\}.$$

Lemma 3.21. *We have the following proper containments:*

(1) $L^2(\mathbb{T}^d) \subset L^1(\mathbb{T}^d)$.

(2) *In general, given any compact and convex set* $\mathcal{P} \subset \mathbb{R}^d$, $L^2(\mathcal{P}) \subseteq L^1(\mathcal{P})$.

Proof. Given $f \in L^2(\mathbb{T}^d)$, we must show that $f \in L^1(\mathbb{T}^d)$. Using the Cauchy–Schwartz inequality for $L^2(\mathbb{T}^d)$ applied to f and the constant function $h(x) \equiv 1$ on $\mathbb{T}^d$, we have:

$$\int_{\mathbb{T}}^d |f(x)|dx = \int_{\mathbb{T}}^d |f(x)h(x)|dx$$

$$\leq \left(\int_{\mathbb{T}}^d |f(x)|^2 dx \right)^{\frac{1}{2}} \left(\int_{\mathbb{T}}^d |h(x)|^2 dx \right)^{\frac{1}{2}}$$

$$= \left(\int_{\mathbb{T}}^d |f(x)|^2 dx \right)^{\frac{1}{2}},$$

so we see that f is absolutely integrable over the torus $\mathbb{T}^d$. To show that the containment in part $((1))$ is proper for $d = 1$, we can consider the following function on $[0, 1]$:

$$f(x) := \begin{cases} \dfrac{1}{\sqrt{x}} & \text{if } x \in (0, 1], \\ 0 & \text{if } x = 0. \end{cases}$$

So $\int_0^1 f(x)dx = 2x^{\frac{1}{2}}\big|_0^1 = 2$, but $\int_0^1 |f(x)|^2 dx = \int_0^1 \frac{1}{x}dx = \infty$. Hence $f \in L^1(\mathbb{T}^d)$, but $f \notin L^2(\mathbb{T}^d)$.

The general case of part $((1))$ for arbitrary dimension follows easily from this example. For part $((2))$, once we know that $L^2(\mathcal{P})$ is a Hilbert space ($[\mathbf{217}]$), it follows that it has a Cauchy–Schwartz inequality, so the same proof of part $((1))$ works. $\qquad\square$

6.1. Fourier series: Fast and loose. Let us see how we can expand (certain) functions in a Fourier series, as well as find a formula for their series coefficients, in a footloose and carefree way, i.e., abandoning all rigor for the moment.

Given that the sequence of exponential functions $\{e_n(x)\}_{n\in\mathbb{Z}^d}$ forms a basis for the infinite dimensional vector space $V := L^2(\mathbb{T}^d)$, we know from linear algebra that any function $f \in V$ may be written in terms of this basis:

$$(3.29) \qquad\qquad f(x) = \sum_{n\in\mathbb{Z}^d} a_n e_n(x).$$

How do we compute the Fourier coefficients a_n? Let us go through the intuitive process, ignoring convergence issues. Again by linear algebra, we take the inner product of both sides with a fixed basis element $e_k(x)$

$$\langle f(x), e_k(x) \rangle = \langle \sum_{n \in \mathbb{Z}^d} a_n e_n(x), e_k(x) \rangle$$

$$= \sum_{n \in \mathbb{Z}^d} a_n \langle e_n(x), e_k(x) \rangle$$

$$= \sum_{n \in \mathbb{Z}^d} a_n \, \delta(n, k)$$

$$= a_k$$

where we have used the orthogonality relations—Theorem 3.20—in the third equality. We also used the standard notation $\delta(n, k) := 0$ if $n \neq k$; and $\delta(n, k) := 1$ if $n = k$. Therefore, it must be the case that

$$a_k = \langle f(x), e_k(x) \rangle$$

$$:= \int_{[0,1]^d} f(x) \overline{e^{2\pi i \langle k, x \rangle}} dx$$

$$= \int_{[0,1]^d} f(x) e^{-2\pi i \langle k, x \rangle} dx,$$

also called the **Fourier coefficients** of f.

6.2. Fourier series: Slow and rigorous. Now let us record the rigorous statements of the intuitive arguments that we constructed in the previous section. We may think of a periodic function on $\mathbb{R}^d$ as a function belonging to $L^2(\mathbb{T}^d)$.

Theorem 3.22 (Fourier series for functions on $\mathbb{T}^d$). *The set of exponentials*

$$\{e_n(x) \mid n \in \mathbb{Z}^d\}$$

*form a **complete orthonormal basis** for $L^2(\mathbb{T}^d)$. Moreover, we have the following:*

(a) *Every function $g \in L^2(\mathbb{T}^d)$ has a **Fourier series***

(3.30) $$g(x) = \sum_{n \in \mathbb{Z}^d} c_n e^{2\pi i \langle n, x \rangle},$$

where the convergence in (3.30) takes place in the L^2 norm on the torus $\mathbb{T}^d$.

(b) *The **Fourier coefficients** c_n may be computed via the formula:*

(3.31) $$c_n = \int_{[0,1]^d} g(t) e^{-2\pi i \langle n, t \rangle} dt,$$

for all $n \in \mathbb{Z}^d$.

(c) (***The Parseval identity***) *The function $g \in L^2(\mathbb{T}^d)$ in (3.30) satisfies*

$$(3.32) \qquad \int_{[0,1]^d} |g(x)|^2 dx = \sum_{n \in \mathbb{Z}^d} |c_n|^2. \qquad \square$$

For a proof, see [**79**, p. 96]. At the risk of stating the obvious, we note that the equality in (3.32) is simply equality between real numbers. We also note that the Fourier coefficients above are integrals over the unit cube $[0,1]^d$, and may also be thought of as $c_n = \langle g, e_n \rangle$, the projection of g onto each basis element. To summarize, we have encountered the following types of transforms so far:

$$(3.33) \qquad \int_{[0,1]^d} g(t)e^{-2\pi i \langle n,t \rangle} dt, \text{ and } \int_{\mathbb{R}^d} g(t)e^{-2\pi i \langle n,t \rangle} dt.$$

To disambiguate, the first integral in (3.33) arises from periodic functions on $\mathbb{R}^d$, and it appears as a Fourier coefficient in Theorem 3.22. The second integral is our old friend the Fourier transform. How are the two integrals related to each other? This is exactly the magic of the Poisson summation formula, Theorem 3.38.

In the pretty proof of Poisson summation, we begin with a Fourier series of a periodized version of f and end up showing that its Fourier coefficients, by a small miracle of nature, turn out to also be Fourier transforms of f.

A natural question is:

Question 3.23. Which functions have a pointwise convergent Fourier series?

But this question turns out to be rather difficult and many lifetimes have been devoted to try to answer Question 3.23. It is a fact of life that the Fourier series of an arbitrary continuous function on $\mathbb{R}^d$ may fail to converge uniformly, or even pointwise. However, there is some good news. As it turns out, if we impose some smoothness conditions on f, then f does have a Fourier series which converges pointwise, as we will see.

7. Piecewise smooth functions have convergent Fourier series

In this section we will restrict attention to the real line. We would like to rigorously define the intuitive idea of a function that is almost continuous, in the sense of being continuous on an interval except for finitely many finite jump discontinuities.

Given real numbers a, b, we define a function $f : [a, b] \to \mathbb{C}$ to be **piecewise continuous** on $[a, b]$ if the following two conditions are met:

(1) f is continuous on (a, b), except possibly on a finite set of points

$$S := \{x_1, \ldots, x_N\} \subset [a, b].$$

(2) The left- and right-hand limits of f exist at each of the points $x_k \in S$:

$$f(x_k^+) := \lim_{\substack{\varepsilon \to 0 \\ \varepsilon > 0}} f(x_k + \varepsilon) \text{ exists and } f(x_k^-) := \lim_{\substack{\varepsilon \to 0 \\ \varepsilon > 0}} f(x_k - \varepsilon) \text{ exists.}$$

Furthermore, we define a function $f : [a, b] \to \mathbb{C}$ to be **piecewise smooth** on $[a, b]$ if both f and its derivative f' are piecewise continuous on $[a, b]$. We will also say that a function $f : \mathbb{R} \to \mathbb{C}$ is piecewise continuous/smooth on $\mathbb{R}$ if it is piecewise continuous/smooth on every finite interval. We have the following refined version of Theorem 3.22, on the real line.

Theorem 3.24. *Let $f : \mathbb{R} \to \mathbb{C}$ be a periodic function with respect to the domain $[0, 1]$, and piecewise smooth on $\mathbb{R}$. Then, for each $t \in \mathbb{R}$, we have*

$$(3.34) \qquad \lim_{N \to \infty} \sum_{n=-N}^{N} c_n e^{2\pi i n t} = \frac{f(t^+) + f(t^-)}{2},$$

where $c_n := \int_0^1 f(x) e^{-2\pi i x n} dx$ are the Fourier coefficients of f.

For a proof of Theorem 3.24 see [251].   □

We will come back to these **partial Fourier sums**, occurring in Theorem 3.24, and defined by

$$(3.35) \qquad S_N f(t) := \sum_{n=-N}^{N} c_n e^{2\pi i n t}.$$

There is also a natural and easy extension of Parseval's identity (3.32). Given any two functions $f, g \in L^2(\mathbb{T}^d)$, we have seen in (3.30) that

$$f(x) = \sum_{n \in \mathbb{Z}^d} a_n \, e^{2\pi i \langle n, x \rangle}, \text{ and } g(x) = \sum_{n \in \mathbb{Z}^d} b_n \, e^{2\pi i \langle n, x \rangle},$$

both converging in the $L^2(\mathbb{T}^d)$ norm.

Theorem 3.25. *If $f, g, \in L^2(\mathbb{T}^d)$ then with the notation above we have*

$$\int_{\mathbb{T}^d} f(x)\overline{g(x)}dx = \sum_{n \in \mathbb{Z}^d} a_n \overline{b_n}. \qquad \square$$

7.1. The first periodic Bernoulli polynomial. To see a concrete instance of Theorem 3.22, we study the function $P_1(x)$, which we have briefly encountered before, as the first periodic Bernoulli polynomial. This function turns out to be so important that it deserves its own section here. We recall its definition:

$$(3.36) \qquad P_1(x) := \begin{cases} \{x\} - \frac{1}{2} & \text{if } x \notin \mathbb{Z}, \\ 0 & \text{if } x \in \mathbb{Z}. \end{cases}$$

It is easy to see that $P_1 \in L^1(\mathbb{T})$ so it has a Fourier series due to Theorem 3.22(a):

$$(3.37) \qquad P_1(x) = \sum_{n \in \mathbb{Z}} c_n e^{2\pi i n x},$$

and the equality here means equality in the $L^2(\mathbb{T})$ norm. Let us compute the Fourier coefficients of P_1, according to Theorem 3.22(b). We will use integration by parts:

$$\begin{aligned} c_n &= \int_0^1 \left(\{x\} - \frac{1}{2} \right) e^{-2\pi i n x} dx \\ &= \int_0^1 x e^{-2\pi i n x} dx - \frac{1}{2} \int_0^1 e^{-2\pi i n x} dx \\ &= x \frac{e^{-2\pi i n x}}{-2\pi i n} \Big|_0^1 - \int_0^1 \frac{e^{-2\pi i n x}}{-2\pi i n} dx \\ &= \frac{1}{-2\pi i n} - 0 = \frac{1}{-2\pi i n}, \end{aligned}$$

when $n \neq 0$. For $n = 0$, we have $c_0 = \int_0^1 (x - \frac{1}{2})dx = 0$. Hence we have the Fourier series

$$(3.38) \qquad P_1(x) = \{x\} - \frac{1}{2} = -\frac{1}{2\pi i} \sum_{\substack{n \in \mathbb{Z} \\ n \neq 0}} \frac{1}{n} e^{2\pi i n x},$$

where the latter equality means convergence in the $L^2(\mathbb{T}^d)$ norm. But we would like pointwise convergence of the latter series! In fact, this follows from Theorem 3.24.

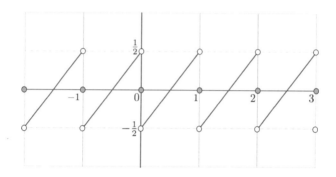

Figure 3.3. The first periodic Bernoulli polynomial $P_1(x)$.

Corollary 3.26. *We have the pointwise convergent Fourier series*

$$(3.39) \qquad \lim_{N \to \infty} -\frac{1}{2\pi i} \sum_{\substack{-N \leq n \leq N \\ n \neq 0}} \frac{1}{n} e^{2\pi i n x} = \{x\} - \frac{1}{2},$$

valid for all $x \in \mathbb{R}$.

Proof. First, we fix any $x \notin \mathbb{Z}$. Theorem 3.24 allows us to conclude that we have pointwise convergent sums:

$$(3.40) \qquad \lim_{N \to \infty} -\frac{1}{2\pi i} \sum_{\substack{-N \leq n \leq N \\ n \neq 0}} \frac{1}{n} e^{2\pi i n x} = \frac{P_1(x^+) + P_1(x^-)}{2}$$

$$(3.41) \qquad \qquad\qquad\qquad = \{x\} - \frac{1}{2},$$

For $x \in \mathbb{Z}$, we can also check that the equality (3.26) holds by observing that

$$\sum_{\substack{-N \leq n \leq N \\ n \neq 0}} \frac{1}{n} e^{2\pi i n x} = \sum_{\substack{-N \leq n \leq N \\ n \neq 0}} \frac{1}{n} = 0,$$

while $\frac{P_1(x^+) + P_1(x^-)}{2} = \frac{1}{2}\left(-\frac{1}{2} + \frac{1}{2}\right) = 0$ as well, which is consistent with the definition (3.36) of $P_1(x)$ at the integers. $\qquad\square$

Next, we can give a classical application of the Fourier series (3.38) using Parseval's identity (3.32):

$$\int_0^1 |P_1(u)|^2 du = \sum_{n \in \mathbb{Z}} |a_n|^2.$$

Let us simplify both sides:

$$\sum_{n \in \mathbb{Z}} |a_n|^2 = \frac{1}{4\pi^2} \sum_{n \in \mathbb{Z}-\{0\}} \frac{1}{n^2} = \frac{1}{2\pi^2} \sum_{n \geq 1} \frac{1}{n^2},$$

while

$$\int_0^1 |P_1(u)|^2 du = \int_0^1 \left(\{x\} - \frac{1}{2}\right)^2 dx = \int_0^1 \left(x - \frac{1}{2}\right)^2 dx = \frac{1}{12}.$$

Therefore

$$\sum_{n \geq 1} \frac{1}{n^2} = \frac{\pi^2}{6},$$

a number-theoretic identity that goes back to Euler. In a similar manner one can evaluate the Riemann zeta function at all positive even integers, using the cotangent function (Exercise (4)).

Another natural question arises.

Question 3.27. What sort of functions $f : \mathbb{T}^d \to \mathbb{C}$ are uniquely determined by all of their Fourier coefficients?

To describe a partial answer, we recall the space of all continuous functions on the torus:

(3.42) $C(\mathbb{T}^d) := \{f : \mathbb{T}^d \to \mathbb{C} \mid f \text{ is continuous on } \mathbb{T}^d\}.$

Theorem 3.28. *Let $f \in C(\mathbb{T}^d)$, and suppose that $\hat{f}(n) = 0$ for all $n \in \mathbb{Z}^d$. Then $f(x) = 0$, for all $x \in [0,1]^d$.*

In particular, if $f, g \in C(\mathbb{T}^d)$ and $\hat{f}(n) = \hat{g}(n)$ for all $n \in \mathbb{Z}^d$, then $f(x) = g(x)$ for all $x \in [0,1]^d$. $\square$

In other words, a continuous function on the torus is uniquely determined by its Fourier coefficients (see [79] for a proof).

8. As f gets smoother, $\hat{f}$ decays faster

There is a very basic and important relationship between the level of smoothness of f and the speed with which $\hat{f}$ tends to 0 as $x \to \infty$. To capture this relation very concretely, let us compute things on the real line to see how the FT interacts with the derivative.

Lemma 3.29. *Let $f \in L^1(\mathbb{R})$.*

(1) *Suppose f is a piecewise smooth function, as defined in Section 7, and $f' \in L^1(\mathbb{R})$ as well. Then*

$$\widehat{f'}(\xi) = (2\pi i)\xi \hat{f}(\xi).$$

(2) *More generally, let $k \geq 0$, suppose that f has k derivatives, $f^{(k)}$ is piecewise smooth, and that we also have $f^{(k+1)} \in L^1(\mathbb{R})$. Then*

$$\widehat{f^{(k+1)}}(\xi) = (2\pi i\xi)^{k+1}\hat{f}(\xi).$$

(3) *Now we suppose that $xf(x) \in L^1(\mathbb{R})$. Then*

$$\frac{d}{d\xi}\mathcal{F}(f)(\xi) = (-2\pi i)\,\mathcal{F}(xf(x))(\xi).$$

Proof. To prove part (1), we notice that

$$\lim_{x \to \infty} f(x) = f(0) + \int_0^\infty f'(x)dx,$$

using the hypothesis $f' \in L^1(\mathbb{R})$. We may also use the the hypothesis $f \in L^1(\mathbb{R})$ to conclude by the Riemann–Lebesgue lemma (Lemma 3.13) that $\lim_{x \to \infty} f(x) = 0$. Similarly, $\lim_{x \to -\infty} f(x) = 0$. Integration by parts now gives us:

$$\begin{aligned}
\widehat{f'}(\xi) &= \int_{\mathbb{R}} f'(x)e^{-2\pi ix\xi}dx \\
&= f(x)e^{-2\pi ix\xi}\Big|_{-\infty}^{\infty} - \int_{\mathbb{R}} f(x)(-2\pi i\xi)e^{-2\pi ix\xi}dx \\
&= 2\pi i\xi \int_{\mathbb{R}} f(x)e^{-2\pi ix\xi}dx \\
&:= 2\pi i\xi \hat{f}(\xi).
\end{aligned}$$

Part (2) follows from part (1) by induction on k. To prove part (3), we have:

$$\mathcal{F}(xf(x))(\xi) := \int_{\mathbb{R}} xf(x)e^{-2\pi ix\xi}dx$$

$$= \frac{1}{-2\pi i} \int_{\mathbb{R}} \frac{d}{d\xi}f(x)e^{-2\pi ix\xi}dx$$

$$= -\frac{1}{2\pi i}\frac{d}{d\xi} \int_{\mathbb{R}} f(x)e^{-2\pi ix\xi}dx$$

$$= -\frac{1}{2\pi i}\frac{d}{d\xi}\hat{f}(\xi).$$

$\square$

It follows from Theorem 3.29(2) that we have an explicit decay rate for the Fourier coefficients of a periodic function f, assuming that f is sufficiently smooth. To obtain Corollary 3.30, we can simply use the fact that $f^{(k+1)} \in L^1(\mathbb{R})$ implies that $\widehat{f^{(k+1)}}$ is uniformly bounded:

$$\left| \frac{1}{(2\pi)^{k+1}}\widehat{f^{(k+1)}}(\xi) \right| < C$$

for a positive constant C.

Corollary 3.30. *If f has k continuous derivatives and we also have $f^{(k+1)} \in L^1(\mathbb{R})$, then there is a constant $C > 0$ such that:*

$$(3.43) \qquad |\hat{f}(\xi)| < C\frac{1}{|\xi|^{k+1}},$$

for all $\xi \neq 0$.

$\square$

In other words, we now understand the dictum "as f gets smoother, $\hat{f}$ decays faster" in a precise quantitative manner: if f has k derivatives, then $\hat{f}$ decays faster than a polynomial of degree k.

9. How fast do Fourier coefficients decay?

In a manner completely analogous to the previous Section 8, we can repeat the important idea of integration by parts to see how fast Fourier coefficients decay, and here we may expect even better results because we will integrate over the compact unit cube (equivalently over $\mathbb{T}^d$) rather than over the noncompact space $\mathbb{R}^d$. We first work things out in dimension 1, recalling that the Fourier coefficients of f are defined by $c_n := \int_0^1 f(x)e^{-2\pi inx}dx$ for all $n \in \mathbb{Z}$. For the sake of the reader, we recall the space of functions $C^k(\mathbb{T})$ from (3.24), which have k continuous derivatives. We also recall that $f \in L^1(\mathbb{T})$ means $\int_0^1 f(x)dx$ is finite, and that $f(x+1) = f(x)$ for all $x \in [0,1]$. Finally, we note that the same conclusion of the Riemann–Lebesgue lemma (Lemma 3.13) also holds for functions $f \in L^1(\mathbb{T}^d)$ with exactly the same proof that we gave in Lemma 3.13.

Theorem 3.31. *Let $f \in L^1(\mathbb{T})$.*

(1) *If $f \in C^1(\mathbb{T})$, then its Fourier coefficients satisfy*

$$(3.44) \qquad \lim_{|n| \to \infty} |nc_n| = 0.$$

In other words, $|c_n| = o\left(\frac{1}{n}\right)$.

(2) *More generally, fix an integer $k \geq 1$. If $f \in C^k(\mathbb{T})$, then its Fourier coefficients satisfy*

$$(3.45) \qquad \lim_{|n| \to \infty} |n^k c_n| = 0.$$

In other words, $|c_n| = o\left(\frac{1}{n^k}\right)$.

Proof. We compute the Fourier coefficients using integration by parts. For each $n \neq 0$, we have:

$$
\begin{aligned}
c_n &:= \int_0^1 f(x)e^{-2\pi inx}dx \\
&= \left[f(x)\frac{e^{-2\pi inx}}{-2\pi in} \right]\Big|_0^1 + \frac{1}{2\pi in}\int_0^1 f'(x)e^{-2\pi inx}dx \\
&= \frac{f(1)-f(0)}{-2\pi in} + \frac{1}{2\pi in}\int_0^1 f'(x)e^{-2\pi inx}dx \\
&= \frac{1}{2\pi in}\int_0^1 f'(x)e^{-2\pi inx}dx,
\end{aligned}
$$

using the periodicity of f. Because f' is continuous, the Riemann–Lebesgue lemma on $L^1(\mathbb{T})$ gives us $\lim_{|n| \to \infty} \int_0^1 f'(x)e^{-2\pi inx}dx = 0$. So we see that

$$|nc_n| \to 0, \text{ as } |n| \to \infty,$$

completing part (1). Part (2) follows easily by induction on k, repeating the same integration by parts computation above, exactly k times. □

We note that the same proof works with even weaker hypotheses in part (2). Namely, given an integer $k \geq 1$, all we require is that $f^{(j)}$ is continuous on $\mathbb{T}$, for $0 \leq j < k$, and $f^{(k)} \in L^1(\mathbb{T})$.

Let us see a concrete application of these ideas (see Note (4)).

Theorem 3.32. *Suppose that $f \in C^k(\mathbb{T})$—defined in (3.24)—for a fixed integer $k \geq 1$. Then*

(3.46)
$$\int_0^1 f(x)dx = \frac{1}{N} \sum_{m=0}^{N-1} f\left(\tfrac{m}{N}\right) + o\left(\tfrac{1}{N^k}\right),$$

as $N \to \infty$.

Proof. Because f is periodic on $\mathbb{R}$, we follow "Hecke's dictum"; namely, we first expand f into its Fourier series, which is guaranteed by Theorem 3.22:

$$f(x) = \sum_{n \in \mathbb{Z}} c_n e^{2\pi i n x}.$$

Since this Fourier series converges absolutely we may interchange the finite sum with the series:

$$\frac{1}{N} \sum_{m=0}^{N-1} f\left(\tfrac{m}{N}\right) = \frac{1}{N} \sum_{m=0}^{N-1} \sum_{n \in \mathbb{Z}} c_n e^{2\pi i n \frac{m}{N}}$$
$$= \sum_{n \in \mathbb{Z}} c_n \left(\frac{1}{N} \sum_{m=0}^{N-1} e^{2\pi i n \frac{m}{N}} \right)$$
$$= \sum_{n \in \mathbb{Z}} c_{Nn},$$

using Exercise (6) (the harmonic detector for divisibility). Next, we recall that the constant term is $c_0 = \int_0^1 f(x)dx$ and we separate out this term from the latter series:

$$\frac{1}{N} \sum_{m=0}^{N-1} f\left(\tfrac{m}{N}\right) = \int_0^1 f(x)dx + \sum_{\substack{n \in \mathbb{Z} \\ n \neq 0}} c_{Nn},$$

Now we can use the (little-o) rate of decay of the Fourier coefficients— given by Theorem 3.31(2)—to write $|c_{Nn}| < \frac{C}{(Nn)^k}$ for *all* constants $C > 0$. We conclude that

$$\sum_{\substack{n \in \mathbb{Z} \\ n \neq 0}} |c_{Nn}| < C \sum_{\substack{n \in \mathbb{Z} \\ n \neq 0}} \frac{1}{N^k |n|^k} = 2C\,\zeta(k)\frac{1}{N^k},$$

for all constants $C > 0$. So as $N \to \infty$, the error term $\sum_{\substack{n \in \mathbb{Z} \\ n \neq 0}} c_N n$ is $o\left(\frac{1}{N^k}\right)$, as claimed. $\square$

It is worth mentioning that although our proof of Theorem 3.32 does not cover the case $k = 0$, this case is also true because it represents the Riemann sum approximation to the integral.

10. The Schwartz space

We saw in Section 8 that a function $f : \mathbb{R}^d \to \mathbb{C}$ that has k derivatives in the space domain corresponds to a function $\hat{f}$ that "decays to order k", the Fourier transform domain. Can we take this idea to the limit by letting $k \to \infty$? Following the ideas of Laurent Schwartz, we can.

We recall that our definition of a "nice function" was any function $f : \mathbb{R}^d \to \mathbb{C}$ for which the Poisson summation formula holds. Here we give our first family of sufficient conditions for a function f to be nice. A **Schwartz function** $f : \mathbb{R} \to \mathbb{C}$ is defined as any infinitely smooth function ($f \in C^\infty(\mathbb{R})$) that satisfies the following growth condition:

$$(3.47) \qquad \left| x^a \frac{d}{dx^k} f(x) \right| \text{ is bounded on } \mathbb{R}$$

for all integers $a, k \geq 0$. In particular, a Schwartz function decreases faster than any polynomial function, as $|x|$ tends to infinity.

Example 3.33. The Gaussian function $G_t(x) := e^{-t\|x\|^2}$ is a Schwartz function for each fixed $t > 0$. To see this we first consider $\mathbb{R}^1$, where we note that the 1-dimensional Gaussian is a Schwartz function, as follows. We observe that for all positive integers k, $\frac{d}{dx^k} G_t(x) = H_n(x) G_t(x)$ where $H_n(x)$ is a univariate polynomial in x (which also depends on the parameter t, but we think of t as a constant). Since $\lim_{x \to \infty} \frac{x^a H_n(x)}{e^{t\|x\|^2}} = 0$ for all positive integers a, we see that $G_t(x)$ is a Schwartz function. Now we note that the product of Schwartz functions is again a Schwartz function; hence the d-dimensional Gaussian $G_t(x) := e^{-t\|x\|^2} = \prod_{k=1}^d e^{-tx_k^2}$, a product of 1-dimensional Gaussians, is a Schwartz function.

Some might say the Gaussian is the quintessential Schwartz function, partly because it is also an eigenfunction of the Fourier transform, as we will see below. $\square$

Example 3.34. We define $f(x) := e^{-2\pi t|x|}$ on the real line for a fixed $t > 0$. To see that f is *not* a Schwartz function, we merely have to observe that f is not differentiable at $x = 0$. To be a Schwartz function, f would have to be infinitely differentiable everywhere on $\mathbb{R}$.

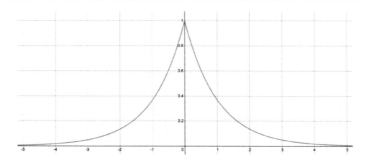

Figure 3.4. The function $e^{-|x|}$.

Interestingly, we can also see that f is not a Schwartz function in another way—by computing its Fourier transform and observing that it is not rapidly decreasing:

$$
\begin{aligned}
\hat{f}(\xi) &:= \int_{\mathbb{R}} e^{-2\pi t|x|-2\pi ix\xi}\,dx \\
&= \int_{-\infty}^{0} e^{2\pi tx-2\pi ix\xi}\,dx + \int_{0}^{+\infty} e^{-2\pi tx-2\pi ix\xi}\,dx \\
&= \int_{-\infty}^{0} e^{2\pi x(t-i\xi)}\,dx + \int_{0}^{+\infty} e^{-2\pi x(t+i\xi)}\,dx \\
&= \frac{e^{2\pi x(t-i\xi)}}{2\pi(t-i\xi)}\Big|_{x=-\infty}^{x=0} + \frac{e^{-2\pi x(t+i\xi)}}{-2\pi(t+i\xi)}\Big|_{x=0}^{x=\infty} \\
&= \frac{1}{2\pi(t-i\xi)} + \frac{1}{2\pi(t+i\xi)} \\
&= \frac{t}{\pi(t^2+\xi^2)},
\end{aligned}
$$

valid for all $\xi \in \mathbb{R}$. Because the Fourier transform

$$
(3.48) \qquad\qquad \hat{f}(\xi) = \frac{t}{\pi(t^2+\xi^2)}
$$

is not a rapidly decreasing function, we have another proof that f is not a Schwartz function.

This example is interesting in that f is infinitely differentiable everywhere except at one point, namely $x = 0$. Yet this local lack of smoothness—*at only a single point*—is enough to cause a global change in decay for its Fourier transform. $\qquad\square$

It is just as easy to define Schwartz functions on $\mathbb{R}^d$ as well. For any $k := (k_1, \ldots, k_d) \in \mathbb{Z}_{\geq 0}^d$, we can define the multivariable differential operator

$$D_k := \frac{\partial}{\partial x_1^{k_1} \cdots \partial x_d^{k_d}}.$$

Example 3.35. In $\mathbb{R}^1$ this is the usual kth derivative, namely $D_k f(x) := \frac{d}{dx^k} f(x)$. In $\mathbb{R}^2$, for example, we have $D_{(1,7)} f(x) := \frac{\partial}{\partial x_1 \partial x_2^7} f(x)$. □

The **order** of the differential operator D_k is by definition $|k| := k_1 + \cdots + k_d$. To define spaces of differentiable functions, we call a function $f : \mathbb{R}^d \to \mathbb{C}$ a C^m-function if all partial derivatives $D_k f$ of order $|k| \leq m$ exist and are continuous. We denote the collection of all such C^m-functions on Euclidean space by $C^m(\mathbb{R}^d)$. When considering **infinitely-differentiable functions on Euclidean space**, we denote this space by $C^\infty(\mathbb{R}^d)$.

So we see that in $\mathbb{R}^d$ we can define **Schwartz functions** similarly to our previous definition: they are infinitely differentiable functions $f : \mathbb{R}^d \to \mathbb{C}$ such that for all vectors $a, k \in \mathbb{Z}_{\geq 0}^d$ we have:

(3.49) $|x^a D_k f(x)|$ is bounded on $\mathbb{R}^d$,

where $x^a := x_1^{a_1} \cdots x_d^{a_d}$ is the standard multi-index notation. We also define the **Schwartz space** $S(\mathbb{R}^d)$ to be set of all Schwartz functions $f : \mathbb{R}^d \to \mathbb{C}$.

Theorem 3.36. *The Fourier transform maps the Schwartz space $S(\mathbb{R}^d)$ one-to-one onto itself (see Exercise (11)).*

In fact, more is true: the mapping $f \to \hat{f}$ from $S(\mathbb{R}^d)$ to itself is an isometry. The proof of this fact uses the Parseval relation below. And now that we know the definition of rapid decay, we see that an obvious consequence of Corollary 3.30 is the following:

(3.50)   If f is infinitely smooth, then $\hat{f}$ is rapidly decreasing.

In fact, we can combine some of the ideas above to record another useful fact.

Lemma 3.37. *Let $\phi : \mathbb{R}^d \to \mathbb{C}$ be compactly supported and infinitely smooth. Then*

$$\phi \in S(\mathbb{R}^d).$$

Proof. Because ϕ is compactly supported, we know that $\hat{\phi}$ is infinitely smooth (differentiation under the integral). Moreover, the assumption that ϕ is infinitely smooth implies that $\hat{\phi}$ is rapidly descreasing by (3.50). So now we know that $\hat{\phi}$ is both rapidly decreasing and infinitely smooth, i.e., a Schwartz function. Applying Theorem 3.36, we see that its Fourier transform is also a Schwartz function. Namely, using Fourier inversion, we conclude that $\hat{\hat{\phi}}(-x) = \phi(x) \in S(\mathbb{R}^d)$. $\qquad\square$

The functions satisfying the conditions of Lemma 3.37 are also called **bump functions**. The curious reader might ask: "Are there any functions at all that satisfy the condition of Lemma 3.37?" The answer is that there are many, though we are almost always interested in their properties rather than their explicit form (see Appendix 3.3).

11. Poisson summation I

We introduce the Poisson summation formula, one of the most useful tools in analytic number theory, and in discrete/combinatorial geometry. This version of Poisson summation holds for Schwartz functions. There are many different families of sufficient conditions that a function f can satisfy in order for Poisson summation to be applicable to f.

Figure 3.5. Function spaces for Poisson summation.

Theorem 3.38 (Poisson summation formula I). *Given a Schwartz function $f : \mathbb{R}^d \to \mathbb{C}$, we have*

$$(3.51) \qquad \sum_{n \in \mathbb{Z}^d} f(n + x) = \sum_{\xi \in \mathbb{Z}^d} \hat{f}(\xi) e^{2\pi i \langle \xi, x \rangle},$$

valid for all $x \in \mathbb{R}^d$. In particular, we have

$$\sum_{n \in \mathbb{Z}^d} f(n) = \sum_{\xi \in \mathbb{Z}^d} \hat{f}(\xi). \tag{3.52}$$

Both sides of (3.51) converge absolutely and are continuous functions on $\mathbb{R}^d$.

Proof. If we let $F(x) := \sum_{n \in \mathbb{Z}^d} f(n+x)$, then we notice that F is periodic on $\mathbb{R}^d$ with the cube $[0, 1)^d$ as a fundamental domain. The argument is easy: fix any $m \in \mathbb{Z}^d$. Then

$$F(x + m) = \sum_{n \in \mathbb{Z}^d} f(n + x + m) = \sum_{k \in \mathbb{Z}^d} f(x + k),$$

because $\mathbb{Z}^d + m = \mathbb{Z}^d$. By Theorem 3.22, F has a fourier series, so let us compute it:

$$F(x) := \sum_{k \in \mathbb{Z}^d} a_k e^{2\pi i \langle k, x \rangle},$$

where $a_k = \int_{[0,1)^d} F(u) e^{2\pi i \langle k, u \rangle} du$ for each fixed $k \in \mathbb{Z}^d$. Let us see what happens if we massage a_k a bit:

$$a_k := \int_{[0,1)^d} F(u) e^{-2\pi i \langle k, u \rangle} du \tag{3.53}$$

$$= \int_{[0,1)^d} \sum_{n \in \mathbb{Z}^d} f(n + u) e^{-2\pi i \langle k, u \rangle} du \tag{3.54}$$

$$= \sum_{n \in \mathbb{Z}^d} \int_{[0,1)^d} f(n + u) e^{-2\pi i \langle k, u \rangle} du. \tag{3.55}$$

The interchange of summation and integral in the latter step is allowed by Theorem B.4, which is an application of the dominated convergence theorem because the integrand satisfies $|f(n+u)e^{-2\pi i \langle k, u \rangle}| = |f(n+u)| \in L^1(\mathbb{R}^d)$. The latter absolute integrability of f is due to the fact that f is a Schwartz function.

Now we fix an $n \in \mathbb{Z}^d$ in the outer sum of (3.55) and make the change of variable in the integral: $n + u := w$, so that $du = dw$. A critical step in this proof is the fact that as u varies over the cube $[0, 1)^d$, $w := n + u$ varies over all of $\mathbb{R}^d$ because we have a tiling of Euclidean space by the unit cube: $[0, 1)^d + \mathbb{Z}^d = \mathbb{R}^d$. We note that under this change of variable, $e^{-2\pi i \langle k, u \rangle} = e^{-2\pi i \langle k, w-n \rangle} = e^{-2\pi i \langle k, w \rangle}$, because $k, n \in \mathbb{Z}^d$ and hence $e^{2\pi i\langle k,n\rangle} = 1$. Therefore, we finally have:

$$(3.56) \qquad a_k = \sum_{n\in\mathbb{Z}^d} \int_{n+[0,1)^d} f(w)e^{-2\pi i\langle k,w\rangle}\,dw$$

$$= \int_{\mathbb{R}^d} f(w)e^{-2\pi i\langle k,w\rangle}\,dw$$

$$:= \hat{f}(k),$$

so that $F(x) = \sum_{k\in\mathbb{Z}^d} a_k e^{2\pi i\langle k,x\rangle} = \sum_{k\in\mathbb{Z}^d} \hat{f}(k)e^{2\pi i\langle k,x\rangle}$. $\qquad\square$

We define a function $f : \mathbb{R}^d \to \mathbb{C}$ to be a **nice function** if both $f, \hat{f} \in L^1(\mathbb{R}^d)$ and if the Poisson summation formula

$$(3.57) \qquad \sum_{n\in\mathbb{Z}^d} f(n+x) = \sum_{\xi\in\mathbb{Z}^d} \hat{f}(\xi)e^{2\pi i\langle\xi,x\rangle}$$

holds for f pointwise for each $x \in \mathbb{R}^d$. In addition, we will always assume absolute convergence of both sides of (3.57).

We will give various different sets of sufficient conditions for a function f to be nice. Figure 3.5 suggests a simple containment relation between some of these function spaces, as we will easily prove.

There are a few things to notice about the classic and pretty proof of Theorem 3.51. The first is that we began with any square-integrable function f defined on all of $\mathbb{R}^d$ and forced a periodization of it, which was by definition F. This is known as the "folding" part of the proof. Then at the end of the proof there was the "unfolding" process where we summed an integral over a lattice, and because the cube tiles $\mathbb{R}^d$, the sum of the integrals transformed into a single integral over $\mathbb{R}^d$.

The second thing we notice is that the integral $\int_{\mathbb{R}^d} f(x)e^{-2\pi i\langle x,\xi\rangle}\,dx$, which is by definition the Fourier transform of f, appears quite naturally due to the tiling of $\mathbb{R}^d$ by the unit cube $[0,1)^d$. Hopefully there will be no confusion about the difference between the integral over the cube and the integral over $\mathbb{R}^d$, as both appeared together in this proof.

12. Useful convergence lemmas in preparation for Poisson summation II

To prepare ourselves for Poisson's original summation formula, which we give in the next section, we will see Poisson's hypotheses for the growth of f and $\hat{f}$ together with the immediate convergence consequences they carry.

Lemma 3.39. *Let $f : \mathbb{R}^d \to \mathbb{C}$ be a function that enjoys the bound*

$$|f(x)| \leq \frac{C}{(1 + \|x\|)^{d+\delta}}$$

for all $x \in \mathbb{R}^d$ and for constants $C, \delta > 0$ that are independent of x. Then $f \in L^1(\mathbb{R}^d)$.

Proof. Consider the cube $Q_n := [-n, n]^d$ and let $D_n := Q_{n+1} - Q_n$ denote the set difference. In other words, D_n is the cubical shell between the cube Q_n and the cube Q_{n+1}. We have $\mathbb{R}^d = \bigcup_{n \geq 0} D_n$, and $D_0 = Q_1$. Also, we note that on each shell D_n, $\frac{1}{\|x\|} \leq \frac{1}{n}$, so that:

$$(3.58) \qquad \int_{\mathbb{R}^d} |f(x)| dx = \sum_{n \geq 0} \int_{D_n} |f(x)| dx$$

$$(3.59) \qquad = \int_{D_0} |f(x)| dx + \sum_{n \geq 1} \int_{D_n} |f(x)| dx$$

$$(3.60) \qquad \leq 2^d C + \sum_{n \geq 1} \int_{D_n} \frac{C}{(1 + n)^{d+\delta}} dx$$

$$(3.61) \qquad = 2^d C + \sum_{n \geq 1} \frac{C}{(1 + n)^{d+\delta}} \int_{D_n} dx$$

$$(3.62) \qquad = 2^d C + \sum_{n \geq 1} \frac{C}{(1 + n)^{d+\delta}} \left((2n + 2)^d - (2n)^d \right)$$

$$(3.63) \qquad = 2^d C + 2^d C \sum_{n \geq 1} \frac{1}{(1 + n)^{d+\delta}} \left((n + 1)^d - n^d \right)$$

$$(3.64) \qquad = 2^d C + \sum_{n \geq 1} \frac{O(n^{d-1})}{(1 + n)^{d+\delta}}$$

$$(3.65) \qquad = 2^d C + \sum_{n \geq 1} O\left(\frac{1}{n^{1+\delta}} \right)$$

$$(3.66) \qquad = 2^d C + O\left(\sum_{n \geq 1} \frac{1}{n^{1+\delta}} \right) < \infty,$$

where we have used the fact that the constant in the big-O of equation (3.64) is independent of n, so that we can move the series inside. $\square$

For the absolute summability of functions satisfying the same growth condition of the previous lemma, we have the following.

Lemma 3.40. *Let* $f : \mathbb{R}^d \to \mathbb{C}$ *be a function that enjoys the bound*

$$|f(x)| \leq \frac{C}{(1 + \|x\|)^{d+\delta}},$$

for all $x \in \mathbb{R}^d$, *and for constants* $C, \delta > 0$ *that are independent of* x. *Then the series*

$$\sum_{k \in \mathbb{Z}^d} f(x + k)$$

converges uniformly and absolutely for all $x \in \mathbb{R}^d$.

Proof. We will restrict attention to $x \in [0, 1)^d$ because the function $F(x) := \sum_{k \in \mathbb{Z}^d} f(k + x)$, if convergent, forms a periodic function of $x \in \mathbb{R}^d$ with the unit cube $[0, 1)^d$ being a period. We also note that for all $x \in [0, 1)^d$ we have the bound $\|x\| \leq \sqrt{d}$.

We consider the tail of the series for any given $N > 0$:

(3.67)
$$\left| \sum_{\substack{k \in \mathbb{Z}^d \\ \|k\| > N}} f(k + x) \right| \leq \sum_{\substack{k \in \mathbb{Z}^d \\ \|k\| > N}} |f(k + x)|$$

$$\leq C \sum_{\substack{k \in \mathbb{Z}^d \\ \|k\| > N}} \frac{1}{(1 + \|k + x\|)^{d+\delta}}$$

(3.68)
$$\leq \sum_{\substack{k \in \mathbb{Z}^d \\ \|k\| > N}} \frac{1}{\left(1 + \frac{\|k+x\|}{1+\sqrt{d}}\right)^{d+\delta}}$$

(3.69)
$$= \sum_{\substack{k \in \mathbb{Z}^d \\ \|k\| > N}} \frac{\left(1 + \sqrt{d}\right)^{d+\delta}}{\left(1 + \sqrt{d} + \|k + x\|\right)^{d+\delta}}$$

(3.70)
$$\leq C_{d,\delta} \sum_{\substack{k \in \mathbb{Z}^d \\ \|k\| > N}} \frac{1}{(1 + \|k\|)^{d+\delta}}$$

(3.71)
$$= C_{d,\delta} \sum_{n \geq N} \frac{1}{(1 + n)^{d+\delta}} O\left(n^{d-1}\right)$$

(3.72)
$$= \sum_{n \geq N} O\left(\frac{1}{n^{1+\delta}}\right)$$

(3.73)
$$= O\left(\sum_{n \geq N} \frac{1}{n^{1+\delta}}\right) \to 0, \text{ as } N \to \infty,$$

and the last bound is independent of x. In passing from (3.69) to (3.70) we used the estimate

$$\|k + x\| \geq \|k\| - \|x\| \geq \|k\| - \sqrt{d} \text{ and } C_{d,\delta} := \left(1 + \sqrt{d}\right)^{d+\delta}.$$

The equality in (3.71) is due to the fact that the number of integer points $k \in \mathbb{Z}^d$ that lie on a sphere of radius n is

$$O\left(\text{surface area of } nS^{d-1}\right) = O\left(n^{d-1}\right).$$

We have shown that the series $\sum_{k \in \mathbb{Z}^d} |f(k + x)|$ converges uniformly on $\mathbb{R}^d$. $\square$

We note that the only reason for having $(1 + \|x\|)^{d+\delta}$ in the denominators of the bounds instead of simply $\|x\|^{d+\delta}$ is to give a bound at the origin as well as any nonzero x simultaneously.

13. Poisson summation II: Á la Poisson

There are various different families of functions for which the adjective "nice" applies, such as in (3.57), and one of the simplest to understand is the Schwartz class of functions. But there is a more general family of nice functions that is extremely useful, which is given by Poisson himself, as follows.

Theorem 3.41 (Poisson summation formula II). *Suppose that for some positive constants δ, C, and all $x \in \mathbb{R}^d$ we have the bounds:*

$$(3.74) \qquad |f(x)| < \frac{C}{(1 + \|x\|)^{d+\delta}} \text{ and } |\hat{f}(x)| < \frac{C}{(1 + \|x\|)^{d+\delta}},$$

and suppose that f is continuous on $\mathbb{R}^d$. Then we have the pointwise equality:

$$(3.75) \qquad \sum_{n \in \mathbb{Z}^d} f(n + x) = \sum_{\xi \in \mathbb{Z}^d} \hat{f}(\xi) e^{2\pi i \langle \xi, x \rangle}$$

for each $x \in \mathbb{R}^d$. In addition, both sides of (3.75) converge absolutely and are continuous functions on $\mathbb{R}^d$.

Proof.

Step 1. The growth conditions (3.74) allow us to conclude that both $f, \hat{f} \in L^1(\mathbb{R}^d)$ by Lemma 3.39. This implies that both $f, \hat{f} \in L^2(\mathbb{R}^d)$ by the elementary lemma (Lemma 3.56). We also know that the Fourier transform of an L^1 function must be uniformly continuous on $\mathbb{R}^d$, and so both f and $\hat{f}$ are uniformly continuous (Lemma 3.11).

Step 2. The hypothesis regarding the growth conditions (3.74) implies that the series defined by $F(x) := \sum_{n \in \mathbb{Z}^d} f(n+x)$ converges uniformly on $[0,1]^d$, as we showed in Lemma 3.40. It follows that this series must also converge in the L^2-norm on $[0,1]^d$. So $F \in L^2(\mathbb{T}^d)$, and it must therefore possess a Fourier series, which converges to it in the L^2-norm:

$$(3.76) \qquad F(x) = \sum_{n \in \mathbb{Z}^d} a_n \, e^{2\pi i \langle n, x \rangle}.$$

Step 3. Next, we compute the Fourier coefficients a_k. This is almost the same step that already appeared in the proof of Theorem 3.38 but we repeat it here for completeness, and also because the interchange of sum and integral below is justified in a different way.

$$(3.77) \qquad a_k := \int_{[0,1)^d} F(u) e^{-2\pi i \langle k, u \rangle} du$$

$$(3.78) \qquad = \int_{[0,1)^d} \sum_{n \in \mathbb{Z}^d} f(n+u) e^{-2\pi i \langle k, u \rangle} du$$

$$(3.79) \qquad = \sum_{n \in \mathbb{Z}^d} \int_{[0,1)^d} f(n+u) e^{-2\pi i \langle k, u \rangle} du.$$

The interchange of summation and integral in the previous step is allowed by the uniform convergence of the series $\sum_{n \in \mathbb{Z}^d} f(n+x)$. We fix an $n \in \mathbb{Z}^d$ in the outer sum of (3.79) and make the change of variables in the integral: $n + u := w$. As u varies over the cube $[0,1)^d$, $w := n + u$ varies over all of $\mathbb{R}^d$ because the unit cube tiles the whole space:

$$[0,1)^d + \mathbb{Z}^d = \mathbb{R}^d.$$

We also have $e^{-2\pi i \langle k, u \rangle} = e^{-2\pi i \langle k, w-n \rangle} = e^{-2\pi i \langle k, w \rangle}$ because $k, n \in \mathbb{Z}^d$ and hence $e^{2\pi i \langle k, n \rangle} = 1$. Finally, we have:

$$a_k = \sum_{n \in \mathbb{Z}^d} \int_{n+[0,1)^d} f(w) e^{-2\pi i \langle k, w \rangle} dw$$

$$= \int_{\mathbb{R}^d} f(w) e^{-2\pi i \langle k, w \rangle} dw$$

$$:= \hat{f}(k).$$

Step 4. Since each summand $f(n+x)$ is a continuous function of x and since the convergence is uniform, the function $F(x)$ must also be continuous. Finally, we would like to pass from the convergence of the Fourier series in the L^2-norm to pointwise and uniform convergence. For this task we can use Lemma B.16, assuming that we can show the absolute convergence of the Fourier series

$$\sum_{n \in \mathbb{Z}^d} a_n \, e^{2\pi i \langle n, x \rangle} = \sum_{n \in \mathbb{Z}^d} \hat{f}(n) e^{2\pi i \langle n, x \rangle}.$$

But this absolute convergence also follows from Lemma 3.40, with f replaced by $\hat{f}$ because the same growth bounds (3.74) are also assumed for $\hat{f}$. To summarize this last step, we know that F is continuous and the previous remarks allow us to use Lemma B.16 to conclude that the Fourier series for F converges pointwise and uniformly to $F(x)$.   □

We call a function that enjoys the bounds in (3.74) a **Poisson function** because Siméon Denis Poisson proved Theorem 3.41 between 1823 and 1827 in [**251**].

Poisson's theorem (Theorem 3.41) is a **stronger** version of Poisson summation than Theorem 3.38. To justify this claim we need to show that any Schwartz function also satisfies the growth conditions in equation (3.74), but this is clear because Schwartz functions (and their transforms) decay faster than any polynomial, thus they decay faster than the bounds given by (3.74).

We call the space of functions that satisfy the hypotheses of Theorem 3.41 the **Poisson space** of functions in honor of the mathematician that discovered this class. As we have just seen, the suggestion of Figure 3.5 is correct, showing that the Schwartz space is contained in the Poisson space.

Question 3.42. Are there some natural necessary and sufficient conditions for Poisson summation?

This is an important open question. In other words, we may ask what the inherent limitations of functions that satisfy Poisson summation are. Although there are well over twenty different versions of sufficient conditions in the literature on Poisson summation, there are currently no known necessary and sufficient conditions for Poisson summation to hold. It is natural to wonder what would happen if we only make the assumption that

$$f \in L^1(\mathbb{R}^d) \text{ and } \hat{f} \in L^1(\mathbb{R}^d).$$

Is such an f always a "nice" function? Sadly, the answer is, in general, "no", and there is an important counterexample by Yitzhak Katznelson in [**131**, Chapter VI, p. 143, Exercise 15].

There are many other families of nice functions in the literature, which include hypotheses such as "functions of bounded variation" and "absolutely continuous" functions. We will not delve into these other families here, but the reader may glance at Figure 3.6 for a slightly more refined relationship between nice functions and the L^1 and L^2 spaces. To justify the new containments that are suggested by Figure 3.6, we recall that a nice function f was defined in (3.57) to include the property that both $f, \hat{f} \in L^1(\mathbb{R}^d)$. By Lemma 3.56, we know, therefore, that both $f, \hat{f} \in L^2(\mathbb{R}^d)$ as well, so Figure 3.6 is correct.

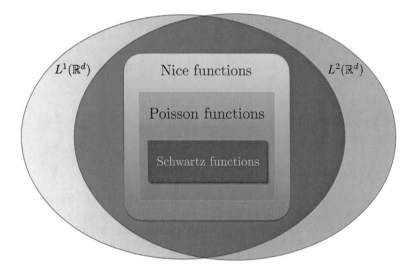

Figure 3.6. A more detailed Venn diagram than Figure 3.5 for function spaces related to nice functions.

14. An initial taste of general lattices in anticipation of Chapter 5

Definition 3.43. A **lattice** is defined by the integer linear span of a fixed set of linearly independent vectors $\{v_1, \dots, v_m\} \subset \mathbb{R}^d$:

$$(3.80) \qquad \mathcal{L} := \left\{ n_1 v_1 + \cdots + n_m v_m \in \mathbb{R}^d \mid \text{all } n_j \in \mathbb{Z} \right\}.$$

Although the **integer lattice** $\mathbb{Z}^d$ is the most common lattice, we often need to consider other types of lattices. Any lattice $\mathcal{L} \subset \mathbb{R}^d$ can also be defined by:

$$
(3.81) \quad \mathcal{L} := \left\{ \begin{pmatrix} | & | & \cdots & | \\ v_1 & v_2 & \cdots & v_m \\ | & | & \cdots & | \end{pmatrix} \begin{pmatrix} n_1 \\ \vdots \\ n_m \end{pmatrix} \mid \begin{pmatrix} n_1 \\ \vdots \\ n_m \end{pmatrix} \in \mathbb{Z}^m \right\} := M(\mathbb{Z}^m),
$$

where, by definition, M is the $d \times m$ matrix whose columns are the vectors $v_1, \ldots, v_m$. This set of basis vectors $\{v_1, \ldots, v_m\}$ is called a **basis** for the lattice $\mathcal{L}$, and m is called the **rank** of the lattice $\mathcal{L}$. In this context, we also use the notation $\mathrm{rank}(\mathcal{L}) = m$. Any invertible matrix M that appears in (3.81) is called a **basis matrix** for the lattice $\mathcal{L}$. Most of the time, we will be interested in **full-rank** lattices, which means that $m = d$. However, sometimes we will also be interested in lattices that have lower rank and it is important to understand them. The **determinant** of a full-rank lattice $\mathcal{L} := M(\mathbb{Z}^d)$ is defined by

$$
\det \mathcal{L} := |\det M|,
$$

and we will see in Chapter 5 that $\det \mathcal{L}$ is independent of the choice of basis matrix M.

15. Poisson summation III: For general lattices

We will use a slightly more general version of the Poisson summation formula, which holds for any lattice, and which follows rather quickly from the Poisson summation formula above. We define a (full-rank) lattice $\mathcal{L} := M(\mathbb{Z}^d) \subset \mathbb{R}^d$, which is the image of the integer lattice under an invertible linear transformation M. The **dual lattice** of $\mathcal{L}$ is defined by $\mathcal{L}^* := M^{-T}(\mathbb{Z}^d)$, where M^{-T} is the inverse transpose matrix of the real matrix M (see Section 7 for more on dual lattices).

As we have seen in Lemma 2.9, Fourier transforms behave beautifully under compositions with any linear transformation. We will use this fact again in the proof of the following extension of Poisson summation, which holds for all lattices $\mathcal{L}$ and is quite standard. We recall that a Poisson function f, by definition, satisfies the growth conditions (3.74).

Theorem 3.44 (Poisson summation formula III). *Given a full-rank lattice $\mathcal{L} \subset \mathbb{R}^d$ and a Poisson function $f : \mathbb{R}^d \to \mathbb{C}$, we have*

$$
(3.82) \qquad \sum_{n \in \mathcal{L}} f(n + x) = \frac{1}{\det \mathcal{L}} \sum_{m \in \mathcal{L}^*} \hat{f}(m) e^{2\pi i \langle x, m \rangle},
$$

valid for all $x \in \mathbb{R}^d$. In particular, we have

$$
(3.83) \qquad \sum_{n \in \mathcal{L}} f(n) = \frac{1}{\det \mathcal{L}} \sum_{\xi \in \mathcal{L}^*} \hat{f}(\xi).
$$

Both sides of (3.82) converge absolutely and are continuous functions on $\mathbb{R}^d$.

Proof. Any (full-rank) lattice may be written as $\mathcal{L} := M(\mathbb{Z}^d)$ so that $\det \mathcal{L} := |\det M|$. Using the Poisson summation formula (3.51) with the change of variable $n = Mk$ with $k \in \mathbb{Z}^d$, we have:

$$\sum_{n \in \mathcal{L}} f(n) = \sum_{k \in \mathbb{Z}^d} (f \circ M)(k)$$

$$= \sum_{\xi \in \mathbb{Z}^d} \widehat{(f \circ M)}(\xi)$$

$$= \frac{1}{|\det M|} \sum_{\xi \in \mathbb{Z}^d} \hat{f}(M^{-T}\xi)$$

$$= \frac{1}{\det \mathcal{L}} \sum_{m \in \mathcal{L}^*} \hat{f}(m),$$

where in the third equality we used the elementary "stretch" lemma (Lemma 2.9), and in the fourth equality we used the definition of the dual lattice $\mathcal{L}^* := M^{-T}\mathbb{Z}^d$. $\qquad\square$

As an aside, it turns out that the special case (3.83) also easily implies the general case, namely (3.82) (Exercise (16)).

A traditional application of the Poisson summation formula is the quick derivation of the functional equation of the theta function. We first define the Gaussian function by

$$(3.84) \qquad\qquad G_t(x) := t^{-\frac{d}{2}} e^{-\frac{\pi}{t}\|x\|^2},$$

for each fixed $t > 0$ and for all $x \in \mathbb{R}^d$, as depicted in Figure 3.7.

Two immediately interesting properties of the Gaussian are:

$$(3.85) \qquad\qquad \int_{\mathbb{R}^d} G_t(x)dx = 1$$

for each $t > 0$ and

$$(3.86) \qquad\qquad \hat{G}_t(m) = e^{-\pi t\|m\|^2},$$

properties which are important in statistics as well (Exercises (17) and (18)). Each fixed ε gives us one Gaussian function and intuitively, as $\varepsilon \to 0$, this sequence of Gaussians approaches the "Dirac delta function" at the origin, which is really known as a "generalized function" or "distribution" (Note (3)).

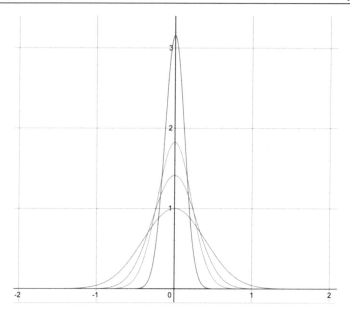

Figure 3.7. The Gaussian family of functions $G_t(x)$ with $t = 1$, $t = .5, t = .3$, and $t = .1$, respectively.

Example 3.45. The classical theta function (for the integer lattice) is defined by:

$$(3.87) \qquad \theta(t) = \sum_{n \in \mathbb{Z}^d} e^{-\pi t \|n\|^2}.$$

This function plays a major role in analytic number theory. One of its first historical applications was carried out by Riemann himself, who proved its functional equation (equation (3.88)) and then applied a "Mellin transform" to it, to prove the functional equation of the Riemann zeta function $\zeta(s) := \sum_{n=1}^{\infty} \frac{1}{n^s}$. We claim that the theta function has the functional equation

$$(3.88) \qquad \theta\left(\frac{1}{t}\right) = t^{\frac{d}{2}} \theta(t),$$

for all $t > 0$. This will follow immediately from the Poisson summation formula for Schwartz functions (3.52), by using $f(x) := G_t(x)$. Using our knowledge of its FT, from (3.86), we have:

$$\sum_{n\in\mathbb{Z}^d} G_t(n) = \sum_{\xi\in\mathbb{Z}^d} \hat{G}_t(\xi)$$

$$= \sum_{\xi\in\mathbb{Z}^d} e^{-\pi t\|\xi\|^2}$$

$$:= \theta(t).$$

Since by definition $\sum_{n\in\mathbb{Z}^d} G_t(n) := t^{-\frac{d}{2}} \sum_{n\in\mathbb{Z}^d} e^{-\frac{\pi}{t}\|n\|^2} := t^{-\frac{d}{2}}\theta\left(\frac{1}{t}\right)$, (3.88) is proved. □

16. The convolution operation

For $f, g \in L^1(\mathbb{R}^d)$, their **convolution** is defined by

$$(3.89) \qquad\qquad (f * g)(x) = \int_{\mathbb{R}^d} f(x - y)g(y)dy.$$

But sometimes it is useful not to assume that we have absolutely integrable functions, and therefore we will also use definition (3.89) to include any functions f, g for which the latter integral still converges (see Examples 3.51 and 3.52). It is possible to think intuitively of this analogue of multiplication as: "this is how waves like to multiply", via Lemma 3.46(2). We have the following basic relations for the convolution operation.

Lemma 3.46. *For all $f, g, h \in L^1(\mathbb{R}^d)$, we have:*

(1) $f * g \in L^1(\mathbb{R}^d)$.

(2) $\widehat{(f * g)}(\xi) = \hat{f}(\xi)\hat{g}(\xi)$.

(3) $f * g = g * f$, $f * (g * h) = (f * g) * h$, and $f * (g + h) = f * g + f * h$.

(4) $\|f * g\|_1 \leq \|f\|_1 \|g\|_1$.

(5) *More generally, when $f \in L^p(\mathbb{R}^d)$ and $g \in L^1(\mathbb{R}^d)$ with $1 \leq p < \infty$, then we have $f * g \in L^p(\mathbb{R}^d)$ and*

$$\|f * g\|_p \leq \|f\|_p \|g\|_1.$$

Proof. To prove part (2), we use Fubini's theorem (Theorem B.2 in the Appendix):

$$\widehat{(f * g)}(\xi) := \int_{\mathbb{R}^d} e^{-2\pi i\langle x,\xi\rangle} \left(\int_{\mathbb{R}^d} f(x-y)g(y)dy \right) dx$$

$$= \int_{\mathbb{R}^d} g(y)e^{-2\pi i\langle y,\xi\rangle}dy \int_{\mathbb{R}^d} f(x-y)e^{-2\pi i\langle x-y,\xi\rangle}dx$$

$$= \int_{\mathbb{R}^d} g(y)e^{-2\pi i\langle y,\xi\rangle}dy \int_{\mathbb{R}^d} f(x)e^{-2\pi i\langle x,\xi\rangle}dx$$

$$:= \hat{f}(\xi)\hat{g}(\xi),$$

where we have used the translation invariance of the measure, in the penultimate equality.

To prove part (4) we use Fubini's theorem again, and the triangle inequality for integrals:

$$\|f * g\|_1 := \int_{\mathbb{R}^d} \left| \int_{\mathbb{R}^d} f(x-y)g(y)dy \right| dx$$

$$\leq \int_{\mathbb{R}^d} \int_{\mathbb{R}^d} |f(x-y)g(y)| \, dydx$$

$$= \int_{\mathbb{R}^d} \int_{\mathbb{R}^d} |f(y)g(y)| \, dydx$$

$$= \int_{\mathbb{R}^d} |f(y)| \, dy \int_{\mathbb{R}^d} |g(y)| \, dx$$

$$:= \|f\|_1\|g\|_1.$$

For the proofs of the remaining parts we recommend Rudin's book [217].
$\square$

Lemma 3.46(2) means that convolution of functions in the space domain corresponds to the usual multiplication of functions in the frequency domain (and vice versa).

Example 3.47. When $\mathcal{P} := [-\frac{1}{2}, \frac{1}{2}]$, the convolution of $1_{\mathcal{P}}$ with itself is drawn in Figure 3.8. We can already see that this convolution is a continuous function, hence a little smoother than the discontinuous function $1_{\mathcal{P}}$. Using Lemma 3.46 we have

$$(\widehat{1_{\mathcal{P}} * 1_{\mathcal{P}}})(\xi) = \hat{1}_{\mathcal{P}}(\xi)\hat{1}_{\mathcal{P}}(\xi) = \left(\frac{\sin(\pi\xi)}{\pi\xi} \right)^2.$$

We used equation (2.2) in the last equality for the Fourier transform of our interval $\mathcal{P}$ here. Considering the graph in Figure 3.9 for the Fourier transform of the convolution $(1_{\mathcal{P}} * 1_{\mathcal{P}})$, we see that this positive function is already much more tightly concentrated near the origin compared with $\mathrm{sinc}(x) := \hat{1}_{\mathcal{P}}(\xi)$. We work out all of the details for this 1-dimensional function—and generalize it—in Example 3.49. □

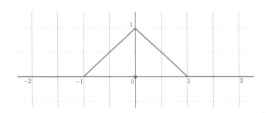

Figure 3.8. The function $(1_{\mathcal{P}} * 1_{\mathcal{P}})(x)$, with $\mathcal{P} := \left[-\frac{1}{2}, \frac{1}{2}\right]$.

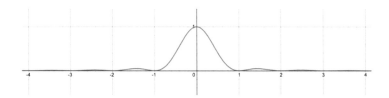

Figure 3.9. The Fourier transform $(\widehat{1_{\mathcal{P}} * 1_{\mathcal{P}}})(\xi)$, which is equal to the infinitely smooth, nonnegative function $\left(\frac{\sin(\pi\xi)}{\pi\xi}\right)^2 := \mathrm{sinc}^2(\xi)$.

Another useful bit of information about convolutions is that they are a kind of averaging process and that the convolution of two functions becomes smoother than either one of them. For our applications, when we consider the indicator function $1_{\mathcal{P}}(x)$ for a polytope $\mathcal{P}$, then this function is not continuous on $\mathbb{R}^d$, so that the Poisson summation formula does not necessarily hold for it. But if we consider the convolution of $1_{\mathcal{P}}(x)$ with a Gaussian, for example, then we arrive at the C^∞ function

$$(1_{\mathcal{P}} * G_t)(x),$$

for which the Poisson summation does hold. In the sequel, we will use the latter convolved function in tandem with Poisson summation to study "solid angles".

Example 3.48. For any bounded sets $K, L \subset \mathbb{R}^d$, we have

$$(3.90) \qquad (1_K * 1_L)(y) := \int_{\mathbb{R}^d} 1_K(x) 1_L(y - x) dx$$

$$(3.91) \qquad\qquad\quad := \int_{\mathbb{R}^d} 1_K(x) 1_{-L+y}(x) dx$$

$$(3.92) \qquad\qquad\quad = \int_{\mathbb{R}^d} 1_{K \cap (-L+y)}(x) dx$$

$$(3.93) \qquad\qquad\quad = \int_{K \cap (-L+y)} dx$$

$$(3.94) \qquad\qquad\quad = \mathrm{vol}(K \cap (-L + y))$$

so that the convolution of indicator functions gives volumes, and this simple connection is one of the entry points of Fourier analysis into convex geometry. □

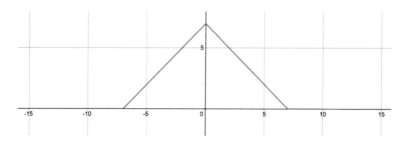

Figure 3.10. The hat function $1_{[-r,r]} * 1_{[-r,r]}$ of Example 3.49 with $r = 3.5$.

Example 3.49. As a special case of Example 3.48, consider the case $K = L := [-r, r] \subset \mathbb{R}$. So we now know, by (3.94), that

$$(3.95) \quad g(x) := \left(1_{[-r,r]} * 1_{[-r,r]}\right)(x) = \mathrm{vol}\left([-r,r] \cap ([-r,r] + x)\right),$$

making it clear that for $x \leq -2r$ and $x \geq 2r$, we have

$$\mathrm{vol}\left([-r,r] \cap ([-r,r] + x)\right) = 0.$$

When $x \in [-2r, 0]$, we have the function

$$g(x) := \mathrm{vol}\left([-r,r] \cap ([-r,r] + x)\right) = |x - 2r| = x + 2r,$$

Finally, when $x \in [0, 2r]$, we have the function

$$g(x) := \text{vol}\left([-r, r] \cap ([-r, r] + x) \right) = |x - 2r| = 2r - x.$$

To summarize, we have

$$g(x) = \begin{cases} 2r - |x| & \text{if } x \in [-2r, 2r] \\ 0 & \text{if not.} \end{cases}$$

Due to its shape, g is sometimes called the **hat function**, which is clearly a continuous function on $\mathbb{R}$. The hat function is extremely useful in many applications. For example, we can use it to build up nonnegative functions that are compactly supported on $\mathbb{R}$, and yet whose Fourier transform is *strictly positive* on $\mathbb{R}$—see Exercise (28). □

Given these examples, it is natural to wonder when the convolution is continuous:

Question 3.50 (Rhetorical). Given any convex sets $A, B \subset \mathbb{R}^d$, is $1_A * 1_B(x)$ continuous for all $x \in \mathbb{R}^d$?

We can answer Question 3.50 in the affirmative in Exercises (20) and (21).

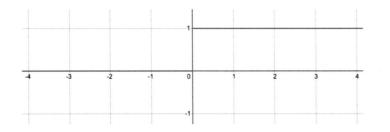

Figure 3.11. The heaviside function $H_0(x)$.

Example 3.51. The **Heaviside function** is defined by

$$(3.96) \qquad H_a(x) := \begin{cases} 1 & \text{if } x \geq a \\ 0 & \text{if } x < a, \end{cases}$$

where a is any fixed real number. Although the Heaviside function is clearly not absolutely integrable over $\mathbb{R}$, we may still use the same definition (3.89) for its convolution with a function $f \in L^1(\mathbb{R})$:

(3.97) $$(f * H_0)(x) := \int_{\mathbb{R}} f(x - y)H_0(y)dy$$

(3.98) $$= \int_0^\infty f(x - y)dy$$

$$= \int_{-\infty}^x f(t)dt,$$

a convergent integral.   □

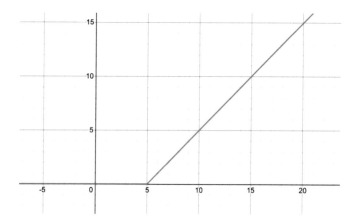

Figure 3.12. The ramp function $r_5(x)$.

Example 3.52. The **ramp function** is defined by

(3.99) $$r_a(x) := \begin{cases} x & \text{if } x \geq a \\ 0 & \text{if } x < a, \end{cases}$$

where a is any fixed real number. It is evident that we also have $r_0(x) = \max\{x, 0\}$. It is also clear that $r'_a(x) = H_a(x)$. The ramp function is ubiquitous in the analysis of machine learning algorithms, where it is called the ReLu (Rectified Linear Unit) function. There is an elegant relationship between the ramp function and the Heaviside function:

(3.100) $$H_0 * H_0 = r_0,$$

so we see that convolution makes sense here despite the fact that none of these functions are in $L^1(\mathbb{R})$! To check the latter claim (3.100), we use (3.97):

$$H_0 * H_0(x) := \int_{-\infty}^{x} H_0(t)dt$$

$$= \begin{cases} \int_0^x dx & \text{if } x \geq 0 \\ 0 & \text{if } x < 0 \end{cases}$$

$$= \begin{cases} x & \text{if } x \geq 0 \\ 0 & \text{if } x < 0 \end{cases} := r_0(x).$$

There is also a straightforward extension: $H_a * H_b = r_{a+b}$ (Exercise (29)).

$\square$

16.1. The support of a convolution. Given two functions whose support is bounded, it is natural to wonder what the support of their convolution looks like. The very first observation is that if we have two closed, convex bodies $A, B \subset \mathbb{R}^d$, then:

$$(3.101) \qquad \text{support}(1_A * 1_B) = A + B,$$

where the right-hand side uses the Minkowski sum of two sets (Exercise (11)). There is a deeper result by Titchmarsh [**248**] in the case of $d = 1$, and J. L. Lions [**160**] in general dimension that gives a very precise answer.

Theorem 3.53 (Titchmarsh and Lions). *Let $f, g : \mathbb{R}^d \to \mathbb{R}$ have bounded support. Then*

$$(3.102) \quad \text{conv}(\text{support}(f * g)) = \text{conv}(\text{support } f) + \text{conv}(\text{support } g),$$

where the right-hand side means we are taking the Minkowski sum of two convex bodies. $\square$

The proof of this theorem is beyond the scope of this book, although Exercise (11) gives another useful special case of Theorem 3.53.

17. More relations between $L^1(\mathbb{R}^d)$ and $L^2(\mathbb{R}^d)$

Having seen convolutions with various examples, we can now return to the question:

Question 3.54. What is the image of the space $L^1(\mathbb{R}^d)$ under the Fourier transform?

It seems that there is no known "complete" answer to this open question yet; however, an apparently lesser-known but elegant result, due to Rudin, is the following correspondence.

Theorem 3.55 (Rudin).

(3.103) $f \in L^1(\mathbb{R}^d) \iff \hat{f} = g * h$, with $g, h \in L^2(\mathbb{R}^d)$.   □

In words, Theorem 3.55 tells us that the image of $L^1(\mathbb{R}^d)$ under the Fourier transform consists precisely of the set of convolutions $g * h$, where $g, h \in L^2(\mathbb{R}^d)$ (See [**218**, Theorem 1.6.3, p. 27]).

Here is an outline of a proof for the easy direction: Suppose that $g, h \in L^2(\mathbb{R}^d)$. Because we want to find a solution in f to the equation $\hat{f} = g * h$, it is natural to try $f := \widehat{g * h} = \hat{g} \cdot \hat{h}$. Let us try it by defining

$$f := \hat{g} \cdot \hat{h}.$$

Because the Fourier transform acting on $L^2(\mathbb{R}^d)$ is an isometry, we have $\hat{g}, \hat{h} \in L^2(\mathbb{R}^d)$. Also, the product of two L^2 functions in an L^1 function (equation (3.2)), so we conclude that $f := \hat{g} \cdot \hat{h} \in L^1(\mathbb{R}^d)$, as required.

This ongoing dance between the L^1 and L^2 spaces has more to offer.

Lemma 3.56. *If $f \in L^1(\mathbb{R}^d)$ and $\hat{f} \in L^1(\mathbb{R}^d)$, then both $f, \hat{f} \in L^2(\mathbb{R}^d)$.*

Proof. Because $\hat{f} \in L^1(\mathbb{R}^d)$, we know by the basic inequality (3.11) that f must be bounded on $\mathbb{R}^d$: $|f(x)| \leq M$ for some $M > 0$. We now compute:

$$\int_{\mathbb{R}^d} |f(x)|^2 dx \leq \int_{\mathbb{R}^d} M|f(x)|dx = M \int_{\mathbb{R}^d} |f(x)|dx < \infty,$$

where the last inequality holds because $f \in L^1(\mathbb{R}^d)$ by assumption. So $f \in L^2(\mathbb{R}^d)$. Precisely the same reasoning applies to $\hat{f}$ so that $\hat{f} \in L^2(\mathbb{R}^d)$ as well.   □

Sometimes we are given a function $f \in L^2(\mathbb{R}^d)$ and we would like to know what extra properties f needs to possess in order to place it in $L^1(\mathbb{R}^d)$.

Lemma 3.57.

(1) *Suppose that f vanishes outside a compact set $E \subset \mathbb{R}^d$. Then:*

$$f \in L^2(\mathbb{R}^d) \implies f \in L^1(\mathbb{R}^d).$$

(2) *Suppose that f is bounded on $\mathbb{R}^d$. Then:*

$$f \in L^1(\mathbb{R}^d) \implies f \in L^2(\mathbb{R}^d).$$

Proof. To prove part (1), we may use the Cauchy–Schwartz inequality:

$$\int_{\mathbb{R}^d} |f(x)|\, dx = \int_E 1 \cdot |f(x)|\, dx$$

$$\leq \left(\int_E dx \right)^{\frac{1}{2}} \left(\int_E |f(x)|^2 dx \right)^{\frac{1}{2}}$$

$$= m(E)^{\frac{1}{2}} \left(\int_E |f(x)|^2 dx \right)^{\frac{1}{2}}$$

$$< \infty.$$

To prove part (2), suppose $|f| < M$ for some bound $M > 0$. Then $|f^2(x)| \leq M|f(x)|$ for all $x \in \mathbb{R}^d$, and we have:

$$\int_{\mathbb{R}^d} |f(x)|^2 dx \leq M \int_{\mathbb{R}^d} |f(x)|\, dx < \infty.$$

$\square$

17.1. How natural is the Fourier transform? We close this section by thinking a bit about another natural question. We have already seen in Lemma 3.46(2) that if $f, \hat{f} \in L^1(\mathbb{R}^d)$, then for each fixed $\xi \in \mathbb{R}^d$ the map

$$\Phi_\xi : f \to \hat{f}(\xi),$$

is a complex homomorphism from $L^1(\mathbb{R}^d)$ to $\mathbb{C}$. In other words, we already know that $\Phi_\xi(fg) := \widehat{(fg)}(\xi) = \hat{f}(\xi)\hat{g}(\xi) := \Phi_\xi(f)\Phi_\xi(g)$.

Are there other linear transforms that act on $L^1(\mathbb{R}^d)$ as a homomorphism into $\mathbb{C}$? It turns out there are not!

The Fourier transform is the unique homomorphism here, which means that it is very natural, and in this algebraic sense the Fourier transform is unavoidable. So we may as well befriend it. The precise statement is the following theorem, following Rudin.

Theorem 3.58. *Suppose $\phi : L^1(\mathbb{R}^d) \to \mathbb{C}$ is a nonzero complex homomorphism. Then for each $f \in L^1(\mathbb{R}^d)$, there exists a unique $t \in \mathbb{R}^d$ such that*

$$\phi(f) = \hat{f}(t).$$

$\square$

The reader may consult Rudin's book [**217**, Theorem 9.23], for a detailed proof. There is also a much more general version of Theorem 3.58, in the context of any locally compact abelian group, which Rudin proves in his book "Fourier analysis on groups" ([**218**, Theorem 1.2.2, p. 7]).

18. The Dirichlet kernel

Using convolutions, we may now also go back to the partial sums of a
Fourier series, which we have defined in (3.35) by

$$(3.104) \qquad S_N f(t) := \sum_{n=-N}^{N} \hat{f}(n) e^{2\pi i n t}.$$

We compute:

$$S_N f(t) := \sum_{n=-N}^{N} \hat{f}(n) e^{2\pi i n t}$$

$$= \sum_{n=-N}^{N} \int_0^1 f(x) e^{-2\pi i x n} dx \, e^{2\pi i n t}$$

$$= \int_0^1 f(x) \sum_{n=-N}^{N} e^{2\pi i (t-x) n} dx$$

$$:= (f * D_N)(t),$$

where this convolution is defined on the 1-Torus (the circle), and where
we introduced the important definition

$$(3.105) \qquad D_N(x) := \sum_{n=-N}^{N} e^{2\pi i x n},$$

known as the **Dirichlet kernel**. But look how naturally another convolution came up! We have just proved the following elementary lemma.

Lemma 3.59. *If $f \in L^2(\mathbb{T})$, then*

$$S_N f(t) = (f * D_N)(t),$$

where this convolution is taken over $[0, 1]$. □

It is therefore very natural to study the behavior of the Dirichlet kernel on its own. In Exercise (32), we showed that the Dirichlet kernel has
the closed form

$$D_N(x) = \frac{\sin(\pi x (2N + 1))}{\sin(\pi x)}.$$

It is clear from the definition of $D_N(x)$ that it is a periodic function of x, with period 1, and if we restrict our attention to the interval
$[-1, 1]$, then its graph appears in Figure 3.13. It turns out the the L^1 norm
of the Dirichlet kernel becomes unbounded as $N \to \infty$, and this phenomenon is responsible for a lot of results about pointwise divergence

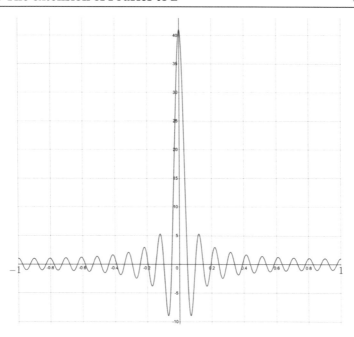

Figure 3.13. The Dirichlet Kernel $D_{20}(x)$, restricted to the interval $[-1, 1]$.

of Fourier series, a very delicate subject that is replete with technical subtleties. There are even examples of continuous functions f whose partial Fourier sums $S_N f(x)$ do not converge anywhere [**251**, Theorem 4.19]. However, the Dirichlet kernel is also useful for proving important pointwise convergence theorems, such as Theorem 3.24.

19. The extension of the Fourier transform to L^2: Plancherel

So far we have worked with the Fourier transform that is defined only for functions that belong to $L^1(\mathbb{R}^d)$. But sometimes we have a function that is *not* in L^1, but we would still like to study its transform. Our prime example was $\hat{1}_C$, a function that is not absolutely integrable for any bounded set C.

So how do we extend the Fourier transform to all of $L^2(\mathbb{R}^d)$? Plancherel did it, and as it turns out there is a unique extension, because $L^1(\mathbb{R}^d) \cap L^2(\mathbb{R}^d)$ is dense in $L^2(\mathbb{R}^d)$.

Theorem 3.60 (Plancherel, 1911). *Let $f \in L^2(\mathbb{R}^d)$. Then there is a map*

$$\Phi : L^2(\mathbb{R}^d) \to L^2(\mathbb{R}^d)$$

such that $\Phi(f)$ has the following properties:

(1) *If $f \in L^1$ as well, then we already have a proper definition of its Fourier transform, so we set $\Phi(f) := \hat{f}$.*

(2) *(Plancherel's formula) $\|\Phi(f)\|_2 = \|f\|_2$.*

(3) *Φ is a surjective Hilbert space isomorphism.*

(4) *(Fourier inversion for L^2) We define:*

$$A_R(\xi) := \int_{\|x\|<R} f(x) e^{-2\pi i \langle x, \xi \rangle} dx,$$

$$B_R(x) := \int_{\|x\|<R} \Phi(f)(\xi) \, e^{2\pi i \langle x, \xi \rangle} d\xi.$$

Then we have:

(3.106) $$\lim_{R\to\infty} \|A_R(\xi) - \Phi(f)\|_2 = 0,$$

(3.107) $$and \lim_{R\to\infty} \|B_R(x) - f\|_2 = 0.$$

This unique extension $\Phi(f)$ of the Fourier transform will henceforth be denoted by the same symbol: $\hat{f}$.   □

We refer the reader to Rudin's book [**217**] for a nice proof. Equations (3.106) and (3.107) are the **Fourier inversion formulas** for L^2-functions. We notice that "there is no free lunch" in following sense. Although we were able to extend the Fourier transform to all of L^2, the convergence is *not* pointwise convergence but rather convergence in norm. This sometimes causes some trouble, but it is part of life.

At the risk of overstating the obvious, we note the good news that the equality in Plancherel's formula, which is part (2) of Plancherel's theorem, is simply an equality between two real numbers. Here is an interesting application for our focused study of indicator functions.

Corollary 3.61. *Given a bounded set $Q \subset \mathbb{R}^d$, we have $\hat{1}_Q \in L^2(\mathbb{R}^d)$. Moreover:*

(3.108) $$\int_{\mathbb{R}^d} |\hat{1}_Q(x)|^2 \, dx = \text{vol } Q.$$

Proof. We know that $1_Q \in L^2(\mathbb{R}^d)$, so by Plancherel's theorem (Theorem 3.60(2)), we have

$$\int_{\mathbb{R}^d} |\hat{1}_Q(x)|^2 \, dx = \int_{\mathbb{R}^d} |1_Q(x)|^2 \, dx = \int_Q dx = \text{vol } Q.$$

$\square$

Now let us consider a related function: $g(x) := (1_A * 1_B)(x)$, which we may equivalently rewrite as

$$(1_A * 1_B)(x) = \text{vol}(A \cap (-B + x)),$$

using (3.94). A natural question is whether or not g is continuous.

Corollary 3.62. *Let $A, B \subset \mathbb{R}^d$ be two bounded sets. For $g(x) := (1_A * 1_B)(x)$, we have:*

(1) $\hat{g} \in L^1(\mathbb{R}^d)$.

(2) *g is continuous on $\mathbb{R}^d$.*

Proof. We know that trivially $1_Q \in L^1(\mathbb{R}^d)$ and $1_{-Q} \in L^1(\mathbb{R}^d)$, and this implies that $\hat{g} := \mathcal{F}(1_Q * 1_{-Q}) = \hat{1}_Q \hat{1}_{-Q}$, via Lemma 3.46(2). The Cauchy–Schwarz inequality now gives us:

$$\int_{\mathbb{R}^d} |\hat{g}(\xi)| \, d\xi = \int_{\mathbb{R}^d} |\hat{1}_Q(\xi)||\hat{1}_{-Q}(\xi)| \, d\xi$$

$$\leq \left(\int_{\mathbb{R}^d} |\hat{1}_Q(\xi)|^2 \, d\xi \right)^{1/2} \left(\int_{\mathbb{R}^d} |\hat{1}_{-Q}(\xi)|^2 \, d\xi \right)^{1/2} < \infty,$$

where the finiteness of the last expression follows from Corollary 3.61. Exercise (21) walks the reader through a detailed proof of Corollary 3.62(2). $\square$

Corollary 3.63. *For all $f, g \in L^2(\mathbb{R}^d)$, we have $\langle f, g \rangle = \langle \hat{f}, \hat{g} \rangle$. In other words:*

(3.109) $$\int_{\mathbb{R}^d} f(x)\overline{g(x)}dx = \int_{\mathbb{R}^d} \hat{f}(x)\overline{\hat{g}(x)}dx.$$

$\square$

Proof. The elementary polarization identity (Exercise (23)) tells us that

$$\langle f, g \rangle = \frac{1}{2} \left(\|f\|^2 + \|g\|^2 - \|f + g\|^2 \right).$$

By Plancherel's theorem (Theorem 3.60(2)), we know that

$$\|f\|^2 = \|\hat{f}\|^2, \|g\|^2 = \|\hat{g}\|^2,$$

and $\|f + g\|^2 = \|\hat{f} + \hat{g}\|^2$, so we have $\langle f, g \rangle = \langle \hat{f}, \hat{g} \rangle$.   □

Example 3.64. As we recall, the sinc function, defined by

$$\text{sinc}(\xi) := \begin{cases} \frac{\sin(\pi\xi)}{\pi\xi}, & \text{if } \xi \neq 0 \\ 1 & \text{if } \xi = 0, \end{cases}$$

plays an important role (in many fields), and was our very first example of the Fourier transform of a polytope: $\text{sinc} = \hat{1}_{\left[-\frac{1}{2}, \frac{1}{2}\right]}$. Here we will glimpse another aspect of the importance of sinc functions as an application of Plancherel's theorem. Let us prove that

$$(3.110) \qquad \int_{\mathbb{R}} \text{sinc}(x - n) \text{sinc}(x - m)dx = \begin{cases} 1 & \text{if } n = m \\ 0 & \text{if } n \neq m. \end{cases}$$

Although $\text{sinc} \notin L^1(\mathbb{R})$, we do have

$$\text{sinc} = \hat{1}_{\left[-\frac{1}{2}, \frac{1}{2}\right]} \in L^2(\mathbb{R})$$

by Corollary 3.61. Using Plancherel's theorem, we know that $\mathcal{F}(\text{sinc}(x - n))(\xi)$ is well-defined as an $L^2(\mathbb{R}^d)$ function, and Corollary 3.63 gives us:

$$\int_{\mathbb{R}} \text{sinc}(x - n) \, \text{sinc}(x - m)dx$$

$$= \int_{\mathbb{R}} \mathcal{F}(\text{sinc}(x - n))(\xi) \, \overline{\mathcal{F}(\text{sinc}(x - m))(\xi)}d\xi$$

$$= \int_{\mathbb{R}} 1_{\mathcal{P}}(\xi)e^{2\pi i\xi n} \, 1_{\mathcal{P}}(\xi)\overline{e^{2\pi i\xi m}}d\xi$$

$$= \int_{\mathcal{P}} e^{2\pi i\xi(n-m)}d\xi$$

$$= \delta(n, m),$$

where $\mathcal{P} := [-\frac{1}{2}, \frac{1}{2}]$ and where we have used the orthogonality of the exponentials over $\mathcal{P}$ (Exercise (3)). So we see that the collection of functions

$$\{\text{sinc}(x - n) \mid n \in \mathbb{Z}\}$$

forms an orthonormal collection of functions in the Hilbert space $L^2([-\frac{1}{2}, \frac{1}{2}])$ relative to its inner product. It turns out that when we study Shannon's sampling theorem, these translated sinc functions are in fact a *complete* orthonormal basis for the Hilbert subspace of $L^2(\mathbb{R})$ that consists of "bandlimited functions".   □

20. Approximate identities

It is a sad fact of life that there is no identity in $L^1(\mathbb{R}^d)$ for the convolution product—in other words, there is no function $h \in L^1(\mathbb{R}^d)$ such that

$$(3.111) \qquad\qquad f * h = f$$

for all $f \in L^1(\mathbb{R}^d)$.

Why is that? Suppose there was such a function $h \in L^1(\mathbb{R}^d)$. Then, taking the Fourier transform of both sides of (3.111), we would also have

$$(3.112) \qquad\qquad \hat{f}\,\hat{h} = \widehat{f * h} = \hat{f}$$

for all $f \in L^1(\mathbb{R}^d)$. Picking an f whose transform is nowhere zero, we can divide both sides of (3.112) by $\hat{f}$ to conclude that $\hat{h} \equiv 1$, the constant function. But by the Riemann–Lebesgue lemma (Lemma 3.13), we know that $\hat{h}$ must go to 0 as $|x| \to \infty$, which is a contradiction.

Nevertheless, it is still interesting to think about what would happen if we were able to apply the inverse Fourier transform to $\hat{h}$, formally applying the Fourier transform to the equation $\hat{h} = 1$ to get

$$(3.113) \qquad\qquad h(x) = \int_{\mathbb{R}^d} e^{2\pi i \langle x, \xi \rangle} dx,$$

an extremely interesting integral that unfortunately diverges. In Note (3), we mention briefly that such observations became critically important for the development of generalized functions that do play the role of the identity for convolutions, and much more.

Although there is no identity element for convolutions, it turns out that by using sequences of functions we can get close! Here is how we may do it, and as a consequence we will be able to rigorously apply the Poisson summation formula to a wider class of functions, including smoothed versions of the indicator function of a polytope.

Fix a function $\phi \in L^1(\mathbb{R}^d)$, such that $\int_{\mathbb{R}^d} \phi(x) dx = 1$. Beginning with any such function ϕ, we construct an **approximate identity** by defining the sequence of functions

$$(3.114) \qquad\qquad \phi_n(x) := n^d \phi(nx),$$

for each $n = 1, 2, 3, \dots$.

It is easy to check that we also have $\int_{\mathbb{R}^d} \phi_n(x) dx = 1$ for all $n \geq 1$ (Exercise (24)). So scaling ϕ by these ns has the effect of squeezing ϕ so that it becomes concentrated near the origin while maintaining a total mass of 1. Then, intuitively, a sequence of such ϕ_n functions approaches the "Dirac delta-function" at the origin (which is a distribution, not a function).

There are many families of functions that give an approximate identity. In practice, we will seldom have to specify exactly which sequence ϕ_n we pick because we will merely use the existence of such a sequence to facilitate the use of Poisson summation. Returning now to the motivation of this section, we can recover the next best thing to an identity for the convolution product, as follows.

Theorem 3.65. *Suppose we are given a function $f \in L^1(\mathbb{R}^d)$, such that $p \in \mathbb{R}^d$ is a point of continuity for f. Fix an approximate identity $\phi_n(x)$ and assume $f * \phi$ exists. Then we have:*

$$(3.115) \qquad \lim_{n \to \infty} (f * \phi_n)(p) = f(p).$$

Proof. We begin by massaging the convolution product:

$$(\phi_n * f)(p) := \int_{\mathbb{R}^d} \phi_n(x) f(p - x) dx$$

$$= \int_{\mathbb{R}^d} \phi_n(x) \Big(f(p - x) - f(p) + f(p) \Big) dx$$

$$= \int_{\mathbb{R}^d} \phi_n(x) \Big(f(p - x) - f(p) \Big) dx + f(p) \int_{\mathbb{R}^d} \phi_n(x) dx$$

$$= f(p) + \int_{\mathbb{R}^d} \phi_n(x) \Big(f(p - x) - f(p) \Big) dx,$$

using the assumption that $\int_{\mathbb{R}^d} \phi_n(x) dx = 1$. Using the definition of $\phi_n(x) := n^d \phi(nx)$ and making a change of variable $u = nx$ in the latter integral, we have:

$$(\phi_n * f)(p) := f(p) + \int_{\mathbb{R}^d} \phi(u) \Big(f\Big(p - \frac{1}{n}u\Big) - f(p) \Big) du.$$

In the second part of the proof, we will show that as $n \to \infty$, the latter integral tends to zero. We will do this in two steps: first, bounding the tails of the integral in a neighborhood of infinity, and then bounding the integral in a neighborhood of the origin.

Step 1. Given any $\varepsilon > 0$, we note that the latter integral converges, so the "tails are arbitrarily small." In other words, there exists an $r > 0$ such that

$$\left| \int_{\|u\| > r} \phi(u) \Big(f\Big(p - \frac{1}{n}u\Big) - f(p) \Big) du \right| < \varepsilon.$$

Step 2. Now we want to bound $\int_{\|u\|<r} \phi(u)\left(f\left(p - \frac{1}{n}u\right) - f(p)\right)du$. We will use the fact that $\int_{\mathbb{R}^d} |\phi(u)|du = M$, a constant. Also, by continuity of f at p, we can pick an n sufficiently large, such that

$$\left|f\left(p - \frac{1}{n}u\right) - f(p)\right| < \frac{\varepsilon}{M}$$

when $\|\frac{1}{n}u\| < r$. Putting all of this together and using the triangle inequality for integrals, we have the bound

$$\left| \int_{\|u\|<r} \phi(u)\left(f\left(p - \frac{1}{n}u\right) - f(p)\right)du \right|$$
$$\leq \int_{\|u\|<r} |\phi(u)| \left|f\left(p - \frac{1}{n}u\right) - f(p)\right| du < \varepsilon.$$

Therefore, as $n \to \infty$, we have $(\phi_n * f)(p) \longrightarrow f(p)$. □

We note that at a point of discontinuity of f, Theorem 3.65 may be false even in dimension 1, as the next example shows.

Example 3.66. Let $f(x) := 1_{[0,1]}(x)$, which is discontinuous at $x = 0$ and $x = 1$. We claim that for $p = 1$, for example, we have

$$\lim_{n\to\infty} (f * \phi_n)(p) = \frac{1}{2}f(p),$$

so that the result of Theorem 3.65 does not hold at this particular p because p lies on the boundary of the 1-dimensional polytope $[0, 1]$. When $p \in \text{int}([0, 1])$, however, Theorem 3.65 does hold. □

21. Poisson summation IV: A practical Poisson summation formula

In practice, we want to apply Poisson summation to indicator functions $1_{\mathcal{P}}$ of polytopes and general convex bodies. With this in mind, it is useful for us to have our own home-cooked version of Poisson summation that is made for this culinary purpose.

Throughout this section, we fix any compactly supported nonnegative function $\varphi \in L^2(\mathbb{R}^d)$, with $\int_{\mathbb{R}^d} \varphi(x)dx = 1$, and we set $\varphi_\varepsilon(x) := \frac{1}{\varepsilon^d}\varphi\left(\frac{x}{\varepsilon}\right)$, for each $\varepsilon > 0$.

Theorem 3.67 (Poisson summation formula IV). *Let $f(x) \in L^2(\mathbb{R}^d)$ be a compactly supported function, and suppose that for each $x \in \mathbb{R}^d$, we have*

(3.116) $$f(x) = \lim_{\varepsilon \to 0^+} (\varphi_\varepsilon * f)(x).$$

Then the following hold:

(1) *For each $\varepsilon > 0$, we have absolute convergence:*

$$\sum_{m \in \mathbb{Z}^d} \left| \widehat{\varphi}(\varepsilon m) \widehat{f}(m) \right| < +\infty.$$

(2) *For all sufficiently small $\varepsilon > 0$, and for each fixed $x \in \mathbb{R}^d$, we have the pointwise equality:*

(3.117)
$$\sum_{n \in \mathbb{Z}^d} (\varphi_\varepsilon * f)(n + x) = \sum_{m \in \mathbb{Z}^d} \widehat{\varphi}(\varepsilon m) \widehat{f}(m) e^{2\pi i \langle m, x \rangle}.$$

(3)

(3.118)
$$\sum_{n \in \mathbb{Z}^d} f(n + x) = \lim_{\varepsilon \to 0} \sum_{m \in \mathbb{Z}^d} \widehat{\varphi}(\varepsilon m) \widehat{f}(m) e^{2\pi i \langle m, x \rangle}.$$

Because both f and φ_ε are compactly supported, the left-hand side of equations (2) and (3.118) are finite sums. $\square$

For a detailed proof of Theorem 3.67, see [**46**].

An interesting aspect of this version of Poisson summation is that it can sometimes even apply to functions f that are only piecewise continuous on $\mathbb{R}^d$, as long as (3.116) holds. Our prime example is, of course,

$$f(x) := 1_{\mathcal{P}}(x),$$

the indicator function of a polytope $\mathcal{P}$, and more generally 1_Q for a compact set Q with reasonable behavior, such as a convex body. In Chapter 4 we will use this version of Poisson summation, Theorem 3.67, to prove Theorem 4.6.

An interesting tool that gets used in the proof of Theorem 3.67 is a **Plancherel–Polya type inequality**, as follows.

Lemma 3.68. *Suppose that $f \in L^1(\mathbb{R}^d)$, $\widehat{f} \in L^1(\mathbb{R}^d)$, and f is compactly supported. Then there exists a constant $c > 0$ depending on the support of f, such that*

(3.119)
$$\sum_{n \in \mathbb{Z}^d} |\widehat{f}(n)| \le c \int_{\mathbb{R}^d} |\widehat{f}(\xi)| d\xi.$$

Proof. We define a new function ψ, which is infinitely smooth—and compactly supported—with $\psi(x) = 1$ for all x in the support of f. So we have $f(x) = \psi(x) f(x), \forall x \in \mathbb{R}^d$, and therefore $\widehat{f}(\xi) = (\widehat{\psi} * \widehat{f})(\xi)$ (using

$\hat{f} \in L^1(\mathbb{R}^d)$). Because ψ is smooth, we know that $\hat{\psi}$ is rapidly decreasing (by Corollary 3.30), and we have

$$(3.120) \qquad \sum_{n \in \mathbb{Z}^d} |\hat{f}(n)| = \sum_{n \in \mathbb{Z}^d} \left| \int_{\mathbb{R}^d} \hat{\psi}(n - \xi) \hat{f}(\xi) d\xi \right|$$

$$(3.121) \qquad \leq \sum_{n \in \mathbb{Z}^d} \int_{\mathbb{R}^d} |\hat{\psi}(n - \xi) \hat{f}(\xi)| \, d\xi$$

$$(3.122) \qquad = \int_{\mathbb{R}^d} \sum_{n \in \mathbb{Z}^d} |\hat{\psi}(n - \xi)| \, |\hat{f}(\xi)| \, d\xi$$

$$(3.123) \qquad \leq \sup_{\xi \in \mathbb{R}^d} \left(\sum_{n \in \mathbb{Z}^d} |\hat{\psi}(n - \xi)| \right) \int_{\mathbb{R}^d} |\hat{f}(\xi)| d\xi$$

$$(3.124) \qquad \leq c \int_{\mathbb{R}^d} |\hat{f}(\xi)| d\xi.$$

The constant c depends on ψ, and hence on the support of f. To justify the last step, we note that $g(\xi) := \sum_{n \in \mathbb{Z}^d} |\hat{\psi}(n - \xi)|$ is a periodic function of ξ, with the unit cube $[0, 1]^d$ being a fundamental domain, so it suffices to show that g is bounded on the unit cube. But due to the rapid decay of $\hat{\psi}$ we may apply the Weierstrass M-test to conclude that the series g is a uniformly convergent sum of continuous functions; hence g is itself a continuous function on a compact set (the cube), and in fact achieves its maximum there. $\qquad \square$

The reader may consult [224], for example, for more information about related Plancherel–Polya type inequalities. In general, there are many functions $f \in L^1(\mathbb{R})$ such that $\sum_{n \in \mathbb{Z}} |\hat{f}(n)|$ diverges yet $\int_{\mathbb{R}} |\hat{f}(\xi)| d\xi$ converges, so that (3.119) is false for these functions (Exercise (30)).

22. The Fourier transform of the ball

Whenever we consider packing or tiling by a convex body B, we have repeatedly seen that taking the Fourier transform of the body, namely $\hat{1}_B$, is very natural, especially from the perspective of Poisson summation. It is also very natural to consider the FT of a ball in $\mathbb{R}^d$.

To compute the Fourier transform of $1_{B(r)}$, a very classical computation, we first define the **Bessel function** J_p of order p [82, p. 147], which comes up naturally here:

$$(3.125) \qquad J_p(x) := \left(\frac{x}{2}\right)^p \frac{1}{\Gamma\left(p + \frac{1}{2}\right)\sqrt{\pi}} \int_0^\pi e^{ix\cos\varphi} \sin^{2p}(\varphi)\, d\varphi,$$

valid for $p > -\frac{1}{2}$, and all $x \in \mathbb{R}$. When $p = n + \frac{1}{2}$ with $n \in \mathbb{Z}$, there are also the following relations with elementary trigonometric functions.

$$(3.126) \qquad J_{n+\frac{1}{2}}(x) = (-1)^n \sqrt{\frac{2}{\pi}} x^{n+\frac{1}{2}} \left(\frac{1}{x}\frac{d}{dx}\right)^n \left(\frac{\sin x}{x}\right).$$

For example,

$$(3.127) \quad J_{\frac{1}{2}}(x) = \sqrt{\frac{2}{\pi x}} \sin x, \quad \text{and } J_{\frac{3}{2}}(x) = \sqrt{\frac{2}{\pi x}} \left(\frac{\sin x}{x} - \cos x\right).$$

We call a function $f : \mathbb{R}^d \to \mathbb{C}$ **radial** if it is invariant under all rotations of $\mathbb{R}^d$. In other words, we have the definition

$$f \text{ is radial} \iff f \circ M = f,$$

for all $M \in SO_d(\mathbb{R})$, the orthogonal group. Another way of describing a radial function is to say that the function f is constant on each sphere that is centered at the origin, so that a radial function only depends on the norm of its input: $f(x) = f(\|x\|)$, for all $x \in \mathbb{R}^d$.

A very useful fact in various applications of Fourier analysis (medical imaging in particular) is that the Fourier transform of a radial function is again a radial function.

Lemma 3.69. *The Fourier transform of $B_d(r)$, the ball of radius r in $\mathbb{R}^d$ centered at the origin, is*

$$\hat{1}_{B_d(r)}(\xi) := \int_{B_d(r)} e^{-2\pi i\langle\xi,x\rangle} dx = \left(\frac{r}{\|\xi\|}\right)^{\frac{d}{2}} J_{\frac{d}{2}}(2\pi r\|\xi\|).$$

Proof. Taking advantage of the inherent rotational symmetry of the ball, and also using the fact that the Fourier transform of a radial function is again radial, we have:

$$\hat{1}_{B_d(r)}(\xi) = \hat{1}_{B_d(r)}(0,\dots,0,\|\xi\|),$$

for all $\xi \in \mathbb{R}^d$. With $r = 1$ for the moment, we therefore have:

$$\hat{1}_B(\xi) = \int_{\|x\|\leq 1} e^{-2\pi i x_d\|\xi\|} dx_1 \dots dx_d.$$

Now we note that for each fixed x_d, the function being integrated is constant and the integration domain for the variables $x_1, \ldots, x_{d-1}$ is a $(d-1)$-dimensional ball of radius $(1 - x_d^2)^{1/2}$. By equation (4.44), the volume of this ball is $(1 - x_d^2)^{\frac{d-1}{2}} \frac{\pi^{\frac{d-1}{2}}}{\Gamma(\frac{d+1}{2})}$, and we have

$$\hat{1}_B(\xi) = \frac{\pi^{\frac{d-1}{2}}}{\Gamma(\frac{d+1}{2})} \int_{-1}^{1} e^{-2\pi i x_d \|\xi\|} (1 - x_d^2)^{\frac{d-1}{2}} \, dx_d$$

$$= \frac{\pi^{\frac{d}{2}}}{\sqrt{\pi} \Gamma\left(\frac{d+1}{2}\right)} \int_0^{\pi} e^{2\pi i \|\xi\| \cos \varphi} \sin^d \varphi \, d\varphi.$$

Using the definition of the J-Bessel function (equation (3.125)), we get

$$\hat{1}_B(\xi) = \|\xi\|^{-\frac{d}{2}} J_{\frac{d}{2}}(2\pi \|\xi\|),$$

and consequently

$$\hat{1}_{B_d(r)}(\xi) = \left(\frac{r}{\|\xi\|}\right)^{\frac{d}{2}} J_{\frac{d}{2}}(2\pi r \|\xi\|). \qquad \square$$

Example 3.70. Using the J-Bessel functions, we work out an explicit evaluation of the following interesting integrals, for all $p > 0$:

$$(3.128) \qquad \int_0^{\pi} \sin^{2p}(\varphi) \, d\varphi = \sqrt{\pi} \frac{\Gamma\left(p + \frac{1}{2}\right)}{\Gamma(p + 1)}.$$

Whenever we raise a negative real number to an arbitrary real exponent, some care has to be taken to avoid "branch problems" with the definition of exponentiation. But over the latter domain of integration, we are considering the nonnegative function $\sin(\varphi) \geq 0$, so everything is copacetic. We will use the following equivalent formulation for the J_p Bessel function in terms of a hypergeometric series [82, p. 684].

$$(3.129) \qquad J_p(x) = \frac{x^p}{2^p} \sum_{k=0}^{\infty} (-1)^k \frac{x^{2k}}{2^{2k} k! \, \Gamma(p + k + 1)}.$$

Using the definition of the Bessel function (equation (3.125)), we can rewrite it slightly:

$$(3.130) \qquad \frac{J_p(x)}{x^p} 2^p \sqrt{\pi} \, \Gamma\left(p + \frac{1}{2}\right) = \int_0^{\pi} e^{ix \cos \varphi} \sin^{2p}(\varphi) \, d\varphi.$$

Taking the limit as $x \to 0$, we can safely move this limit inside the integral in (3.130) because we are integrating a differentiable function over a compact interval

$$\int_0^\pi \sin^{2p}(\varphi)\, d\varphi = \lim_{x \to 0} \frac{J_p(x)}{x^p} 2^p \sqrt{\pi}\, \Gamma\left(p + \frac{1}{2}\right).$$

So, if we knew the asymptotic limit $\lim_{x \to 0} \frac{J_p(x)}{x^p}$, we would be in business. From (3.129), we may divide both sides by x^p, and then take the limit as $x \to 0$ to obtain the constant term of the remaining series, giving us

$$\lim_{x \to 0} \frac{J_p(x)}{x^p} = \frac{1}{2^p \Gamma(p+1)}.$$

Altogether, we have

$$\int_0^\pi \sin^{2p}(\varphi)\, d\varphi = \lim_{x \to 0} \frac{J_p(x)}{x^p} 2^p \sqrt{\pi}\, \Gamma\left(p + \frac{1}{2}\right)$$

$$= \frac{1}{2^p \Gamma(p+1)} 2^p \sqrt{\pi}\, \Gamma\left(p + \frac{1}{2}\right)$$

$$= \sqrt{\pi}\, \frac{\Gamma\left(p + \frac{1}{2}\right)}{\Gamma(p+1)},$$

valid for all $p > 0$.

In the special case that p is a positive integer, the latter identity can of course be written in terms of a ratio of factorials. □

23. Uncertainty principles

> "Uncertainty is the only certainty there is, and knowing how to live with insecurity is the only security."
> – John Allen Paulos

Perhaps the most basic type of an *uncertainy principle* is the fact that if a function f is compactly supported, then its Fourier transform $\hat{f}$ cannot be compactly supported—see Theorem 3.73. Similar impossible constraints, placed simultaneously on both f and $\hat{f}$, have become known as **uncertainty principles**. Perhaps the most famous of these, originating in quantum mechanics, is Heisenberg's discovery, as follows.

Theorem 3.71 (Heisenberg uncertainty principle). *Let* $f \in L^2(\mathbb{R}^d)$, *with the normalization assumption that* $\int_{\mathbb{R}^d} |f(x)|^2 dx = 1$. *Then*

$$(3.131) \qquad \int_{\mathbb{R}^d} \|x\|^2 |f(x)|^2 dx \int_{\mathbb{R}^d} \|x\|^2 |\hat{f}(x)|^2 dx \geq \frac{1}{16\pi^2},$$

with equality holding if and only if f *is equal to a Gaussian.*

For a proof see [**189**] or [**73**]. □

Theorem 3.72 (Hardy uncertainty principle). *Let* $f \in L^1(\mathbb{R}^d)$ *be a function that enjoys the property that*

$$|f(x)| \leq A e^{-\pi c x^2} \text{ and } |\hat{f}(\xi)| \leq B e^{-\pi \xi^2/c},$$

for all $x, \xi \in \mathbb{R}^d$, *and for some constants* $A, B, c > 0$.

Then $f(x)$ *is a scalar multiple of the Gaussian* $e^{-\pi c x^2}$.

For a proof see [**108**]. □

But perhaps the most "elementary" kind of uncertainty principle is the following basic fact, which is useful to keep in mind.

Theorem 3.73. *Let* $f \in L^1(\mathbb{R}^d)$ *be a function that is supported on a compact set in* $\mathbb{R}^d$. *Then* $\hat{f}$ *is not supported on any compact set in* $\mathbb{R}^d$.

For a proof see [**82**]. □

Notes

(1) There are some wonderful introductory books that develop Fourier analysis from first principles, such as the books by Stein and Shakarchi [**245**] and Giancarlo Travaglini [**251**]. The reader is also encouraged to read more advanced but fundamental introductions to Fourier analysis, in particular the books by Körner [**143**], Pinsky [**193**], Titchmarsh [**249**], Zygmund [**270**], Einsiedler and Ward [**79**], Dym and McKean [**73**], and, of course, the classic by Stein and Weiss [**244**]. In addition, the book by Terras [**253**] is a good introduction to Fourier analysis on finite groups, with applications. Another excellent introduction to Fourier analysis, which is more informal and focuses on various applications, is given by Osgood [**189**].

(2) There are some "elementary" techniques that we will use, such as the calculus of a complex variable, but which require essentially no previous knowledge in this field. In particular, suppose we have two analytic functions $f : \mathbb{C} \to \mathbb{C}$ and $g : \mathbb{C} \to$

$\mathbb{C}$, such that $f(z_k) = g(z_k)$ for a convergent sequence of complex numbers $z_k \to L$, where L is any fixed complex number. Then $f(z) = g(z)$ for all $z \in \mathbb{C}$.

The same conclusion is true even if the hypothesis is relaxed to the assumption that both f and g are meromorphic functions, as long as the sequence and its limit stay away from the poles of f and g.

(3) The "Dirac delta function" is part of the theory of "generalized functions" and may be intuitively defined by the full sequence of Gaussians $G_t(x) := t^{-\frac{d}{2}} e^{-\frac{\pi}{t}\|x\|^2}$, taken over all $t > 0$. The observation that there is no identity for the convolution product on $\mathbb{R}^d$ is a clear motivation for a theory of generalized functions beginning with the Dirac delta function. Another intuitive way of "defining" the Dirac delta function is

$$\delta_0(x) := \begin{cases} \infty & \text{if } x = 0 \\ 0 & \text{if not,} \end{cases}$$

even though this is not a function. But in the sense of distributions (i.e., generalized functions), we have $\lim_{\to 0} G_t(x) = \delta_0(x)$.

More rigorously, the δ-function belongs to a theory of distributions that was developed by Laurent Schwartz in the 1950s and by Sobolev in 1936, where we can think of generalized functions as linear functionals on the space of all bump functions on $\mathbb{R}^d$ (see the book by Lighthill [158] for a nice introduction to generalized functions).

Such generalized functions were originally used by the physicist Paul Dirac in 1920—before the rigorous mathematical theory was even created for it—in order to better understand quantum mechanics.

(4) I would like to thank Greg Kuperberg for very helpful comments, and in particular for introducing me to the statement of Theorem 3.32, for which we still cannot find a published reference.

(5) It is sometimes interesting to derive analogues between norms in $\mathbb{R}^d$ and norms in an infinite dimensional function space. Among the many norm relations in $\mathbb{R}^d$, we mention one elementary but interesting relation:

$$\|x\|_1 \le \sqrt{n}\|x\|_2,$$

for all vectors $x \in \mathbb{R}^d$, where $\|x\|_1 := |x_1| + \cdots + |x_d|$, and $\|x\|_2 := \sqrt{x_1^2 + \cdots + x_d^2}$. (see Exercise (1) for more practice with related norm relations). At this point the curious reader might wonder "are there any other inner products on $\mathbb{R}^d$, besides the usual inner product $\langle x, y \rangle := \sum_{k=1}^{d} x_k y_k$?" A classification of all inner products that exist on $\mathbb{R}^d$ is given in Exercise (13).

(6) Of great practical importance—and historical significance—a **bump function** is defined as any infinitely smooth function on $\mathbb{R}^d$, which is compactly supported. In other words, a bump function enjoys the following properties:
   - ϕ has compact support on $\mathbb{R}^d$.
   - $\phi \in C^\infty(\mathbb{R}^d)$.

Bump functions are also called **test functions**, and if we consider the set of all bump functions on $\mathbb{R}^d$, under addition we get a vector space V whose dual vector space is called the space of **distributions on** $\mathbb{R}^d$.

(7) Theorem 3.41, originally appearing in Poisson's work, also appear in Stein and Weiss's book [**244**]; here we gave a slightly different exposition.

(8) The cotangent function, appearing in some of the exercises below, is the unique *meromorphic function* that has a simple pole at every integer, with residue 1 (up to multiplication by an entire function with the same residues). The cotangent function also gives an entry point for Eisenstein series in number theory, through the corresponding partial fraction expansion of its derivatives.

(9) A deeper exploration into projections and sections of the unit cube in $\mathbb{R}^d$ can be found in "The cube—a window to convex and discrete geometry", by Zong [**267**]. In [**138**], Koldobsky gives a thorough introduction to sections of convex bodies, intersection bodies, and the Busemann–Petty problem.

(10) There are numerous other identities throughout mathematics that are equivalent to special cases of Poisson summation, such as the Euler–MacLaurin summation formula, the Abel–Plana formula, and the approximate sampling formula of signal analysis (see [**45**] for a nice treatment of such equivalences for functions of 1 real variable and functions of 1 complex variable).

(11) There is an important and fascinating result of Cordoba [61] which states the following. Let $A := \{x_k\}_{k \in \mathbb{Z}}, B := \{y_k\}_{k \in \mathbb{Z}}$ be two discrete sets in $\mathbb{R}^d$. Suppose that for all Schwartz functions f, we have

$$\sum_{k \in \mathbb{Z}} f(x_k) = \sum_{k \in \mathbb{Z}} \hat{f}(y_k).$$

Then both of the sequences A and B must be lattices in $\mathbb{R}^d$, and $B = A'$, its dual lattice.

(12) Finally, we mention that the term "harmonic analysis" simply means a more general theory than Fourier analysis, extending the ideas of Fourier analysis to other groups besides Euclidean space.

Exercises

"In theory, there is no difference between theory and practice; but in practice, there is!"
  – Walter J. Savitch

(1) ♣ On $\mathbb{R}^d$ the L^2-norm is defined by $\|x\|_2 := \sqrt{x_1^2 + \cdots + x_d^2}$, the L^1-norm is defined by $\|x\|_1 := |x_1| + \cdots + |x_d|$, and the L^∞-norm is defined by $\|x\|_\infty := \max\{|x_1|, \ldots, |x_d|\}$.
  Prove the following four norm relations:

$$\|x\|_\infty \leq \|x\|_2 \leq \|x\|_1 \leq \sqrt{d}\, \|x\|_2 \leq d\, \|x\|_\infty,$$

for all $x \in \mathbb{R}^d$.

(2) We know that the functions $u(t) := \cos t = \frac{e^{it} + e^{-it}}{2}$ and $v(t) := \sin t = \frac{e^{it} - e^{-it}}{2i}$ are natural, partly because they parametrize the unit circle: $u^2 + v^2 = 1$. Here we see that there are other similarly natural functions, parametrizing the hyperbola.

  (a) Show that the following functions parametrize the hyperbola $u^2 - v^2 = 1$:

$$u(t) := \frac{e^t + e^{-t}}{2}, \quad v(t) := \frac{e^t - e^{-t}}{2}.$$

(This is the reason that the function $\cosh t := \frac{e^t + e^{-t}}{2}$ is called the hyperbolic cosine, and the function $\sinh t := \frac{e^t - e^{-t}}{2}$ is called the hyperbolic sine)

(b) The hyperbolic cotangent is defined as $\coth t := \frac{\cosh t}{\sinh t} = \frac{e^t + e^{-t}}{e^t - e^{-t}}$. Using Bernoulli numbers, show that $t \coth t$ has the Taylor series:

$$t \coth t = \sum_{n=0}^{\infty} \frac{2^{2n}}{(2n)!} B_{2n} t^{2n}.$$

(3) ♣ Prove that:

$$\frac{t}{\pi} \sum_{n \in \mathbb{Z}} \frac{1}{n^2 + t^2} = \sum_{m \in \mathbb{Z}} e^{-2\pi t |m|}.$$

Hint: Think of Poisson summation applied to the function $f(x) := e^{-2\pi t |x|}$.

(4) ♣ Here we evaluate the Riemann zeta function at the positive even integers.

(a) Show that

$$\sum_{n \in \mathbb{Z}} e^{-2\pi t |n|} = \frac{1 + e^{-2\pi t}}{1 - e^{-2\pi t}} := \coth(\pi t),$$

for all $t > 0$.

(b) Show that the cotangent function has the following well-known partial fraction expansion:

$$\pi \cot(\pi x) = \frac{1}{x} + 2x \sum_{n=1}^{\infty} \frac{1}{x^2 - n^2},$$

valid for any $x \in \mathbb{R} - \mathbb{Z}$.

(c) Let $0 < t < 1$. Show that

$$\frac{t}{\pi} \sum_{n \in \mathbb{Z}} \frac{1}{n^2 + t^2} = \frac{1}{\pi t} + \frac{2}{\pi} \sum_{m=1}^{\infty} (-1)^{m+1} \zeta(2m) \, t^{2m-1},$$

where $\zeta(s) := \sum_{n=1}^{\infty} \frac{1}{n^s}$ is the Riemann zeta function, initially defined by the latter series, which is valid for all $s \in \mathbb{C}$ with $Re(s) > 1$.

(5) Here we show that we may quickly evaluate the Riemann zeta function at all even integers, as follows. We recall the definition of the

Bernoulli numbers, namely:

$$\frac{z}{e^z - 1} = 1 - \frac{z}{2} + \sum_{m \geq 1} \frac{B_{2m}}{2m!} z^{2m}.$$

Prove that for all $m \geq 1$,

$$\zeta(2m) = \frac{(-1)^{m+1}}{2} \frac{(2\pi)^{2m}}{(2m)!} B_{2m}.$$

Thus, for example, using the first three Bernoulli numbers, we have $\zeta(2) = \frac{\pi^2}{6}$, $\zeta(4) = \frac{\pi^4}{90}$, and $\zeta(6) = \frac{\pi^6}{945}$.

(6) For each $n \geq 1$, let $T_n(x) = \cos(nx)$. For example, $T_2(x) = \cos(2x) = 2\cos^2(x) - 1$, so $T_2(x) = 2u^2 - 1$, a polynomial in $u := \cos x$.
   (a) Show that for all $n \geq 1$, $T_n(x)$ is a polynomial in $\cos x$.
   (b) Can you write $x^n + \frac{1}{x^n}$ as a polynomial in the variable $x + \frac{1}{x}$? Would your answer be related to the polynomial $T_n(x)$? What is the relationship in general? For example, $x^2 + \frac{1}{x^2} = \left(x + \frac{1}{x}\right)^2 - 2$.

Notes. The polynomials $T_n(x)$ are very important in applied fields such as approximation theory and optimization because they have many useful extremal properties. They are called Chebyshev polynomials.

(7) The hyperbolic secant is defined by

$$\operatorname{sech}(\pi x) := \frac{2}{e^{\pi x} + e^{-\pi x}}, \text{ for } x \in \mathbb{R}.$$

   (a) Show that $\operatorname{sech}(\pi x)$ is its own Fourier transform:

$$\mathcal{F}(\operatorname{sech})(\xi) = \operatorname{sech}(\xi),$$

   for all $\xi \in \mathbb{R}$.
   (b) Show that $\operatorname{sech}(\pi x)$ can never be bounded above by any Gaussian in the precise sense that the following claim is **impossible**: there exists a constant $c > 0$ such that for all $x \in \mathbb{R}$ we have:

$$\operatorname{sech}(\pi x) \leq e^{-cx^2}.$$

Notes. For part (7a), the easiest path is through the use of basic complex analysis. For part (7b), it may be helpful to look at Hardy's uncertainty principle, Theorem 3.72. We can also conclude from Hardy's uncertainty principle that any eigenfunction f of the Fourier transform cannot be bounded above by a Gaussian apart from the case that f is itself a Gaussian.

(8) Using the previous exercise, conclude that

$$\int_{\mathbb{R}} \frac{1}{e^{\pi x} + e^{-\pi x}} dx = \frac{1}{2}.$$

(9) ♣ Prove that

$$\int_0^1 \left(\{ax\} - \frac{1}{2}\right)\left(\{bx\} - \frac{1}{2}\right) dx = \frac{\gcd^2(a,b)}{12ab}$$

for all positive integers a, b. As always, $\{x\}$ is the fractional part of x.

Notes. This integral is called a **Franel integral**, and there is a substantial literature about related integrals. In 1924, Jérôme Franel [87] related this integral to the Riemann hypothesis and to Farey fractions.

(10) Given an even function $f \in L^1(\mathbb{R}^d)$, such that $\hat{f} \in L^1(\mathbb{R}^d)$ as well, we clearly always have $f(x) := \frac{1}{2}\left(f(x) + \hat{f}(x)\right) + \frac{1}{2}\left(f(x) - \hat{f}(x)\right)$. Show that:
   (a) The function $g(x) := \frac{1}{2}\left(f(x) + \hat{f}(x)\right)$ is an eigenfunction of the Fourier transform acting on $L^1(\mathbb{R}^d)$, with eigenvalue equal to $+1$.
   (b) Similarly, the function $h(x) := \frac{1}{2}\left(f(x) - \hat{f}(x)\right)$ is an eigenfunction of the Fourier transform acting on $L^1(\mathbb{R}^d)$, with eigenvalue equal to -1.

(11) ♣ Let $f : \mathbb{R} \to \mathbb{C}$ belong to the Schwartz class of functions on $\mathbb{R}$, denoted by $S(\mathbb{R})$. Show that $\hat{f} \in S(\mathbb{R})$ as well.

(12) Here we define $f(x) := 1 + \sin(2\pi x)$ for all $x \in \mathbb{R}$. We note that f is a periodic function of $x \in \mathbb{R}$ with period 1, so it may be considered as a function on the torus $\mathbb{T}$.
   (a) Using Theorem 3.32, find the little-o asymptotics (with $N \to \infty$) for the finite sum:

   $$\sum_{m=0}^{N-1} f\left(\frac{m}{N}\right).$$

   (b) Show directly that $\sum_{m=0}^{N-1} f(\frac{m}{2N}) = N + \frac{N}{2^{N-1}}$.
   (c) From part (12b), conclude (independently of Theorem 3.32) that we get the same little-o asymptotics that Theorem 3.32 predicts.

Notes. For part (12b), you might begin with the polynomial identity

$$1 + z + z^2 + \cdots + z^{N-1} = \prod_{r=1}^{N-1} (z - e^{\frac{2\pi i r}{N}}).$$

(13) ♣ Here we answer the very natural question "What are the other inner products on $\mathbb{R}^d$ besides the usual inner product $\langle x, y \rangle :=$ $\sum_{k=1}^{d} x_k y_k$?" (See Appendix 3.3 for the general definition of an inner product). Here we show that all inner products are related to each other via positive definite matrices, as follows. We recall from linear algebra that a symmetric matrix is called positive definite if all of its eigenvalues are positive. Prove that the following two conditions are equivalent:
  (a) $L(x, y)$ is an inner product on $\mathbb{R}^d$.
  (b) $L(x, y) := x^T M y$ for some positive definite matrix M.

(14) For any positive real numbers $a < b < c < d$, define

$$f(x) := 1_{[a,b]}(x) + 1_{[c,d]}(x).$$

Can you find a, b, c, d such that $\hat{f}(\xi)$ is nonzero for all $\xi \in \mathbb{R}$?

(15) ♣ Show that for $f, \hat{f} \in L^1(\mathbb{R}^d)$, the only eigenvalues of the linear operator

$$f \to \hat{f}$$

are $\{1, -1, i, -i\}$, and find functions in $L^1(\mathbb{R}^d)$ that achieve each of these eigenvalues.

(16) ♣ Show that the special case of Poisson summation(equation (3.83)) implies the general case, Theorem 3.44.

(17) ♣ We recall the definition of the Gaussian: for each fixed $\varepsilon > 0$, and for all $x \in \mathbb{R}^d$, they are defined by

(3.132)

$$G_\varepsilon(x) := \frac{1}{\varepsilon^{\frac{d}{2}}} e^{-\frac{\pi}{\varepsilon} \|x\|^2}.$$

Show that:

$$\int_{\mathbb{R}^d} G_\varepsilon(x) dx = 1.$$

(18) ♣ (Hard-ish) Show that, for all $m \in \mathbb{R}^d$, the Fourier transform of the Gaussian $G_\varepsilon(x)$ is:

$$\hat{G}_\varepsilon(m) = e^{-\pi \varepsilon \|m\|^2}.$$

Conclude that for each fixed $n \in \mathbb{R}^d$

$$\mathcal{F}\left(\frac{1}{\varepsilon^{\frac{d}{2}}} e^{-\frac{\pi}{\varepsilon}\|x+n\|^2}\right)(\xi) = e^{-\pi\varepsilon\|\xi\|^2} e^{2\pi i\langle\xi,n\rangle}.$$

(19) We define the translation operator $T_h : L^2(\mathbb{R}^d) \rightarrow L^2(\mathbb{R}^d)$ by $(T_h f)(x) := f(x - h)$, for any fixed $h \in \mathbb{R}^d$. Show that convolution commutes with the translation operator, as follows:

$$T_h(f * g) = (T_h f) * g = f * (T_h g).$$

Notes. Using standard linear algebra terminology, this is called *translational equivariance*.

(20) Prove that if $f, g \in L^1(\mathbb{R}^d)$ are bounded functions, then $f * g$ is continuous on $\mathbb{R}^d$.

(21) ♣ Suppose that we fix any $f, g \in L^2(\mathbb{R}^d)$. Here we carry the reader through a detailed proof that $f * g$ is always continuous on $\mathbb{R}^d$ by using a mixture of convergence in $L^2(\mathbb{R}^d)$ and pointwise convergence.
   (a) For any sequence of functions $f_n \in L^2(\mathbb{R}^d)$ with the property that $\lim_{n\to\infty} f_n = f$ in $L^2(\mathbb{R}^d)$, show that

(3.133)
$$\lim_{n\to\infty} (f_n * g)(x) = (f * g)(x),$$

   for each $x \in \mathbb{R}^d$.
   (b) Define the translation operator $T_h : L^2(\mathbb{R}^d) \rightarrow L^2(\mathbb{R}^d)$ by $(T_h f)(x) := f(x - h)$, for a fixed vector $(h_1, \dots, h_d) \in \mathbb{R}^d$ with positive coordinates. Show that

$$\lim_{h\to 0} T_h f = f, \text{ in } L^2(\mathbb{R}^d).$$

   (c) Show that $\lim_{h\to 0}(T_h f * g)(x) = (f * g)(x)$ for each fixed $x \in \mathbb{R}^d$.
   (d) Conclude that $f * g$ is continuous on $\mathbb{R}^d$.

Notes. It follows from either Exercise (20) or Exercise (21) that if $A, B \subset \mathbb{R}^d$ are convex bodies (or finite unions of convex bodies), then $(1_A * 1_B)(x) = \text{vol}(A \cap (-B + x))$ is a continuous function of $x \in \mathbb{R}^d$.

(22) Show by example that $f, g \in L^1(\mathbb{R}^d)$ does not necessarily imply that $fg \in L^1(\mathbb{R}^d)$ (here fg is the usual product of functions).

(23) ♣ For all $f, g \in L^2(\mathbb{R}^d)$, prove that:
   (a)
$$\langle f, g \rangle = \frac{1}{2}\left(\|f\|^2 + \|g\|^2 - \|f + g\|^2\right),$$
   (b)
$$\langle f, g \rangle = \langle \hat{f}, \hat{g} \rangle.$$

(24) ♣ Given any approximate identity sequence ϕ_ε, as defined in (3.114), show that for each $\varepsilon > 0$,

$$\int_{\mathbb{R}^d} \phi_\varepsilon(x)dx = 1.$$

(25) ♣ Let $E \subset \mathbb{R}^d$ be any set, and suppose we have two continuous functions $f, g : E \to \mathbb{C}$.
If $f = g$ for almost every $x \in E$, prove that $f = g$ for all $x \in E$.

(26) ♣ Under some positivity assumptions for f, the Fourier transform of f achieves its *unique maximum* at the origin. More precisely, we have the following.
(a) Suppose $f \in L^1(\mathbb{R}^d)$, and $f(x) > 0$ for all $x \in \mathbb{R}^d$. Prove that

$$|\hat{f}(\xi)| < \hat{f}(0)$$

for all $\xi \in \mathbb{R}^d$.
(b) Now let $\mathcal{P} \subset \mathbb{R}^d$ be a d-dimensional bounded set. Prove that for all $\xi \neq 0$, we have

(3.134)
$$|\hat{1}_{\mathcal{P}}(\xi)| < \text{vol } \mathcal{P}.$$

(27) Show that the ramp function, defined in (3.99), also has the representation

(3.135)
$$r_0(x) = \frac{x + |x|}{2}$$

for all $x \in \mathbb{R}$.

Notes. Some books, particularly in approximation theory, use the notation $r_0(x) := x_+$.

(28) ♣ Here we show how to construct compactly supported functions $f : \mathbb{R} \to \mathbb{C}$ whose Fourier transform is **strictly positive** on all of $\mathbb{R}$. Fix any two incommensurable real numbers r, s (meaning that $\frac{r}{s} \notin \mathbb{Q}$), and define

$$f := 1_{[-r,r]} * 1_{[-r,r]} + 1_{[-s,s]} * 1_{[-s,s]},$$

which is a sum of two hat functions, as depicted in Figure 3.14. Prove that for all $\xi \in \mathbb{R}$, we have $\hat{f}(\xi) > 0$.

Notes. This construction can be extended to higher dimensions, once we know more about the Fourier transforms of balls in $\mathbb{R}^d$.

(29) ♣ Show that for all $a, b \in \mathbb{R}$, we have

$$H_a * H_b = r_{a+b},$$

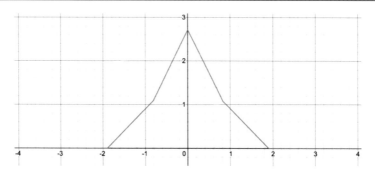

Figure 3.14. The function f of Exercise (28), a sum of two hat functions, with $s = \sqrt{\frac{2}{3}}$, and $r = 1.9$.

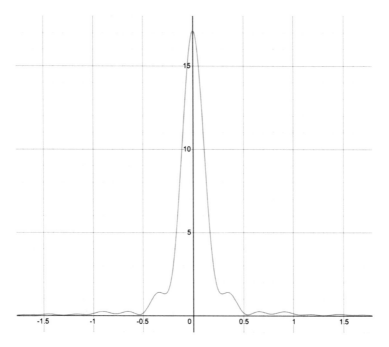

Figure 3.15. The *strictly positive* Fourier transform $\hat{f}(\xi)$ of Exercise (28), with the incommensurable numbers $s = \sqrt{\frac{2}{3}}, r = 1.9$.

where H_a is the heaviside function of (3.96), and r_a is the ramp function of (3.99).

(30) ♣ Here we show that the absolute convergence of a series—and the absolute convergence of the corresponding integral—are independent of each other.

    (a) Find a function $f : \mathbb{R} \to \mathbb{C}$ such that $\sum_{n\in\mathbb{Z}} |\hat{f}(n)|$ diverges, yet $\int_{\mathbb{R}} |\hat{f}(\xi)|\,d\xi$ converges.

    (b) On the other hand, find a function $f : \mathbb{R} \to \mathbb{C}$ such that $\sum_{n\in\mathbb{Z}} |\hat{f}(n)|$ converges, yet $\int_{\mathbb{R}} |\hat{f}(\xi)|\,d\xi$ diverges.

Notes. Exercise (30) shows that there the Plancherel–Polya inequality holds only for a special class of functions.

(31) We recall that $C(\mathbb{R}^d)$ is the function space consisting of all continuous functions on $\mathbb{R}^d$. Show that

    (a) $C(\mathbb{R}^d) \cap L^1(\mathbb{R}^d) \not\subset C(\mathbb{R}^d) \cap L^2(\mathbb{R}^d)$.

    (b) $C(\mathbb{R}^d) \cap L^2(\mathbb{R}^d) \not\subset C(\mathbb{R}^d) \cap L^1(\mathbb{R}^d)$.

(32) Here is a slightly different version of Poisson summation, which is easy to prove. If $g : \mathbb{R}^d \to \mathbb{C}$ is infinitely smooth, and compactly supported, prove that

$$\sum_{n\in\mathbb{Z}^d} \hat{g}(n) = \sum_{n\in\mathbb{Z}^d} g(n),$$

and, of course, the right-hand side is a finite sum.

    Exercises (33)–(44) give the reader more practice with some of the important inequalities. Most of these inequalities follow from either the convexity or the concavity of some simple function.

(33) (Jensen's inequality for convex functions). Suppose $E \subset \mathbb{R}^d$ is a convex set. A function $f : E \to \mathbb{R}$ is called a **convex function** on E if

$$f\left(tx + (1-t)y\right) \le tf(x) + (1-t)f(y),$$

for all $x, y \in E$, and for all $t \in [0,1]$. Prove that if f is a convex function on E, then:

(3.136) $f(\lambda_1 x_1 + \cdots + \lambda_n x_n) \le \lambda_1 f(x_1) + \cdots + \lambda_n f(x_n),$

for all nonnegative real numbers $\lambda_1, \ldots, \lambda_n$, such that $\lambda_1 + \cdots + \lambda_n = 1$, and for all $x_1, \ldots, x_n \in E$.

    An observation: **equality holds** in (3.136) $\iff$

(3.137)   Either f is a linear function on E, or $x_1 = x_2 = \cdots = x_n$.

(34) Prove that for all real numbers x, the function $f(x) := e^x$ is a convex function.

Notes. Here you may quote the elementary calculus fact that if a function f has a continuous second derivative on $[a, b]$, then it is convex on $[a, b]$ $\iff$ $f''(x) \geq 0$ on $[a, b]$.

(35) (Jensen's inequality for concave functions). Suppose $E \subset \mathbb{R}^d$ is a concave set. A function $f : E \to \mathbb{R}$ is called a **concave function** on E if $-f$ is convex on E. In other words, f is concave on E means that

$$f\left(tx + (1-t)y\right) \geq tf(x) + (1-t)f(y),$$

for all $x, y \in E$, and for all $t \in [0, 1]$. Prove that if f is a concave function on E, then

(3.138) $$f(\lambda_1 x_1 + \cdots + \lambda_n x_n) \geq \lambda_1 f(x_1) + \cdots + \lambda_n f(x_n),$$

for all nonnegative real numbers $\lambda_1, \ldots, \lambda_n$, such that $\lambda_1 + \cdots + \lambda_n = 1$, and for all $x_1, \ldots, x_n \in E$.

An observation: **equality holds** in (3.138) $\iff$

(3.139) f is a linear function on E, or $x_1 = x_2 = \cdots = x_n$.

(36) Let $f : [a, b] \to \mathbb{R}$ be an increasing function, where we allow $a = -\infty$ and/or $b = +\infty$. The image of f is defined by $\text{Image}(f) := \{y \in \mathbb{R} \mid f(x) = y, \text{for some } x \in [a, b]\}$.
   (a) Prove that f is convex on $[a, b]$ $\iff$ its inverse $f^{-1} : \text{Image}(f) \to [a, b]$ is a concave function.
   (b) Conclude that for all $x > 0$, the function $f(x) := \ln(x)$ is a concave function (You can use Exercise (34)).

(37) (Young's inequality). Let $a, b \geq 0$, $p, q > 0$, and $\frac{1}{p} + \frac{1}{q} = 1$.
   (a) Show that:

(3.140) $$ab \leq \frac{a^p}{p} + \frac{b^q}{q}.$$

   (b) Show that equality holds in (3.140) $\iff$ $a^p = b^q$.

(38) (Arithmetic-geometric inequality). Using equation (3.136) of Exercise (33), prove that for all nonnegative real numbers $x_1, \ldots, x_n$, we have

$$\left(x_1 x_2 \cdots x_n\right)^{\frac{1}{n}} \leq \frac{x_1 + \cdots x_n}{n},$$

with equality holding if and only if all of the x_is are equal to each other.

(39) (Arithmetic-Geometric inequality, with weights). Prove that

$$x_1^{\lambda_1} x_2^{\lambda_2} \cdots x_n^{\lambda_n} \leq \lambda_1 x_1 + \cdots \lambda_n x_n,$$

for all positive real numbers $x_1, \ldots, x_n$, and for all nonnegative real numbers $\lambda_1, \ldots, \lambda_n$, such that $\lambda_1 + \cdots + \lambda_n = 1$, with equality holding if and only if all of the x_is are equal to each other.

For the next few exercises, we define the p-**norm of a vector** $(x_1, \ldots, x_d) \in \mathbb{R}^d$ by

$$(3.141) \qquad \|x\|_p := \left(\sum_{m=1}^{d} |x_m|^p \right)^{\frac{1}{p}} ,$$

for each $1 \le p < \infty$.

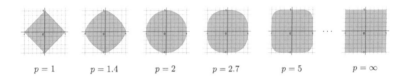

$$p = 1 \qquad p = 1.4 \qquad p = 2 \qquad p = 2.7 \qquad p = 5 \qquad \cdots \qquad p = \infty$$

Figure 3.16. The unit ball in the p-norm, for various values of p.

(40) For "$p = \infty$" we define the p-norm by:

$$\|x\|_\infty := \max\{|x_1|, |x_2|, \cdots, |x_d|\} .$$

Prove that

$$\|x\|_\infty = \lim_{p \to \infty} \left(\sum_{m=1}^{d} |x_m|^p \right)^{\frac{1}{p}} .$$

Notes. The point of this exercise is that definition (3.141) is now extended to include the "$p = \infty$" case. We notice that in $\mathbb{R}^d$, the unit ball in the 1-norm is the crosspolytope, and the unit ball in the ∞-norm is the cube, as Figure 3.16 suggests.

(41) (Hölder's inequality). Fix two real numbers p, q with the property that $\frac{1}{p} + \frac{1}{q} = 1$, and with $1 < p, q < \infty$. Show that

$$\sum_{m=1}^{d} |x_m y_m| \le \left(\sum_{m=1}^{d} |x_m|^p \right)^{\frac{1}{p}} \left(\sum_{m=1}^{d} |y_m|^q \right)^{\frac{1}{q}} ,$$

for all vectors $(x_1, \ldots, x_d), (y_1, \ldots, y_d) \in \mathbb{R}^d$.

(42) (Minkowski's inequality). Let $1 \le p < \infty$, and prove that

$$(3.142) \qquad \left(\sum_{m=1}^{d} |x_m + y_m|^p \right)^{\frac{1}{p}} \le \left(\sum_{m=1}^{d} |x_m|^p \right)^{\frac{1}{p}} + \left(\sum_{m=1}^{d} |y_m|^p \right)^{\frac{1}{p}},$$

for all vectors $(x_1, \dots, x_d), (y_1, \dots, y_d) \in \mathbb{R}^d$.

Notes. Minkowski's inequality (3.142) can be thought of geometrically as:
$$\|x + y\|_p \le \|x\|_p + \|y\|_p,$$
which is the triangle inequality for the p-norm (3.141). There are important integral analogues of some of the latter inequalities, a couple of which we give below.

Each of the latter inequalities also has a continuous/integral analogue. We give just two of these below.

(43) (Hölder's inequality for integrals). Fix two functions $f \in L^p(\mathbb{R}^d)$, and $g \in L^q(\mathbb{R}^d)$ with the property that $\frac{1}{p} + \frac{1}{q} = 1$, and with $1 < p, q < \infty$. Using the definition (equation (3.15)) of the L^p-norm of a function, show that

$$(3.143) \qquad \|fg\|_{L^1(\mathbb{R}^d)} \le \|f\|_{L^p(\mathbb{R}^d)} \|g\|_{L^q(\mathbb{R}^d)}.$$

(44) (Minkowski's inequality for integrals). Let $1 \le p < \infty$, and let $f \in L^p(\mathbb{R}^d)$. Prove that

$$(3.144) \qquad \|f + g\|_{L^p(\mathbb{R}^d)} \le \|f\|_{L^p(\mathbb{R}^d)} + \|g\|_{L^p(\mathbb{R}^d)}.$$

Chapter 4

Geometry of numbers
Part I: Minkowski meets
Siegel

Hermann Minkowski

"Henceforth space by itself, and time by itself, are doomed to fade away into mere shadows, and only a kind of union of the two will preserve an independent reality."

– Hermann Minkowski

1. Intuition

To see a wonderful and fun application of Poisson summation, we give a relatively easy extension of Minkowski's first theorem in the geometry of numbers. Minkowski's theorem gives the existence of an integer point inside symmetric bodies in $\mathbb{R}^d$ once we know their volume is sufficiently large.

We will explore, and prove, a more powerful identity which is now a classical result of Carl Ludwig Siegel (Theorem 4.4), yielding an identity between Fourier transforms of convex bodies and their volume. Our proof of this identity of Siegel uses Poisson summation applied to the convolution of an indicator function with itself.

The geometry of numbers is an incredibly beautiful field, and too vast to encompass in just one chapter (see Note (6)). This chapter, as well as Chapter 6, together give just a taste of a giant and thriving forest.

2. Minkowski's first convex body theorem

Minkowski initiated the field that we call today *the geometry of numbers*, around 1890. To begin, we define a **body** $\mathcal{P}$ in $\mathbb{R}^d$ as a compact set. In other words, $\mathcal{P}$ is a bounded, closed set. Most of the time, it is useful to work with convex bodies that enjoy the following symmetry. We call a body $\mathcal{P}$ **centrally symmetric**—also called **symmetric about the origin**—if for all $x \in \mathbb{R}^d$ we have

$$x \in \mathcal{P} \iff -x \in \mathcal{P}.$$

A body $\mathcal{P}$ is called **symmetric** if some translation of $\mathcal{P}$ is symmetric about the origin. For example, the ball $\{x \in \mathbb{R}^d \mid \|x\| \leq 1\}$ is centrally symmetric, and the translated ball $\{x \in \mathbb{R}^d \mid \|x - w\| \leq 1\}$, for $w \neq 0$, is symmetric, but not centrally symmetric. An initial, motivating question in the geometry of numbers is:

Question 4.1 (Rhetorical). How large does a convex body $\mathcal{P}$ have to be in order to contain a nonzero integer point?

If we are not careful, then Figure 4.2, for example, shows that $\mathcal{P}$ can be as large as we like, and yet never contain an integer point. So without further hypotheses, there are no positive answers to Question 4.1. Therefore, it is natural to assume that our body $\mathcal{P}$ is positioned in a "nice" way relative to the integer lattice, and centrally symmetry is a natural assumption in this respect.

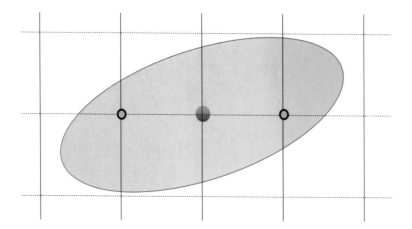

Figure 4.1. A convex, centrally symmetric body in $\mathbb{R}^2$, with area bigger than 4, containing two nonzero integer points.

Theorem 4.2 (Minkowski's first convex body theorem for $\mathbb{Z}^d$). *Let K be a d-dimensional convex body in $\mathbb{R}^d$, symmetric about the origin.*

If $\operatorname{vol} K > 2^d$, then K must contain a nonzero integer point in its interior.   □

Sometimes this classical and very useful result of Minkowski is stated in its contrapositive form: Let $K \subset \mathbb{R}^d$ be any convex body, symmetric about the origin. If the only integer point in the interior of K is the origin, then:

$$(4.1) \qquad\qquad \operatorname{vol} K \leq 2^d.$$

It is natural—and straightforward—to extend this result to any lattice $\mathcal{L} := M(\mathbb{Z}^d)$, by simply applying the linear transformation M to both the integer lattice, and to the convex body K. The conclusion is the following, which is the version that we will prove as a consequence of Siegel's theorem (Theorem 4.4).

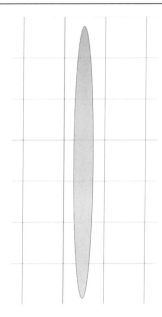

Figure 4.2. A convex symmetric body in $\mathbb{R}^2$, which is not centered at the origin, may be constructed with arbitrarily large volume and simultaneously with no integer points.

Theorem 4.3 (Minkowski's first convex body theorem for a lattice $\mathcal{L}$). *Let K be a d-dimensional convex body in $\mathbb{R}^d$, symmetric about the origin, and let $\mathcal{L}$ be a (full rank) lattice in $\mathbb{R}^d$.*

> *If $\operatorname{vol} K > 2^d(\det \mathcal{L})$, then K must contain a nonzero point of $\mathcal{L}$ in its interior.*

Proof. The proof appears below—see "first proof of Minkowski". We also give a second proof in Section 2, using Blichfeldt's methods—see "second proof of Minkowski". □

These very important initial results of Minkowski [**178**] have found applications in algebraic number theory, diophantine analysis, combinatorial optimization, and other fields. In the next section we show that Minkowski's result (Theorem 4.3) follows as a special case of Siegel's formula.

3. A Fourier transform identity for convex bodies

"Behind every inequality there is an equality—find it."
  – Basil Gordon

Minkowski's theorem (Theorem 4.3) suggests that behind his inequality

$$2^d > \operatorname{vol} K$$

there may hide an interesting equality:

$$2^d = \operatorname{vol} K + (\text{some positive error term}).$$

A natural and motivating question is, "what form does this positive error term take?"

Siegel found it, and as we will soon see, it naturally leads us to the Fourier transform of K. First, a basic construction in the geometry of numbers is the **Minkowski sum** of convex bodies. Given two convex bodies $K, L \subset \mathbb{R}^d$, their Minkowski sum is defined by

$$K + L := \{x + y \mid x \in K, y \in L\},$$

and turns out to also be a convex body (Exercise (2)). Another related construction, appearing in some of the results below, is

$$K - L := \{x - y \mid x \in K, y \in L\},$$

the Minkowski difference of K and L. Of course, we also have $K - L = K + (-L)$, where $-L := \{-x \mid x \in \mathcal{L}\}$. A very useful special case is the gadget known as the **difference body** of K, defined by

$$(4.2) \qquad\qquad\qquad K - K.$$

Given any set $K \subset \mathbb{R}^d$, the difference body $K - K$ is centrally symmetric. To see this, suppose $x \in K - K$, so we may write $x = y - z$, with $y, z \in K$. Then $-x = z - y \in K - K$.

The body $\frac{1}{2}K - \frac{1}{2}K$ is called the **Minkowski symmetrized body** of K, and one example is shown in Figure 4.3. In addition, we have the fortuitous and easy fact that a set $K \subset \mathbb{R}^d$ is convex and centrally symmetric if and only if

$$(4.3) \qquad\qquad\qquad \frac{1}{2}K - \frac{1}{2}K = K.$$

(see Exercise (5)). Another important geometric notion is the dilation of a convex body by a positive real number t:

$$tK := \{tx \mid x \in K\}.$$

The most basic version of Siegel's theorem is the following identity, which assumes that a convex body K is symmetric about the origin.

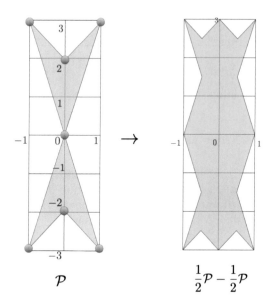

Figure 4.3. Left: A nonconvex body $\mathcal{P}$. Right: Its Minkowski symmetrization $\frac{1}{2}\mathcal{P} - \frac{1}{2}\mathcal{P}$.

Theorem 4.4 (Siegel). *Let K be any d-dimensional convex body in $\mathbb{R}^d$, symmetric about the origin, and suppose that the only integer point in the interior of K is the origin. Then*

$$(4.4) \qquad 2^d = \operatorname{vol} K + \frac{4^d}{\operatorname{vol} K} \sum_{\xi \in \mathbb{Z}^d - \{0\}} \left| \hat{1}_{\frac{1}{2}K}(\xi) \right|^2. \qquad \square$$

We now prove the following extension of Siegel's theorem (Theorem 4.4), namely (4.5), which applies to bodies that are neither necessarily convex, nor necessarily symmetric about the origin. Our proof of Theorem 4.5 consists of yet another application of Poisson summation. It turns out that if K is any convex body, then $f := 1_{\{\frac{1}{2}K\}} * 1_{\{-\frac{1}{2}K\}}$ is a nice function (Exercise (14)), in the sense that Poisson summation (3.57) holds for f. So Theorem 4.4 is a consequence of the following extension to bodies that are not necessarily convex or symmetric.

Theorem 4.5 (Siegel's formula, for a body K, and a lattice $\mathcal{L}$). *Let $K \subset \mathbb{R}^d$ be a body (compact set) for which the convolution $1_{\frac{1}{2}K} * 1_{-\frac{1}{2}K}$ is a nice function. If the only integer point in the interior of the difference body $\frac{1}{2}K - \frac{1}{2}K$ is the origin, then*

$$(4.5) \qquad 2^d = \operatorname{vol} K + \frac{4^d}{\operatorname{vol} K} \sum_{\xi \in \mathbb{Z}^d - \{0\}} \left| \hat{1}_{\frac{1}{2}K}(\xi) \right|^2.$$

More generally, if we replace the lattice $\mathbb{Z}^d$ by any full-rank lattice $\mathcal{L}$, and assume that the only lattice point of $\mathcal{L}$ in the interior of $\frac{1}{2}K - \frac{1}{2}K$ is the origin, then we have:

$$(4.6) \qquad 2^d \det \mathcal{L} = \operatorname{vol} K + \frac{4^d}{\operatorname{vol} K} \sum_{\xi \in \mathcal{L}^* - \{0\}} \left| \hat{1}_{\frac{1}{2}K}(\xi) \right|^2.$$

Proof. We start with the function

$$(4.7) \qquad f(x) := \left(1_{\frac{1}{2}K} * 1_{-\frac{1}{2}K} \right)(x),$$

which is continuous on $\mathbb{R}^d$, and we plug f into Poisson summation (3.52).

$$(4.8) \qquad \sum_{n \in \mathbb{Z}^d} f(n) = \sum_{\xi \in \mathbb{Z}^d} \hat{f}(\xi).$$

We first compute the left-hand side of Poisson summation, using the definition of f:

$$(4.9) \qquad \sum_{n \in \mathbb{Z}^d} f(n) = \sum_{n \in \mathbb{Z}^d} \int_{\mathbb{R}^d} 1_{\frac{1}{2}K}(y) 1_{-\frac{1}{2}K}(n - y) dy$$

$$(4.10) \qquad = \sum_{n \in \mathbb{Z}^d} \int_{\mathbb{R}^d} 1_{\frac{1}{2} \operatorname{int} K}(y) 1_{-\frac{1}{2} \operatorname{int} K}(n - y) dy,$$

where the last step follows from the fact that the integral does not distinguish between a convex set or its closure. Now we follow the definition of containment: $y \in \frac{1}{2}K$ and $n - y \in -\frac{1}{2}K$ imply that the integer point $n \in \frac{1}{2}K - \frac{1}{2}K$. But by hypothesis $\frac{1}{2}K - \frac{1}{2}K$ contains the origin as its *only* interior integer point, so the left-hand side of the Poisson summation formula contains only one term, namely the $n = 0$ term:

$$(4.11) \qquad \sum_{n \in \mathbb{Z}^d} f(n) = \sum_{n \in \mathbb{Z}^d} \int_{\mathbb{R}^d} 1_{\frac{1}{2}K}(y) 1_{-\frac{1}{2}K}(n - y) dy$$

$$(4.12) \qquad = \int_{\mathbb{R}^d} 1_{\frac{1}{2}K}(y) 1_{-\frac{1}{2}K}(-y) dy$$

$$(4.13) \qquad = \int_{\mathbb{R}^d} 1_{\frac{1}{2}K}(y) dy$$

$$(4.14) \qquad = \mathrm{vol}\left(\frac{1}{2}K\right) = \frac{\mathrm{vol}\,K}{2^d}.$$

On the other hand, the right-hand side of Poisson summation gives us

$$(4.15) \qquad \sum_{\xi \in \mathbb{Z}^d} \hat{f}(\xi) = \sum_{\xi \in \mathbb{Z}^d} \hat{1}_{\frac{1}{2}K}(\xi) \hat{1}_{-\frac{1}{2}K}(\xi)$$

$$(4.16) \qquad = \sum_{\xi \in \mathbb{Z}^d} \int_{\frac{1}{2}K} e^{2\pi i \langle \xi, x \rangle} dx \int_{-\frac{1}{2}K} e^{2\pi i \langle \xi, x \rangle} dx$$

$$(4.17) \qquad = \sum_{\xi \in \mathbb{Z}^d} \int_{\frac{1}{2}K} e^{2\pi i \langle \xi, x \rangle} dx \int_{\frac{1}{2}K} e^{2\pi i \langle -\xi, x \rangle} dx$$

$$(4.18) \qquad = \sum_{\xi \in \mathbb{Z}^d} \int_{\frac{1}{2}K} e^{2\pi i \langle \xi, x \rangle} dx \overline{\int_{\frac{1}{2}K} e^{2\pi i \langle \xi, x \rangle} dx}$$

$$(4.19) \qquad = \sum_{\xi \in \mathbb{Z}^d} \left| \hat{1}_{\frac{1}{2}K}(\xi) \right|^2$$

$$(4.20) \qquad = \left| \hat{1}_{\frac{1}{2}K}(0) \right|^2 + \sum_{\xi \in \mathbb{Z}^d - \{0\}} \left| \hat{1}_{\frac{1}{2}K}(\xi) \right|^2$$

$$(4.21) \qquad = \frac{\mathrm{vol}^2\,K}{4^d} + \sum_{\xi \in \mathbb{Z}^d - \{0\}} \left| \hat{1}_{\frac{1}{2}K}(\xi) \right|^2,$$

where we have pulled out the $\xi = 0$ term from the series (4.19). So we have arrived at

$$\frac{\mathrm{vol}\,K}{2^d} = \frac{\mathrm{vol}^2\,K}{4^d} + \sum_{\xi \in \mathbb{Z}^d - \{0\}} \left| \hat{1}_{\frac{1}{2}K}(\xi) \right|^2,$$

yielding the required identity:

$$2^d = \operatorname{vol} K + \frac{4^d}{\operatorname{vol} K} \sum_{\xi \in \mathbb{Z}^d - \{0\}} \left| \hat{1}_{\frac{1}{2}K}(\xi) \right|^2.$$

Finally, to prove the stated extension to all lattices $\mathcal{L}$, we use the slightly more general form of Poisson summation (Theorem 3.44), valid for any lattice $\mathcal{L}$:

$$(4.22) \qquad \sum_{n \in \mathcal{L}} f(n) = \frac{1}{\det \mathcal{L}} \sum_{\xi \in \mathcal{L}^*} \hat{f}(\xi).$$

All the steps of the proof above are identical, except for the factor of $\frac{1}{\det \mathcal{L}}$, so that we arrive at the required identity of Siegel for arbitrary lattices:

$$(4.23) \qquad \frac{\operatorname{vol} K}{2^d} = \frac{\operatorname{vol}^2 K}{4^d \det \mathcal{L}} + \frac{1}{\det \mathcal{L}} \sum_{\xi \in \mathcal{L}^* - \{0\}} \left| \hat{1}_{\frac{1}{2}K}(\xi) \right|^2. \qquad \square$$

The proof of Minkowski's convex body theorem for lattices, namely Theorem 4.3, now follows immediately.

Proof of Theorem 4.3. [Minkowski's convex body theorem for a lattice $\mathcal{L}$] Applying Siegel's theorem (Theorem 4.5) to the centrally symmetric body K, we see that the lattice sum on the right-hand side of identity (4.5) contains only nonnegative terms. It follows that we immediately get the analogue of Minkowski's result for a given cenetrally symmetric body K and a lattice $\mathcal{L}$, in its contrapositive form:

> If the only lattice point of $\mathcal{L}$ in the interior of K is the origin, then $2^d \det \mathcal{L} \geq \operatorname{vol} K$. $\square$

In fact, we can easily extend Minkowski's theorem (Theorem 4.3) using the same ideas of the latter proof by using Siegel's theorem (Theorem 4.5) so that it applies to nonsymmetric bodies as well (but there iss a small "catch"—see Exercise (23)).

Enrico Bombieri [42] found an extension of Siegel's formula (Theorem 4.5), allowing the body to contain any number of lattice points. In recent work, Martins and Robins [168] found an extension of Bombieri's results, using the cross-covariogram of two bodies.

Figure 4.4. The Rhombic dodecahedron, a 3-dimensional symmetric polytope that tiles $\mathbb{R}^3$ by translations, and is another extremal body for Minkowski's convex body theorem.

4. Tiling and multi-tiling Euclidean space by translations of polytopes

First, we give a "spectral" equivalence for the tiling of Euclidean space by a single polytope using only translations by a lattice. It will turn out that the case of equality in Minkowski's convex body theorem is characterized precisely by the polytopes that tile $\mathbb{R}^d$ by translations. These bodies are called extremal bodies.

More generally, we would also like to consider the notion of multi-tiling, as follows. We say that a polytope $\mathcal{P}$ k-**tiles** $\mathbb{R}^d$ **by using a set of translations** $\mathcal{L}$ if for some integer k, we have

$$(4.24) \qquad\qquad \sum_{n \in \mathcal{L}} 1_{\mathcal{P}+n}(x) = k$$

for all $x \in \mathbb{R}^d$, except those points x that lie on the boundary of $\mathcal{P}$ or its translates under $\mathcal{L}$ (and, of course, these exceptions form a set of measure 0 in $\mathbb{R}^d$). In other words, $\mathcal{P}$ is a k-tiling body if almost every $x \in \mathbb{R}^d$ is covered by exactly k translates of $\mathcal{P}$.

Other synonyms for k-tilings in the literature are **multi-tilings** of $\mathbb{R}^d$, or **tiling at level** k. When $\mathcal{L}$ is a lattice, we will say that such a k-tiling is **periodic**. A common research theme is to search for tilings which are not necessarily periodic, but this is a difficult problem in general. The classical notion of tiling, such that there are no overlaps between the interiors of any two tiles, corresponds here to the case $k = 1$. We have the following wonderful dictionary between multi-tiling $\mathbb{R}^d$ by translations of a convex body $\mathcal{P}$, and a certain vanishing property of the Fourier transform of $\mathcal{P}$ due to Mihalis Kolountzakis [**139**], [**140**].

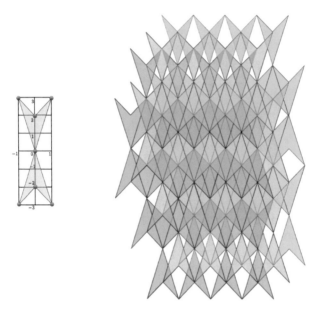

Figure 4.5. Left: A nonconvex body K, which is centrally symmetric. Right: The body K 2-tiles by translations with a lattice.

Theorem 4.6 (Kolountzakis). *Let $\mathcal{P} \subset \mathbb{R}^d$ be a compact set with positive d-dimensional volume, and let $\mathcal{L} \subset \mathbb{R}^d$ be a full-rank lattice. We define $k := \frac{\text{vol}\,\mathcal{P}}{\det \mathcal{L}}$. The following two properties are equivalent:*

(1) *$\mathcal{P}$ k-tiles $\mathbb{R}^d$ by translations with $\mathcal{L}$.*

(2) *$\hat{1}_{\mathcal{P}}(\xi) = 0$, for all nonzero $\xi \in \mathcal{L}^*$, the dual lattice.*

We note that part (2) implies that $k := \frac{\text{vol}\,\mathcal{P}}{\det \mathcal{L}}$ must be an integer.

Proof. We begin with the definition of multi-tiling, so that by assumption

$$(4.25) \qquad \sum_{n \in \mathcal{L}} 1_{\mathcal{P}+n}(x) = k$$

for all $x \in \mathbb{R}^d$ except those points x that lie on the boundary of $\mathcal{P}$ or its translates under $\mathcal{L}$ (and, of course, these exceptions form a set of measure 0 in $\mathbb{R}^d$). A trivial but useful observation is that

$$1_{\mathcal{P}+n}(x) = 1 \iff 1_{\mathcal{P}}(x - n) = 1,$$

so we can rewrite the defining identity (4.25) as $\sum_{n \in \mathcal{L}} 1_{\mathcal{P}}(x - n) = k$. Now we notice that the left-hand side is a periodic function of x, namely,

$$F(x) := \sum_{n \in \mathcal{L}} 1_{\mathcal{P}}(x - n)$$

is periodic in x with $\mathcal{L}$ as its set of periods. This is easy to see: if we let $l \in \mathcal{L}$, then $F(x + l) = \sum_{n \in \mathcal{L}} 1_{\mathcal{P}}(x + l - n) = \sum_{m \in \mathcal{L}} 1_{\mathcal{P}}(x + m) = F(x)$, because the lattice $\mathcal{L}$ is invariant under a translation by any vector that belongs to it.

The following "intuitive proof" would in fact be rigorous if we were allowed to use "generalized functions", but since we do not use them in this book, we label this part of the proof as "intuitive", and we then give a rigorous proof using functions rather than generalized functions.

Intuitive proof. By Theorem 3.22, we may expand F into its Fourier series because it is a periodic function on $\mathbb{R}^d$. Now by Poisson summation, namely Theorem 3.44, we know that its Fourier coefficients are the following.

$$(4.26) \qquad \sum_{m \in \mathcal{L}} 1_{\mathcal{P}}(x + m) = \frac{1}{\det \mathcal{L}} \sum_{\xi \in \mathcal{L}^*} \hat{1}_{\mathcal{P}}(\xi) e^{2\pi i \langle \xi, x \rangle}.$$

If we now make the assumption that $\hat{1}_{\mathcal{P}}(\xi) = 0$ for all nonzero $\xi \in \mathcal{L}^*$, then by (4.26) this assumption is equivalent to

$$\sum_{m \in \mathcal{L}} 1_{\mathcal{P}}(x + m) = \frac{\hat{1}_{\mathcal{P}}(0)}{\det \mathcal{L}} = \frac{\mathrm{vol}\, \mathcal{P}}{\det \mathcal{L}}.$$

This relation means that we have a k-tiling where $k := \frac{\mathrm{vol}\, \mathcal{P}}{\det \mathcal{L}}$. Now we replace the intuitive portion of the proof with a rigorous proof.

Rigorous proof. In order to apply Poisson summation, it is technically necessary to replace $1_{\mathcal{P}}(x)$ by a smoothed version of it in (4.26). Because this process is so common and useful in applications, this proof is instructive. We pick an approximate identity ϕ_n, which is also compactly supported and continuous. Applying the Poisson summation formula of

Theorem 3.67 to the smoothed function $1_P * \phi_n$, we get

$$(4.27) \qquad \sum_{m \in \mathcal{L}} (1_\mathcal{P} * \phi_n)(x+m) = \frac{1}{\det \mathcal{L}} \sum_{\xi \in \mathcal{L}^*} \hat{1}_\mathcal{P}(\xi) \hat{\phi}_n(\xi) e^{2\pi i \langle \xi, x \rangle}.$$

Using the fact that the convolution of two compactly supported functions is itself compactly supported, we see that $1_\mathcal{P} * \phi_n$ is again compactly supported. Thus the sum on the LHS of (4.27) is a finite sum. Performing a separate computation, we take the limit as $n \to \infty$ inside this finite sum, and, using Theorem 3.65 (due to the continuity of $1_\mathcal{P} * \phi_n$), we obtain

$$\lim_{n \to \infty} \sum_{m \in \mathcal{L}} (1_\mathcal{P} * \phi_n)(x+m) = \sum_{m \in \mathcal{L}} \lim_{n \to \infty} (1_\mathcal{P} * \phi_n)(x+m)$$
$$= \sum_{m \in \mathcal{L}} 1_\mathcal{P}(x+m),$$

at all points $x + m$ for which $(1_\mathcal{P} * \phi_n)(x+m)$ is continuous. Now, using our Poisson summation IV (Theorem 3.67(2)), we have

$$(4.28) \qquad \sum_{m \in \mathcal{L}} 1_\mathcal{P}(x+m) = \frac{1}{\det \mathcal{L}} \sum_{\xi \in \mathcal{L}^*} \hat{1}_\mathcal{P}(\xi) \hat{\phi}_n(\xi) e^{2\pi i \langle \xi, x \rangle}$$

for all sufficiently large values of n. Separating the term $\xi = 0$ on the RHS of this Poisson summation formula, we have

$$(4.29) \qquad \sum_{m \in \mathcal{L}} 1_\mathcal{P}(x+m) = \frac{\hat{1}_\mathcal{P}(0)}{\det \mathcal{L}} + \sum_{\xi \in \mathcal{L}^* - \{0\}} \hat{1}_\mathcal{P}(\xi) \hat{\phi}_n(\xi) e^{2\pi i \langle \xi, x \rangle}$$

$$(4.30) \qquad = \frac{\mathrm{vol}\,\mathcal{P}}{\det \mathcal{L}} + \sum_{\xi \in \mathcal{L}^* - \{0\}} \hat{1}_\mathcal{P}(\xi) \hat{\phi}_n(\xi) e^{2\pi i \langle \xi, x \rangle}.$$

Now, $\hat{1}_\mathcal{P}(\xi) = 0$ for all $\xi \in \mathcal{L}^* - \{0\}$ in (4.30) will hold

$$\iff \sum_{m \in \mathcal{L}} 1_\mathcal{P}(x+m) = \frac{\mathrm{vol}\,\mathcal{P}}{\det \mathcal{L}},$$

an equivalent condition which we may write as $\sum_{m \in \mathcal{L}} 1_\mathcal{P}(x+m) = k$, where $k := \frac{\mathrm{vol}\,\mathcal{P}}{\det \mathcal{L}}$. The condition $\sum_{m \in \mathcal{L}} 1_\mathcal{P}(x+m) = k$ means that $\mathcal{P}$ k-tiles $\mathbb{R}^d$ by translations with the lattice $\mathcal{L}$, and also implies that k must be an integer. $\qquad \square$

In 1905, Minkowski gave necessary conditions for a polytope $\mathcal{P}$ to tile $\mathbb{R}^d$ by translations. Later, Venkov and McMullen independently found sufficient conditions as well, culminating in the following fundamental result.

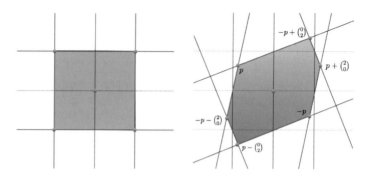

Figure 4.6. The square on the left is an extremal body in $\mathbb{R}^2$ relative to the integer lattice, and has area 4 as expected. More generally, there is a continuous (2-parameter) family of extremal hexagons, each having area 4, with no integer points in their interior. This continuous family is parametrized by the point $p \in \mathbb{R}^2$ in the figure on the right.

Theorem 4.7 (Minkowski–Venkov–McMullen). *A polytope $\mathcal{P}$ tiles $\mathbb{R}^d$ by translations if and only if the following 3 conditions hold:*

(1) *$\mathcal{P}$ is a symmetric polytope.*

(2) *The facets of $\mathcal{P}$ are symmetric polytopes.*

(3) *Fix any face $F \subset \mathcal{P}$ of codimension 2 and project $\mathcal{P}$ onto the 2-dimensional plane that is orthogonal to the $(d-2)$-dimensional affine span of F. Then this projection is either a parallelogram or a centrally symmetric hexagon.*

5. Extremal bodies

An **extremal body**, relative to a lattice $\mathcal{L}$, is a convex symmetric body K which contains exactly one lattice point of $\mathcal{L}$ in its interior, such that

$$\operatorname{vol} K = 2^d (\det \mathcal{L}).$$

In other words, an extremal body satisfies the hypotheses of Minkowski's inequality (Theorem 4.3), and attains the equality case.

If we look at equation (4.5) a bit more closely, we quickly get a nice corollary that arises by combining Theorem 4.6 and Siegel's theorem (Theorem 4.4). Namely, equality occurs in Minkowski's convex body theorem if and only if K tiles $\mathbb{R}^d$ by translations. Let us prove this.

Theorem 4.8 (Extremal bodies). *Let K be any convex, centrally symmetric subset of $\mathbb{R}^d$, and fix a full-rank lattice $\mathcal{L} \subset \mathbb{R}^d$. Suppose that the only point of $\mathcal{L}$ in the interior of K is the origin. Then*

$$2^d \det \mathcal{L} = \operatorname{vol} K \iff \tfrac{1}{2} K \text{ tiles } \mathbb{R}^d \text{ by translations}$$
with the lattice $\mathcal{L}$.

Proof. By formula (4.6), we have

$$(4.31) \qquad 2^d \det \mathcal{L} = \operatorname{vol} K + \frac{4^d}{\operatorname{vol} K} \sum_{\xi \in \mathcal{L}^* - \{0\}} \left| \hat{1}_{\frac{1}{2} K}(\xi) \right|^2 .$$

Therefore, the assumption $2^d \det \mathcal{L} = \operatorname{vol} K$ holds $\iff$

$$(4.32) \qquad 0 = \frac{4^d}{\operatorname{vol} K} \sum_{\xi \in \mathcal{L}^* - \{0\}} \left| \hat{1}_{\frac{1}{2} K}(\xi) \right|^2 ,$$

$\iff$ all of the nonnegative summands $\hat{1}_{\frac{1}{2} K}(\xi) = 0$ for all nonzero $\xi \in \mathcal{L}^*$. Now we would like to use Theorem 4.6 to show the required tiling equivalence, namely that $\frac{1}{2} K$ tiles $\mathbb{R}^d$ by translations with the lattice $\mathcal{L}$. We have already verified Theorem 4.6(1), applied to the body $\frac{1}{2} K$, namely that $\hat{1}_{\frac{1}{2} K}(\xi) = 0$, for all nonzero $\xi \in \mathcal{L}^*$.

To verify Theorem 4.6(2), we notice that because $\operatorname{vol}\left(\frac{1}{2} K\right) = \frac{1}{2^d} \operatorname{vol} K$, it follows that $2^d \det \mathcal{L} = \operatorname{vol} K$ is equivalent to

$$1 = \frac{\operatorname{vol}\left(\frac{1}{2} K\right)}{\det \mathcal{L}},$$

so that we may apply Theorem 4.6 with $\mathcal{P} := \frac{1}{2} K$ and the multiplicity $k := 1$. $\qquad \square$

There is an extension of Theorem 4.7 (the Minkowski–Venkov–McMullen result) to multi-tilings, as follows.

Theorem 4.9 ([100]). *If a polytope $\mathcal{P}$ multi-tiles $\mathbb{R}^d$ by translations with a discrete set of vectors, then*

(1) *$\mathcal{P}$ is a symmetric polytope.*

(2) *The facets of $\mathcal{P}$ are symmetric polytopes.*

In the case that $\mathcal{P} \subset \mathbb{R}^d$ is a rational polytope, meaning that all the vertices of $\mathcal{P}$ have rational coordinates, the latter two necessary conditions for multi-tiling become sufficient conditions as well [100].

Figure 4.7. The truncated octahedron, one of the 3-dimensional polytopes that tiles $\mathbb{R}^3$ by translations.

Question 4.10 (Rhetorical). Is it possible to find two distinct polytopes $\mathcal{P}, Q$ such that

$$(4.33) \qquad \hat{1}_{\mathcal{P}}(\xi) = \hat{1}_Q(\xi) \text{ for all } \xi \in \mathbb{Z}^d?$$

Example 4.11. We finish this section by answering Question 4.10 in the affirmative. Let us pick any two distinct extremal bodies relative to the lattice $\mathbb{Z}^d$, say, $\mathcal{P}, Q \subset \mathbb{R}^d$. By definition of an extremal body, we know that their volumes must be both equal to 2^d, so that

$$\hat{1}_{\mathcal{P}}(0) = \text{vol } \mathcal{P} = 2^d = \text{vol } Q = \hat{1}_Q(0).$$

Moreover, by Theorem 4.6 we also have

$$\hat{1}_{\mathcal{P}}(\xi) = 0 = \hat{1}_Q(\xi) \text{ for all } \xi \in \mathbb{Z}^d \setminus \{0\}. \qquad \square$$

6. Zonotopes and centrally symmetric polytopes

It is both fun and instructive to see how very simple Fourier methods can give us deeper insight into the geometry of symmetric polytopes. The reader may glance at the definitions in Section 2.

Example 4.12. Consider the cross-polytope $\lozenge \subset \mathbb{R}^3$, defined in Chapter 2. This is a centrally symmetric polytope, but each of its facets is *not* a symmetric polytope because its facets are triangles. $\qquad \square$

If *all* of the k-dimensional faces of a polytope $\mathcal{P}$ are symmetric, for each $1 \leq k \leq d$, then $\mathcal{P}$ is called a **zonotope**. Zonotopes form an extremely important class of polytopes, and have various equivalent formulations.

Lemma 4.13. *A polytope $\mathcal{P} \subset \mathbb{R}^d$ is a zonotope $\iff \mathcal{P}$ has one of the following properties:*

(1) *$\mathcal{P}$ is a projection of some n-dimensional cube.*

(2) *$\mathcal{P}$ is the Minkowski sum of a finite number of line segments.*

(3) *Every face of $\mathcal{P}$ is symmetric.*   □

A projection here means any affine transformation of $\mathcal{P}$ where the rank of the associated matrix may be less than d.

Zonotopes have been very useful in the study of tilings [265], [25]. For instance, in dimension 3, the only polytopes that tile $\mathbb{R}^3$ by translations with a lattice are zonotopes, and there is a list of five of them (up to an isomorphism of their face posets) called the **Fedorov solids**, drawn in Figure 4.10 (see Note (8)).

By definition, any zonotope is a symmetric polytope but the converse is not true; for example, the cross-polytope is symmetric but it has triangular faces which are not symmetric, so the crosspolytope is not a zonotope.

Example 4.14. Consider the following 3 line segments in $\mathbb{R}^2$:

$$\text{conv}\{\left(\begin{smallmatrix} 0 \\ 0 \end{smallmatrix}\right), \left(\begin{smallmatrix} 1 \\ 0 \end{smallmatrix}\right)\}, \text{conv}\{\left(\begin{smallmatrix} 0 \\ 0 \end{smallmatrix}\right), \left(\begin{smallmatrix} 2 \\ 1 \end{smallmatrix}\right)\}, \text{ and } \text{conv}\{\left(\begin{smallmatrix} 0 \\ 0 \end{smallmatrix}\right), \left(\begin{smallmatrix} 1 \\ 3 \end{smallmatrix}\right)\}.$$

The Minkowski sum of these three line segments, by definition a zonotope in $\mathbb{R}^2$, is the symmetric hexagon whose vertices are

$$\left(\begin{smallmatrix} 0 \\ 0 \end{smallmatrix}\right), \left(\begin{smallmatrix} 1 \\ 0 \end{smallmatrix}\right), \left(\begin{smallmatrix} 2 \\ 1 \end{smallmatrix}\right), \left(\begin{smallmatrix} 3 \\ 3 \end{smallmatrix}\right), \left(\begin{smallmatrix} 3 \\ 1 \end{smallmatrix}\right), \left(\begin{smallmatrix} 4 \\ 3 \end{smallmatrix}\right).$$

Notice that once we graph it in Figure 4.8, the graph is hinting to us that this body is a projection of a 3-dimensional cube, and indeed this turns out to be always true for Minkowski sums of line segments.   □

Example 4.15. A particular embedding of the truncated octahedron $\mathcal{P}$ (drawn in Figure 4.7) is given by the convex hull of the set of 24 vertices defined by all permutations of $(0, \pm 1, \pm 2)$. We note that this set of vertices can also be thought of as the orbit of just the one point $(0, 1, 2) \in \mathbb{R}^3$ under the hyperoctahedral group (see [56] for more on the hyperoctahedral group). It turns out that this truncated octahedron $\mathcal{P}$ tiles $\mathbb{R}^3$ by translations with a lattice (Exercise (17)).   □

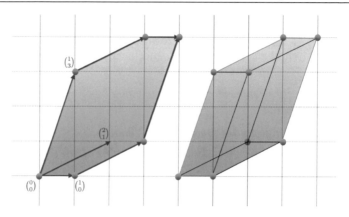

Figure 4.8. The Minkowski sum of three line segments in the plane, forming a 2-dimensional zonotope, as described in Example 4.14.

Figure 4.9. A 3-dimensional zonotope, called the rhombic dodecahedron, showing in bold its 4 line segments whose Minkowski sums generate the object.

Next, we show that it is possible to detect whether any compact set S is centrally symmetric by observing whether its Fourier transform is real-valued.

Lemma 4.16. *Suppose that $S \subset \mathbb{R}^d$ is a compact set. Then*

$$S \text{ is symmetric about the origin} \iff \hat{1}_S(\xi) \in \mathbb{R}$$

for all $\xi \in \mathbb{R}^d$.

Proof. Suppose that S is symmetric about the origin, meaning that $S = -S$. Then we have

$$\overline{\hat{1}_S(\xi)} := \overline{\int_S e^{2\pi i \langle \xi, x \rangle} dx} \tag{4.34}$$

$$= \int_S e^{-2\pi i \langle \xi, x \rangle} dx$$

$$= \int_{-S} e^{2\pi i \langle \xi, x \rangle} dx \tag{4.35}$$

$$= \int_S e^{2\pi i \langle \xi, x \rangle} dx := \hat{1}_S(\xi), \tag{4.36}$$

showing that the complex conjugate of $\hat{1}_S$ is itself, hence that it is real-valued.

Conversely, suppose that $\hat{1}_S(\xi) \in \mathbb{R}$ for all $\xi \in \mathbb{R}^d$. We must show that $S = -S$. We first compute

$$\hat{1}_{-S}(\xi) := \int_{-S} e^{2\pi i \langle \xi, x \rangle} dx \tag{4.37}$$

$$= \int_S e^{-2\pi i \langle \xi, x \rangle} dx$$

$$= \overline{\int_S e^{2\pi i \langle \xi, y \rangle} dy} \tag{4.38}$$

$$:= \overline{\hat{1}_S(\xi)} \tag{4.39}$$

$$= \hat{1}_S(\xi) \tag{4.40}$$

for all $\xi \in \mathbb{R}^d$, where we have used the assumption that $\hat{1}_S(\xi)$ is real-valued in the last equality. But Theorem 3.18 tells us that in this case $\hat{1}_S(\xi) = \hat{1}_{-S}(\xi)$ for all $\xi \in \mathbb{R}^d \iff S = -S$. □

Example 4.17. The interval $\mathcal{P} := [-\frac{1}{2}, \frac{1}{2}]$ is a symmetric polytope, and we can see that its Fourier transform $\hat{1}_{\mathcal{P}}(\xi)$ is real-valued, since we have $\hat{1}_{\mathcal{P}}(\xi) = \text{sinc}(\xi)$, as we saw in equation (2.4). □

Example 4.18. The cross-polytope $\Diamond_2$ is a symmetric polytope, and as we verified in dimension 2, equation (2.58), its Fourier transform $1_{\Diamond_2}(\xi)$ is real-valued. □

Alexandrov [2], and Shephard [231] independently proved the following remarkable fact.

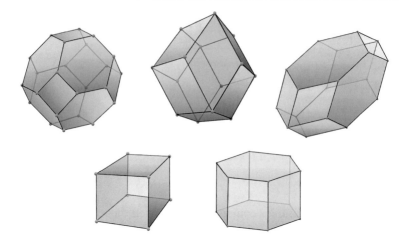

Figure 4.10. The Fedorov solids, the only 3-dimensional polytopes that tile $\mathbb{R}^3$ by translations. All five of them are zonotopes, and they are also extremal bodies for Minkowski's convex body theorem. The top three, from left to right, are: the truncated octahedron, the rhombic dodecahedron, and the hexarhombic dodecahedron. The bottom two are the cube and the hexagonal prism.

Theorem 4.19 (Alexandrov and Shephard). *Let P be any real d-dimensional polytope, with $d \geq 3$. If all of the facets of P are symmetric, then P is symmetric.*   □

Example 4.20. The converse to the latter result is clearly false, as demonstrated by the cross-polytope in dimension $d > 2$: it is centrally symmetric, but its facets are not symmetric because they are simplices and we know that no simplex (of dimension ≥ 2) is symmetric.   □

Suppose we consider 3-dimensional polytopes $\mathcal{P}$, and ask which ones enjoy the property that all of their 2-dimensional faces are symmetric. Because 1-dimensional faces are always symmetric, and because Theorem 4.19 tells us that $\mathcal{P}$ itself must also be symmetric, the answer is that $\mathcal{P}$ must be a zonotope—in other words all of its faces are symmetric.

Moving up to 4-dimensional polytopes, our curiosity might take the next step: Which 4-dimensional polytopes enjoy the property that all of their 3-dimensional faces are symmetric? Must they also be zonotopes? The 24-cell is a good counterexample because it has triangular 2-dimensional faces, and hence is not a zonotope. On the other hand, the 24-cell tiles $\mathbb{R}^4$ by translations with a lattice (it is the Voronoi cell of the D4 lattice), and therefore by Theorem 4.7 its 3-dimensional facets must be symmetric.

What if we ask which 4-dimensional polytopes enjoy the property that all of their 2-dimensional faces are symmetric? Peter McMullen [**175**] discovered the wonderful conclusion that all of their faces must be symmetric—in other words, they must be zonotopes—and that much more is true.

Figure 4.11. A 3-dimensional zonotope that does not tile $\mathbb{R}^3$ by translations.

Theorem 4.21 (McMullen). *Let P be any real d-dimensional polytope with $d \geq 4$. Fix any positive integer k with $2 \leq k \leq d - 2$.*

If the k-dimensional faces of $\mathcal{P}$ are symmetric, then $\mathcal{P}$ is a zonotope.

$\square$

One might wonder what happens if we "discretize the volume" of a symmetric body K, by counting integer points, and then ask for an analogue of Minkowski Theorem 4.2. In fact, Minkowski already had a result about this too. (And he had so many beautiful ideas that it is hard to put them all in one place!) We give Minkowski's own elegant and short proof.

Theorem 4.22 (Minkowski, 1910). *Let $K \subset \mathbb{R}^d$ be any d-dimensional, convex, centrally symmetric set. If the only integer point in the interior of K is the origin, then*

$$(4.41) \qquad \left| K \cap \mathbb{Z}^d \right| \leq 3^d.$$

Proof. We define the map $\phi : \mathbb{Z}^d \to (\mathbb{Z}/3\mathbb{Z})^d$ by reducing each coordinate modulo 3. Now we claim that when restricted to the set $K \cap \mathbb{Z}^d$, our map ϕ is $1 - 1$. The statement of the theorem follows directly from this claim. So let $x, y \in K \cap \mathbb{Z}^d$, and suppose $\phi(x) = \phi(y)$. Then, by definition of the map ϕ, we have

$$(4.42) \qquad n := \frac{1}{3}(x - y) \in \mathbb{Z}^d.$$

Now we define C to be the **interior** of the convex hull of $x, -y$, and 0. Because K is symmetric, and $x, y \in K$, we know that $-y \in K$ as well, so that $C \subset \text{int}(K)$. Now using the convexity of C, we also see that $n \in C$, because n is a nontrivial convex linear combination of $0, x, -y$.

Therefore $n \in \text{int}(K)$ as well. Altogether, $n \in \text{int}(K) \cap \mathbb{Z}^d = \{0\}$, which forces $n = 0$. Hence $x - y = 0$.   □

Theorem 4.22 is often called **Minkowski's 3^d theorem**. An immediate and natural question is: Which bodies account for the "equality case"? One direction is easy to see: if K is the integer cube $[-1, 1]^d$, then it is clear that K is symmetric about the origin, and the only integer point in its interior is the origin. In addition, vol $K = 2^d$, and K contains precisely 3^d integer points. It is a bit surprising, perhaps, that only in 2012 was it proved that this integer cube is the only case of equality in Minkowski's 3^d theorem [**180**].

7. Sums of two squares via Minkowski's theorem

In 1625, Albert Girard appears to have been the first to observe (without proof) that if we have a prime $p \equiv 1 \pmod 4$, then $p = a^2 + b^2$ for some positive integers a, b, and that up to order such a representation is unique. It is easy to see that if a prime $p \equiv 3 \pmod 4$ then it cannot be written as a sum of two integer squares, because every square mod 4 is congruent to either 0 or 1 $\pmod 4$, and hence a sum of two integer squares must be congruent to either $0, 1$, or 2 $\pmod 4$.

Fermat popularized this result, which now bears his name, although Fermat did not provide a proof of this statement. The first recorded proof was discovered by Euler in 1752, and employs the idea of infinite descent. Here we will give a proof of this result by appealing to Minkowski's convex body theorem, namely Theorem 4.3.

To warm up, the reader may want to solve the following elementary and classical number theory problem: Given a prime $p \equiv 1 \pmod 4$, prove that there exists an integer m such that $-1 \equiv m^2 \pmod p$ (Exercise (22)).

Theorem 4.23 (Sum of two squares). *Let p be an odd prime. Then $p = a^2 + b^2$ is solvable in integers $a, b \iff p \equiv 1 \pmod 4$.*

Proof. We know from above that there exists an integer k such that $-1 \equiv k^2 \pmod 4$, and we have also seen that the prime p must satisfy $p \equiv 1 \pmod 4$. We define the lattice $\mathcal{L} := M(\mathbb{Z}^2)$ with $M := \left(\begin{smallmatrix} 1 & 0 \\ k & p \end{smallmatrix} \right)$, a lattice which manifestly has determinant p. For our convex body, we will pick the ball $B := \{x \in \mathbb{R}^2 \mid \|x\| \le \sqrt{2p}\}$. The volume of B is $2p\pi$, and we can now check that the hypotheses of Theorem 4.3 are satisfied:

$$\text{vol } B > 2^2 \det M \iff (2p)\pi > 4p,$$

which is true. Hence there exists a lattice point $\left(\begin{smallmatrix} a \\ b \end{smallmatrix}\right) \in \mathcal{L}$ in the interior of B. But any point in $\left(\begin{smallmatrix} a \\ b \end{smallmatrix}\right) \in \mathcal{L}$ must satisfy

$$\left(\begin{smallmatrix} a \\ b \end{smallmatrix}\right) = \left(\begin{smallmatrix} 1 & 0 \\ k & p \end{smallmatrix}\right)\left(\begin{smallmatrix} m \\ n \end{smallmatrix}\right) = \left(\begin{smallmatrix} m \\ mk+np \end{smallmatrix}\right)$$

for some $m, n \in \mathbb{Z}$. We now have

$$a^2 + b^2 = m^2 + (mk + np)^2 \equiv m^2(1 + k^2) \equiv 0 \quad (\text{mod } p),$$

so $p \mid a^2 + b^2$. Finally, we will use the fact that $\left(\begin{smallmatrix} a \\ b \end{smallmatrix}\right)$ is also in the interior of the body B, giving us $a^2 + b^2 < 2p$. Together with $p \mid a^2 + b^2$, we arrive at $p = a^2 + b^2$. □

This proof shows one small aspect of Minkowski's powerful geometry of numbers using simple ideas in geometry to conclude nontrivial number-theoretic facts. Minkowski's theorem (Theorem 4.3) can also be used to prove Lagrange's theorem, namely that every integer may be written as a sum of 4 squares (for a proof, see [**110**]).

8. The volume of the ball and the sphere

The most symmetric of all convex bodies is the ball, and here we will explicitly compute the volumes of d-dimensional balls and the volumes of $(d - 1)$-dimensional spheres. For these very classical computations, we need the Gamma function

$$(4.43) \qquad \Gamma(x) := \int_0^\infty e^{-t} t^{x-1} dt,$$

valid for all $x > 0$. The Gamma function $\Gamma(x)$ interpolates smoothly between the integer values of the factorial function $n!$, in the following sense.

Lemma 4.24. *Fix $x > 0$. Then*

(1) $\Gamma(x + 1) = x\Gamma(x)$.

(2) $\Gamma(n + 1) = n!$, *for all nonnegative integers n.*

(3) $\Gamma\left(\frac{1}{2}\right) = \sqrt{\pi}$.

(4) Γ *extends to an infinitely smooth function on the complex plane, except at 0 and the negative integers, where it has simple poles.*

The verifications of parts (1), (2), and (3) are good exercises (Exercise (24)), and we do not want to deprive the reader of that pleasure. Part (4) requires some knowledge of complex analysis, but we include the statement here for general knowledge.

What is the volume of the unit ball $B := \{x \in \mathbb{R}^d \mid \|x\| \leq 1\}$? And what about the volume of the unit sphere

$$S^{d-1} := \{x \in \mathbb{R}^d \mid \|x\| = 1\}?$$

Lemma 4.25. *For the unit ball B and unit sphere S^{d-1}, we have*

(4.44) $$\mathrm{vol}\, B = \frac{\pi^{\frac{d}{2}}}{\Gamma\left(\frac{d}{2}+1\right)}, \text{ and } \mathrm{vol}\left(S^{d-1}\right) = \frac{2\pi^{\frac{d}{2}}}{\Gamma\left(\frac{d}{2}\right)}.$$

Proof. We let $\kappa_{d-1} := \mathrm{vol}(S^{d-1})$ denote the surface area of the unit sphere $S^{d-1} \subset \mathbb{R}^d$. We use polar coordinates in $\mathbb{R}^d$, meaning that we may write each $x \in \mathbb{R}^d$ in the form $x = (r, \theta)$, where $r > 0$ and $\theta \in S^{d-1}$. Thus $\|x\| = r$, and we also have the calculus fact that $dx = r^{d-1}dr d\theta$.

Returning to our Gaussians $e^{-\pi\|x\|^2}$, we may recompute their integrals using polar coordinates in $\mathbb{R}^d$:

$$1 = \int_{\mathbb{R}^d} e^{-\pi\|x\|^2}dx$$

$$= \int_{S^{d-1}} \int_0^\infty e^{-\pi r^2} r^{d-1}dr\, d\theta$$

$$= \kappa_{d-1} \int_0^\infty e^{-\pi r^2} r^{d-1}dr$$

$$= \kappa_{d-1} \frac{1}{2\pi^{\frac{d}{2}}} \int_0^\infty e^{-t} t^{\frac{d}{2}-1}dt,$$

where we have used $t := \pi r^2$, implying that

$$r^{d-1}dr = r^{d-2}rdr = \left(\frac{t}{\pi}\right)^{\frac{d-2}{2}} \frac{dt}{2\pi}.$$

Recognizing the latter integral as $\Gamma\left(\frac{d}{2}\right)$, we find that

$$1 = \frac{\kappa_{d-1}}{2\pi^{\frac{d}{2}}} \Gamma\left(\frac{d}{2}\right),$$

as desired.

For the volume of the unit ball B, we have

$$\mathrm{vol}\, B = \int_0^1 \kappa_{d-1} r^{d-1}dr = \frac{\kappa_{d-1}}{d} = \frac{\pi^{\frac{d}{2}}}{\frac{d}{2}\Gamma\left(\frac{d}{2}\right)} = \frac{\pi^{\frac{d}{2}}}{\Gamma\left(\frac{d}{2}+1\right)}. \qquad \square$$

It is an easy fact—but worth mentioning—that we may also rewrite the formulas (4.44) in terms of ratios of factorials by using the recursive properties of the Γ function (Exercise (21)). While we are at it, let us dilate the unit ball by $r > 0$, and recall our definition of the ball of radius r:

$$B_d(r) := \left\{ x \in \mathbb{R}^d \mid \|x\| \leq r \right\}.$$

We know that for any d-dimensional body K we have $\operatorname{vol}(rK) = r^d \operatorname{vol} K$, so we also get the volumes of the ball of radius r and the sphere of radius r:

$$(4.45) \qquad \operatorname{vol} B_d(r) = \frac{\pi^{\frac{d}{2}}}{\Gamma\left(\frac{d}{2} + 1\right)} r^d, \text{ and } \operatorname{vol}\left(rS^{d-1}\right) = \frac{2\pi^{\frac{d}{2}}}{\Gamma\left(\frac{d}{2}\right)} r^{d-1}.$$

Intuitively, the derivative of the volume is the surface area and now we can confirm this intuition:

$$\begin{aligned}
\frac{d}{dr} \operatorname{vol} B_d(r) &= \frac{d\pi^{\frac{d}{2}}}{\Gamma\left(\frac{d}{2} + 1\right)} r^{d-1} \\
&= \frac{2\frac{d}{2}\pi^{\frac{d}{2}}}{\frac{d}{2}\Gamma\left(\frac{d}{2}\right)} r^{d-1} \\
&= \frac{2\pi^{\frac{d}{2}}}{\Gamma\left(\frac{d}{2}\right)} r^{d-1} \\
&= \operatorname{vol}\left(rS^{d-1}\right).
\end{aligned}$$

9. Classical geometric inequalities

It turns out that the volume of the difference body $\frac{1}{2}K - \frac{1}{2}K$, which appeared quite naturally in some of the proofs above, can be related in a rather precise manner to the volume of K itself. The consequence is the following **Rogers–Shephard inequality**:

$$(4.46) \qquad \operatorname{vol} K \leq \operatorname{vol}\left(\frac{1}{2}K - \frac{1}{2}K\right) \leq \binom{2d}{d} \operatorname{vol} K,$$

where equality on the left holds $\iff K$ is a symmetric body, and equality on the right holds $\iff K$ is a simplex (see [**214**], [**55**]). There is also an extension of the Rogers–Shephard inequality to two distinct convex bodies $K, L \subset \mathbb{R}^d$ ([**214**] and [**13**]):

$$(4.47) \qquad \operatorname{vol}(K - L) \operatorname{vol}(K \cap L) \leq \binom{2d}{d} \operatorname{vol} K \operatorname{vol} L.$$

A quick way of proving equation (4.46) is to use the ubiquitous **Brunn–Minkowski inequality**. To set it up, two sets $A, B \subset \mathbb{R}^d$ are called **homothetic** if $A = \lambda B + v$ for some fixed $v \in \mathbb{R}^d$, and some $\lambda > 0$ (or either A or B consist of just one point).

Theorem 4.26 (Brunn–Minkowski inequality). *If K and L are convex subsets of $\mathbb{R}^d$, then*

$$(4.48) \qquad \operatorname{vol}(K + L)^{\frac{1}{d}} \geq \operatorname{vol}(K)^{\frac{1}{d}} + \operatorname{vol}(L)^{\frac{1}{d}}$$

with equality if and only if K and L lie in parallel hyperplanes or are homothetic to each other. (See [225, Section 7.1] for a proof and a thorough introduction to this inequality.)   □

10. Minkowski's theorems on linear forms

There is a quick and wonderful application of Minkowski's first theorem to products of linear forms.

Theorem 4.27 (Minkowski—homogeneous linear forms). *For each $1 \leq i \leq d$, let*

$$L_i(x) := a_{i,1}x_1 + \cdots + a_{i,d}x_d$$

be linear forms with real coefficients $a_{i,j}$, and suppose that the matrix A formed by these coefficients $a_{i,j}$ is invertible. Suppose further that there exists positive numbers $\lambda_1, \ldots, \lambda_d$ with the property that $\lambda_1 \lambda_2 \ldots, \lambda_d \geq |\det A|$.

Then there exists a nonzero integer vector $n \in \mathbb{Z}^d$, such that

$$(4.49) \qquad |L_1(n)| \leq \lambda_1, \cdots, |L_d(n)| \leq \lambda_d.$$

Proof. We define the body

$$(4.50) \qquad \mathcal{P} := \{x \in \mathbb{R}^d \mid |L_k(x)| \leq \lambda_k, \text{ for each } 1 \leq k \leq d\},$$

which is a centrally symmetric parallelepiped. To compute $\operatorname{vol} \mathcal{P}$, we note that the image of $\mathcal{P}$ under the linear transformation A is $Q := A(\mathcal{P}) = \{x \in \mathbb{R}^d \mid |x_k| \leq \lambda_k, 1 \leq k \leq d\}$, which clearly has volume $\operatorname{vol} Q = 2^d \lambda_1 \cdots \lambda_d$. Therefore,

$$\operatorname{vol} \mathcal{P} = \operatorname{vol} A^{-1} Q = \frac{1}{\det A} \operatorname{vol} Q = \frac{1}{\det A} 2^d \lambda_1 \cdots \lambda_d \geq 2^d,$$

the last inequality holding by assumption. By Theorem 4.3, $\mathcal{P}$ contains a nonzero integer point, and we are done.   □

Corollary 4.28 (Minkowski—product theorem for homogeneous linear forms). *For each $1 \leq i \leq d$, let*

$$(4.51) \qquad L_i(x) := a_{i,1}x_1 + \cdots + a_{i,d}x_d$$

be linear forms with real coefficients $a_{i,j}$, and suppose that the matrix A formed by these coefficients $a_{i,j}$ is invertible. If $d > 1$, then there exists a nonzero integer vector $n \in \mathbb{Z}^d$ such that

$$(4.52) \qquad |L_1(n)L_2(n) \cdots L_d(n)| \leq |\det A|.$$

Proof. We can simply use Theorem 4.27 with $\lambda_1 = \lambda_2 = \cdots = \lambda_d :=$ $|\det A|^{\frac{1}{d}}$. Since $\lambda_1 \cdots \lambda_d = |\det A|$, the conclusion of Theorem 4.27 gives us the existence of a nonzero integer point n that satisfies the following:

$$|L_1(n)| \, |L_2(n)| \cdots |L_d(n)| \leq \lambda_1 \cdots \lambda_d = |\det A|. \qquad \square$$

It is worth mentioning that there are various ways to strengthen Corollary 4.28. For example, it is possible to replace the inequality in (4.52) by a strict inequality [120].

11. Poisson summation as the trace of a compact linear operator

Now that we have seen a few applications of Poisson summation (and there will more throughout the book), it is natural to wonder if there is something a little deeper going on here. In this brief section we carry the reader through a more general context for Poisson summation, as the trace of a certain linear operator. The modern context for this extension is called the spectral theory of compact operators. For more about the spectral theory of noncompact operators, the reader is invited to peruse Audrey Terras's book [252].

Suppose we are given a compact set $\mathcal{P} \subset \mathbb{R}^d$ of positive d-dimensional volume, and a continuous function $K(x, y) : \mathcal{P} \times \mathcal{P} \to \mathbb{C}$. Then we can define a corresponding operator $T_K : L^2(\mathcal{P}) \to L^2(\mathcal{P})$ by

$$(4.53) \qquad T_K(f)(x) := \int_{\mathcal{P}} K(x, y) f(y) dy.$$

The function $K(x, y)$ is called a **kernel**. The operator T_K is clearly linear, and indeed $T_K(\alpha f + \beta g) = \alpha \, T_K(f) + \beta \, T_K(g)$ follows from the linearity of the integral. We call T_K a **positive operator** if $\langle T_K(f), f \rangle > 0$ for all nonzero functions f. Finally, the kernel (as well as the operator) is called **self-adjoint** if $K(x, y) = \overline{K(y, x)}$ for all $x, y \in \mathcal{P}$. A standard fact is that all of the eigenvalues of T_K are real. By the spectral theorem for compact, self-adjoint linear operators (see [**79**]), we know that T_K has an orthonormal basis of eigenvectors $\{v_1, v_2, v_3, \dots\}$, which correspond to its nonzero eigenvalues $\{\lambda_1, \lambda_2, \lambda_3, \dots\}$.

James Mercer proved Theorem 4.29 in [**176**].

Theorem 4.29 (Mercer, 1909). *Suppose that T_K is a positive, self-adjoint operator on a compact set $\mathcal{P} \subset \mathbb{R}^d$. Then*

$$(4.54) \qquad K(x, y) = \sum_{n=1}^{\infty} \lambda_n v_n(x)\overline{v_n(y)},$$

and the series converges absolutely and uniformly.   □

The **trace** of the linear operator T_K is defined by

$$\mathrm{Trace}(T_K) := \sum_{n=1}^{\infty} \lambda_n.$$

If T_K satisfies the hypotheses of Mercer's theorem, then we have also have the following immediate corollary:

$$(4.55) \qquad \int_{\mathcal{P}} K(x, x)\,dx = \int_{\mathcal{P}} \sum_{n=1}^{\infty} \lambda_n v_n(x)\overline{v_n(x)}\,dx$$

$$= \sum_{n=1}^{\infty} \lambda_n \int_{\mathcal{P}} |v_n(x)|^2\,dx$$

$$(4.56) \qquad\qquad\qquad = \sum_{n=1}^{\infty} \lambda_n,$$

which is the trace of T_K.

So what does all of this abstraction have to do with Poisson summation, the reader might ask? Well, let us pick $\mathcal{P} := \mathbb{T}^d$, the d-dimensional torus, and let us fix a Schwartz function $f : \mathbb{R}^d \to \mathbb{C}$. We may now consider the linear operator defined by

$$(4.57) \qquad L_f(g)(x) := (f * g)(x) := \int_{\mathbb{R}^d} f(x - y)g(y)\,dy$$

for all $x \in \mathbb{R}^d$, and for all $g \in L^2(\mathbb{T}^d)$. The interplay between the torus and $\mathbb{R}^d$ is intended here, and in fact we have

$$L_f(g)(x) := \int_{\mathbb{R}^d} f(x-y)g(y)dy$$

$$= \sum_{n \in \mathbb{Z}^d} \int_{(\mathbb{R}^d/\mathbb{Z}^d)-n} f(x-y)g(y)dy$$

$$= \sum_{n \in \mathbb{Z}^d} \int_{\mathbb{T}}^d f(x-y+n)g(y)dy$$

$$= \int_{\mathbb{T}}^d \left(\sum_{n \in \mathbb{Z}^d} f(x-y+n) \right) g(y)dy$$

$$:= \int_{\mathbb{T}}^d K(x,y)g(y)dy,$$

where we have defined our kernel

$$K(x,y) := \sum_{n \in \mathbb{Z}^d} f(x-y+n)$$

in the last equality above. What are the eigenfunctions of L_f? We claim that they are precisely the exponentials $e_k(x) := e^{2\pi i \langle x,k \rangle}$, indexed by $k \in \mathbb{Z}^d$! We can compute

$$L_f(e_k)(x) := \int_{\mathbb{R}^d} f(y)e^{2\pi i \langle x-y,k \rangle}dy$$

$$= e^{2\pi i \langle x,k \rangle} \int_{\mathbb{R}^d} f(y)e^{-2\pi i \langle y,k \rangle}dy$$

$$= \hat{f}(k)e_k(x),$$

proving that each function $e_k(x)$ is an eigenfunction of L_f, with eigenvalue $\hat{f}(k)$. Using the completeness of this set of orthonormal exponentials $\{e_k(x) \mid k \in \mathbb{Z}^d\}$ in the Hilbert space $L^2(\mathbb{T}^d)$, it is also possible to show that these are all of the eigenfunctions. So we see that the trace of L_f equals

(4.58) $$\text{Trace}(L_f) := \sum_{n=1}^{\infty} \lambda_n = \sum_{k \in \mathbb{Z}^d} \hat{f}(k).$$

On the other hand, if we assume that L_f is a self-adjoint positive operator (for this particular f), then (4.55) tells us that the trace may also be computed in another way:

$$\text{Trace}(L_f) = \int_{\mathbb{T}^d} K(x,x)dx$$

$$:= \int_{\mathbb{T}}^d \sum_{n\in\mathbb{Z}^d} f(n)dx$$

$$= \sum_{n\in\mathbb{Z}^d} f(n) \int_{\mathbb{T}}^d dx$$

$$= \sum_{n\in\mathbb{Z}^d} f(n).$$

So we have arrived at the Poisson summation formula (for Schwartz functions)

$$\sum_{n\in\mathbb{Z}^d} f(n) = \sum_{k\in\mathbb{Z}^d} \hat{f}(k)$$

by computing the trace of the linear operator L_f, acting on the Hilbert space $L^2(\mathbb{T}^d)$.

Notes

(1) Siegel's original proof of Theorem 4.4 used Parseval's identity, but the "Fourier-spirit" of the two proofs is similar.

(2) Minkowski's book [178] in 1896 was the first treatise to develop the threads between convex geometry, Diophantine approximation, and the theory of quadratic forms. This book marked the birth of the geometry of numbers.

(3) In Exercise (8), we see three equivalent conditions for a 2-simplex to be unimodular. In higher dimensions, a d-simplex will not satisfy all three conditions, and hence this exercise shows one important "breaking point" between 2-dimensional and 3-dimensional discrete geometry.

(4) There is a very important tool in number theory, called the Selberg trace formula, which extends Poisson summation to hyperbolic space. See, for example, Audrey Terras's book [252].

(5) The Poisson summation formula also extends to all locally compact abelian groups, and this field has a vast literature— for an example, see [252].

(6) There are a growing number of interesting books on the geometry of numbers. An excellent encyclopedic text is Gruber and

Lekkerkerker's [99] *Geometry of Numbers*. Another encyclopedic reference is Peter Gruber's own book [98].

Two other excellent and classic introductions are Siegel's book [233], and Cassels's book [55]. An expository introduction to some of the elements of the Geometry of numbers, at a level that is even appropriate for high school students, is given by Olds, Lax, and Davidoff [187]. For upcoming books, the reader may also consult Martin Henk's lecture notes "Introduction to geometry of numbers" [116] and the book by Lenny Fukshansky and Stephan Ramon Garcia, *Geometry of Numbers* [89].

(7) The Brunn–Minkowski inequality is fundamental to many branches of mathematics, including the geometry of numbers. A wonderful and encyclopedic treatment of the Brunn–Minkowski inequality, with its many interconnections, appears in Rolf Schneider's book *The Brunn–Minkowski Theory* [225].

(8) The Fedorov solids are depicted and explained via the modern ideas of Conway and Sloane in an excellent expository article by David Austin [4]. For a view into the life and work of Evgraf Stepanovich Fedorov, as well as a fascinating account of how Fedorov himself thought about the 5 parallelohedra, the reader may consult the article by Marjorie Senechal and R. V. Galiulin [228]. The authors of [228] also discuss the original book of Fedorov, *An Introduction to the Theory of Figures*, published in 1885, which is now considered a pinnacle of modern crystallography. Fedorov later became one of the great crystallographers of his time.

In $\mathbb{R}^4$, it is known that there are fifty-two different combinatorial types of 4-dimensional parallelohedra. In $\mathbb{R}^5$, the complete classification of all the combinatorial types of 5-dimensional paralellohedra was completed in 2016 [72], where the authors found $110,244$ of them.

(9) The field of multi-tiling is still rapdily growing. One of the first important papers in this field was by Mihalis Koloutzakis [139], who related the multi-tiling problem to a famous technique known as the idempotent theorem, and thereby proved that if we have a multi-tiling in $\mathbb{R}^2$ with any discrete set of translations, then we also have a multi-tiling with a finite union of lattices. A recent advance is an equivalence between multi-tiling and certain Hadwiger-type invariants, given by Nir Lev

and Bochen Liu [156]. Here the authors show that for a generalized polytope $\mathcal{P} \subset \mathbb{R}^d$ (not necessarily convex or connected), if $\mathcal{P}$ is spectral, then $\mathcal{P}$ is equidecomposable by translations to a cube of equal volume.

Another natural question in multi-tiling which is still open is the following:

Question 4.30. Suppose that $\mathcal{P}$ multi-tiles with a discrete set of translations D. Do we really need D to be arbitrary, or is it true that just a finite union of lattices suffices? Even better, perhaps one lattice always suffices?

In this direction, Bochen Liu recently proved that if we assume that $\mathcal{P}$ multi-tiles with a finite union of lattices, then $\mathcal{P}$ also multi-tiles with a single lattice [161]. This is big step in the direction of answering Question 4.30 in general. An earlier, and smaller step, was taken in [95], where the authors answered part of Question 4.30 in $\mathbb{R}^3$, reducing the search from an arbitrary discrete set of translations to translations by a finite union of lattices. Taken together, the latter two steps imply that in $\mathbb{R}^3$ (and in $\mathbb{R}^2$), any multi-tiling with a discrete set of translations also occurs with just one lattice.

In a different direction, the work of Gennadiy Averkov [5] analyzes the equality cases for an extension of Minkowski's theorem, relating those extremal bodies to multi-tilers. In [262], Qi Yang and Chuanming Zong show that the smallest k for which we can obtain a nontrivial k-tiling in $\mathbb{R}^2$ is $k = 5$, and the authors characterize those 5-tiling bodies, showing, in particular, that if a convex polygon is a 5-tiler, then it must be either an octagon or a decagon. In [104], Zong and his collaborators continue their research to show that the smallest k for which we can obtain a nontrivial k-tiling in $\mathbb{R}^3$ is $k = 5$. These investigations naturally lead to the general question:

Question 4.31. In $\mathbb{R}^d$ (for $d \geq 4$), what is the smallest integer k such that there exists a d-dimensional polytope $\mathcal{P}$ that k-tiles $\mathbb{R}^d$ (nontrivially) by translations?

(10) We say that a compact set $\mathcal{P}$ is **spectral** if $L^2(\mathcal{P})$ possesses an orthonormal complete basis of exponentials. There is a fascinating and vast literature about such spectral bodies, relating them to multi-tiling problems. A natural question in this direction is the following conjecture by Bent Fuglede.

Conjecture 4.32 (Fuglede, 1974 [**88**]). $\mathcal{P}$ tiles $\mathbb{R}^d$ by translations $\iff$ $\mathcal{P}$ is spectral.

Terry Tao disproved the Fuglede conjecture for some nonconvex bodies. Indeed, in 2003, Alex Iosevich, Nets Katz, and Terry Tao [**122**] proved that the Fuglede conjecture is true for all convex domains in $\mathbb{R}^2$. In 2021, this conjecture was proved for all convex domains (which must necessarily be polytopes by an additional simple argument) in the fundamental work of Nir Lev and Máté Matolcsi [**157**].

In a related direction, Sigrid Grepstad and Nir Lev [**93**] showed that for any bounded subset $S \subset \mathbb{R}^d$, if S multi-tiles by translations with a discrete set, then S has a Riesz basis of exponentials.

(11) We have seen that the zero set of the Fourier transform of a polytope is very important in that Theorem 4.6 gave us a necessary and sufficient condition for multi-tiling. But the zero set of the FT also gives more information, and an interesting application of the information content in the zero set is the Pompeiu problem. The Pompeiu problem is an ancient problem (defined in 1929 by Pompeiu) that asks the following: Which bodies $\mathcal{P} \in \mathbb{R}^d$ are uniquely characterized by the collection of their integrals over $\mathcal{P}$, and over all rigid motions of $\mathcal{P}$? An equivalent formulation is the following.

Question 4.33. Given a body $\mathcal{P}$ with nonempty interior, does there exist a nonzero continuous function f that allows for the the vanishing of all of the integrals

$$(4.59) \qquad \int_{M(\mathcal{P})} f(x)dx = 0,$$

taken over all rigid motions M, including translations?

A body $\mathcal{P} \subset \mathbb{R}^d$, for which the answer to the question above is affirmative, is said to have the Pompeiu property. Even for convex bodies $\mathcal{P}$, it is still an open problem in general dimension whether $\mathcal{P}$ has the Pompeiu property. It is known, by the work of Brown, Schreiber, and Taylor [**50**], that $\mathcal{P}$ has the Pompeiu property $\iff$ the collection of Fourier transforms $\hat{1}_{\sigma(\mathcal{P})}(z)$, taken over all rigid motions σ of $\mathbb{R}^d$, have a common zero z. It was also known that all polytopes have the Pompeiu property. Recently, in [**164**], Fabricio Machado and Sinai Robins showed that the zero set of the FT does not contain (almost all) circles whose center is the origin, and as a consequence we get a simple new proof that all polytopes have the "Pompeiu property".

Exercises

"Every problem has a creative solution."
  – Folklore

"Every problem has a solution that is simple, neat, and wrong."
  – Mark Twain

(1) Suppose that in $\mathbb{R}^2$ we are given a symmetric convex body K of area 4, which contains only the origin. Prove that K must tile $\mathbb{R}^2$ by translations.

(2) ♣ Given d-dimensional compact, convex sets $K, L \subset \mathbb{R}^d$, prove that $K + L$ is convex, and that $K - L$ is convex.

(3) Given d-dimensional compact convex sets $A, B \subset \mathbb{R}^d$, prove that
$$A \cap B \subseteq \tfrac{1}{2}A + \tfrac{1}{2}B \subseteq \mathrm{conv}(A \cup B),$$
and show that equality holds in either of the two containments $\iff$ $A = B$.

(4) It is easy to see that, essentially by definition, $A \subset \mathbb{R}^d$ is convex $\iff A + A \subset 2A$.
  (a) Given any convex subset $A \subset \mathbb{R}^d$, prove that
$$A + A = 2A.$$
  (b) Find a counterexample to show that the converse is false; in other words, it is false that $A + A = 2A \implies A$ is convex.

(5) ♣ Suppose initially that $C \subset \mathbb{R}^d$ is any set.
  (a) Show that

(4.60) $\dfrac{1}{2}C - \dfrac{1}{2}C = C \implies C$ is centrally symmetric.

  (b) Show that the following are equivalent:
      (i) C is centrally symmetric and convex.
      (ii) $\tfrac{1}{2}C - \tfrac{1}{2}C = C$.

(6) Find an example of a centrally symmetric set C that is not convex and satisfies
$$\frac{1}{2}C - \frac{1}{2}C \neq C.$$

(7) ♣ Given any convex sets $A, B \subset \mathbb{R}^d$, show that

$$\mathrm{conv}(A + B) = \mathrm{conv}\,A + \mathrm{conv}\,B.$$

(8) ♣ Suppose we have a triangle Δ whose vertices v_1, v_2, v_3 are integer points. Prove that the following properties are equivalent:
   (a) Δ has no other integer points inside or on its boundary (besides its vertices).
   (b) $Area(\Delta) = \frac{1}{2}$.
   (c) Δ is a unimodular triangle, which, in this case, means that $v_3 - v_1$ and $v_2 - v_1$ form a basis for $\mathbb{Z}^2$.
   (Hint: You might begin by "doubling" the triangle to form a parallelogram.)

(9) Show that in $\mathbb{R}^d$, an integer simplex Δ is unimodular $\iff$ vol $\Delta = \frac{1}{d!}$.

(10) In $\mathbb{R}^3$, find an integer simplex Δ that has no other integer points inside or on its boundary (other than its vertices of course), but such that Δ is not a unimodular simplex.

(11) ♣ Recalling the definition of the support of a function f from (1.14), show that:
   (a) Suppose that we are given two closed, convex bodies $A, B \subset \mathbb{R}^d$. Show that

$$\mathrm{support}(1_A * 1_B) = A + B,$$

   where the addition is the Minkowski addition of sets.
   (b) More generally, if two functions $f, g : \mathbb{R}^d \to \mathbb{C}$ are compactly supported, show that

$$\mathrm{support}(f * g) \subseteq \mathrm{clos}(\mathrm{support}(f) + \mathrm{support}(g)),$$

   the closure of the Minkowski sum of their individual supports.

Notes. For a vast generalization, see Theorem 3.53.

(12) Let $K \subset \mathbb{R}^d$ be a convex body, and let its $(d-1)$-dimensional boundary be denoted by B. Show that we have the equality of Minkowski sums

$$B + B = K + K.$$

(13) Prove that for any polytope $\mathcal{P}$, $\hat{1}_{\mathcal{P}}$ is not a Schwartz function.

(14) ♣ (hard-ish) Show that if K is any convex body, then $1_K * 1_{-K}$ is a nice function, in the sense of (3.57). In other words, show that the Poisson summation formula holds for the function

$$f(x) := (1_K * 1_{-K})(x).$$

(Hint: Use the Parseval identity, valid for functions $f \in L^2(\mathbb{R}^d)$. For this particular exercise, feel free to use the results of all of the later sections (though in general we refrain from such a "look ahead").)

(15) We first define the following sets recursively:

$$C_0 := [0, 1], \ C_1 := [0, \tfrac{1}{3}] \cup [\tfrac{2}{3}, 1], \ldots, C_n := \tfrac{1}{3}C_{n-1} \cup \{\tfrac{1}{3}C_{n-1} + \tfrac{2}{3}\},$$

and now the classical **Cantor set** is defined by their infinite intersection

$$\mathcal{C} := \cap_{n=0}^{\infty} C_n.$$

It is a standard fact (which you may assume here) that the Cantor set $\mathcal{C}$ is compact, uncountable, and has measure 0. Despite these facts, show that its difference body satisfies the somewhat surprising identity

$$\mathcal{C} - \mathcal{C} = [-1, 1].$$

Notes. There is a nice article about such difference sets written for undergraduates [145].

(16) Show that any regular hexagon in the plane cannot tile by translations with the integer lattice $\mathbb{Z}^2$.

(17) Show that the truncated octahedron, defined in Example 4.15, tiles $\mathbb{R}^3$ by using only translations with a lattice. Which lattice can you use for this tiling?

(18) Define $f(x) := a \sin x + b \cos x$ for constants $a, b \in \mathbb{R}$. Show that the maximum value of f is $\sqrt{a^2 + b^2}$ and occurs when $\tan x = \frac{a}{b}$.

(19) Find an example of a symmetric polygon $\mathcal{P} \subset \mathbb{R}^2$ that multi-tiles (nontrivially) with multiplicity $k = 5$.

Notes. A trivial multi-tiling for $\mathcal{P}$ is by definition a multi-tiling that uses $\mathcal{P}$, with some multiplicity $k > 1$, but such that there also exists a 1-tiling (classical) using the same $\mathcal{P}$ (but perhaps using a different lattice).

(20) Let $K \subset \mathbb{R}^d$ be a convex and centrally symmetric set. Show that

$$\frac{1}{2}K \cap \left(\frac{1}{2}K + n\right) \neq \phi \iff n \in K.$$

(21) Using Lemma 4.25, show that for the unit ball B and unit sphere S^{d-1} in $\mathbb{R}^d$, we have
   (a)

$$\text{vol } S^{d-1} = \begin{cases} \dfrac{(2\pi)^{\frac{d}{2}}}{2 \cdot 4 \cdot 6 \cdots (d-2)}, & \text{if } d \text{ is even}, \\[4mm] \dfrac{2(2\pi)^{\frac{d-1}{2}}}{1 \cdot 3 \cdot 5 \cdots (d-2)}, & \text{if } d \text{ is odd}, \end{cases}$$

(b)

$$\text{vol } B = \begin{cases} \dfrac{(2\pi)^{\frac{d}{2}}}{2\cdot4\cdot6\cdots d}, & \text{if } d \text{ is even,} \\[2mm] \dfrac{2(2\pi)^{\frac{d-1}{2}}}{1\cdot3\cdot5\cdots d}, & \text{if } d \text{ is odd.} \end{cases}$$

(22) ♣ Suppose we are given a prime $p \equiv 1 \pmod 4$. Prove that there exists an integer m such that $-1 \equiv m^2 \pmod p$.
(Hint: you can assume "Euler's little theorem"

$$a^{\phi(n)} \equiv 1 \pmod n, \text{ for all coprime integers } a, n,$$

where $\phi(n)$ is the Euler ϕ-function.)

(23) ♣ Here we use Seigel's theorem (Theorem 4.5) to give the following extension of Minkowski's classical theorem (Theorem 4.3), but for bodies K that are not necessarily symmetric, nor necessarily convex.
Namely, let K be any bounded subset of $\mathbb{R}^d$ with positive d-dimensional volume. Let $B := \frac{1}{2}K - \frac{1}{2}K$ be the symmetrized body of K (hence B is a centrally symmetric set containing the origin). Let $\mathcal{L}$ be a (full rank) lattice in $\mathbb{R}^d$. Prove the following statement:
If $\text{vol } K > 2^d(\det \mathcal{L})$, then B must contain a nonzero point of $\mathcal{L}$ in its interior.

Notes. We note that the positive conclusion of the existence of a nonzero integer point holds only for the symmetrized body B, with no guarantees for any integer points in K.

(24) ♣ Prove the elementary properties of the Γ function (namely parts (1), (2), and (3)) in Lemma 4.24.

(25) Using the Möbius μ-function, defined in Exercose (10), prove the following inversion formula for infinite series.

$$\text{If } g(x) := \sum_{n=1}^{\infty} f(nx), \text{ then } f(x) = \sum_{m=1}^{\infty} \mu(m)g(mx).$$

To make everything completely rigorous, can you formulate a sufficient convergence criterion for f in order to make the latter statement true?

(26) We recall that a polytope $\mathcal{P} \subset \mathbb{R}^d$ was called symmetric if there exists a vector $v \in \mathbb{R}^d$ such that $\mathcal{P} - v$ is symmetric about the origin.
Prove that the following are equivalent:
(a) $\mathcal{P}$ is symmetric.
(b) There exists a vector $v \in \mathbb{R}^d$ such that for all $\xi \in \mathbb{R}^d$ we have

$$\hat{1}_{\mathcal{P}}(\xi)\, e^{2\pi i \langle \xi, v \rangle} \in \mathbb{R}.$$

Chapter 5

An introduction to Euclidean lattices

"Less is more... more or less."
 – Ludwig Mies van der Rohe

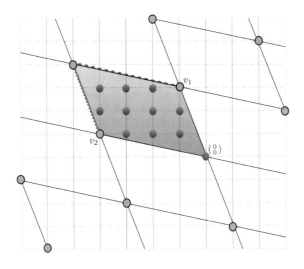

Figure 5.1. A fundamental parallelepiped (half-open) for a lattice $\mathcal{L}$, generated by the vectors v_1 and v_2.

1. Intuition

John H. Conway

We introduce Euclidean lattices here, which may be thought of intuitively as regularly spaced points in $\mathbb{R}^d$, with some hidden number-theoretic structure. Another intuitive way to think of lattices is that they are one of the most natural ways to **discretize Euclidean space**. A lattice in $\mathbb{R}^d$ is also the most natural extension of an infinite set of equally spaced points on the real line. In the real world, lattices come up very naturally when we study crystals, for example.

Perhaps it is not surprising that number theory comes in through study of the integer lattice $\mathbb{Z}^d$ and more general lattices, as they are a d-dimensional extension of the integers $\mathbb{Z}$. Moreover, whenever we study almost any periodic behavior, lattices naturally come up, essentially from the definition of **periodicity** in Euclidean space. John Conway and Neil Sloane have an encyclopedic treatment of lattices [**59**], and have contributed greatly to the development of the subject. And of course, wherever there are lattices, there are also Fourier series, as we saw in Chapter 3.

2. Introduction to lattices

For the sake of completeness, we recall again the definition of a general lattice, and in this chapter we will understand lattices in more detail.

Definition 5.1. A **lattice** is defined by the integer linear span of a fixed set of linearly independent vectors $\{v_1, \ldots, v_m\} \subset \mathbb{R}^d$:

$$(5.1) \qquad \mathcal{L} := \{n_1 v_1 + \cdots + n_m v_m \in \mathbb{R}^d \mid \text{all } n_j \in \mathbb{Z}\}.$$

The first thing we might notice is that, by equation (5.1), a lattice may also be written as follows:

$$(5.2) \quad \mathcal{L} := \left\{ \begin{pmatrix} | & | & \cdots & | \\ v_1 & v_2 & \cdots & v_m \\ | & | & \cdots & | \end{pmatrix} \begin{pmatrix} n_1 \\ \vdots \\ n_m \end{pmatrix} \;\middle|\; \begin{pmatrix} n_1 \\ \vdots \\ n_m \end{pmatrix} \in \mathbb{Z}^m \right\} := M(\mathbb{Z}^m),$$

where by definition, M is the $d \times m$ matrix whose columns are the vectors $v_1, \ldots, v_m$. This set of basis vectors $\{v_1, \ldots, v_m\}$ is called a **basis** for the lattice $\mathcal{L}$, and m is called the **rank** of the lattice $\mathcal{L}$. In this context, we also use the notation $\operatorname{rank}(\mathcal{L}) = m$.

We will call M a **basis matrix** for the lattice $\mathcal{L}$. But there are always infinitely many other bases for $\mathcal{L}$ as well, and Lemma 5.3 shows how they are related to each other.

Most of the time, we will be interested in **full-rank** lattices, which means that $m = d$; however, sometimes we will also be interested in lattices that have lower rank, and it is important to understand them. The **determinant** of a full-rank lattice $\mathcal{L} := M(\mathbb{Z}^d)$ is defined by

$$\det \mathcal{L} := |\det M|.$$

The determinant of a lattice measures how *coarseness* of the lattice—the larger the determinant, the coarser the lattice.

It is easy (and necessary) to prove that our definition of $\det \mathcal{L}$ is independent of the choice of basis matrix M, which is the content of Lemma 5.3. To better understand lattices, we need the **unimodular group**, which we write as $GL_d(\mathbb{Z})$, under matrix multiplication:

$$GL_d(\mathbb{Z}) := \left\{ M \;\middle|\; M \text{ is a } d \times d \text{ integer matrix, with } |\det M| = 1 \right\}.$$

The elements of $GL_d(\mathbb{Z})$ are called **unimodular matrices**. By definition, this group of matrices includes both the identity I and the negative identity $-I$. The easy fact that $GL_d(\mathbb{Z})$ really is a group under matrix multiplication is a standard and easy fact [183].

Example 5.2. Some typical elements of $GL_2(\mathbb{Z})$ are

$$S = \begin{pmatrix} 0 & 1 \\ -1 & 0 \end{pmatrix}, T := \begin{pmatrix} 1 & 1 \\ 1 & 0 \end{pmatrix}, -I := \begin{pmatrix} -1 & 0 \\ 0 & -1 \end{pmatrix}, \text{ and } \begin{pmatrix} 1 & n \\ 0 & 1 \end{pmatrix},$$

where $n \in \mathbb{Z}$. Interestingly, there is still no complete understanding of all of the subgroups of $GL_2(\mathbb{Z})$ (see Newman's book [183]). $\square$

Now, we suppose a lattice $\mathcal{L}$ is defined by two different basis matrices: $\mathcal{L} = M_1(\mathbb{Z}^d)$ and $\mathcal{L} = M_2(\mathbb{Z}^d)$. Is there a nice relationship between M_1 and M_2?

Lemma 5.3. *If a full-rank lattice $\mathcal{L} \subset \mathbb{R}^d$ is defined by two different basis matrices M_1 and M_2, then*

$$M_1 = M_2 U,$$

where $U \in \mathrm{GL_d}(\mathbb{Z})$, a unimodular matrix. In particular, $\det \mathcal{L}$ is independent of the choice of basis matrix M.

Proof. By hypothesis, we know that the columns of M_1, say, $v_1, \ldots, v_d$, form a basis of $\mathcal{L}$, and that the columns of M_2, say, $w_1, \ldots, w_d$, also form a basis of $\mathcal{L}$. So we can begin by writing each fixed basis vector v_j in terms of all the basis vectors w_k:

$$v_j = \sum_{k=1}^{d} c_{j,k} w_k,$$

for each $j = 1, \ldots, d$, and for some $c_{j,k} \in \mathbb{Z}$. We may collect all d of these identities into matrix form:

$$M_1 = M_2 C,$$

where C is the integer matrix whose entries are defined by the integer coefficients $c_{j,k}$ above. Conversely, we may also write each basis vector w_j in terms of the basis vectors v_k: $w_j = \sum_{k=1}^{d} d_{j,k} v_k$, for some $d_{j,k} \in \mathbb{Z}$, getting another matrix identity:

$$M_2 = M_1 D.$$

Altogether we have

$$M_1 = M_2 C = (M_1 D)C,$$

and since M_1^{-1} exists by assumption, we get $DC = I$, the identity matrix. Taking determinants, we see that

$$|\det D||\det C| = 1,$$

and since both C and D are integer matrices, they must belong to $\mathrm{GL_d}(\mathbb{Z})$ by definition. Finally, because a unimodular matrix U has $|\det U| = 1$, we see that any two basis M_1, M_2 matrices satisfy $|\det M_1| = |\det M_2|$. $\square$

Lemma 5.4. *The group of one-to-one onto linear transformations from $\mathbb{Z}^d$ to itself is equal to the unimodular group $GL_d(\mathbb{Z})$.* $\square$

Try to prove this yourself, and for more about the delicate internal structure of $GL_d(\mathbb{Z})$, even for $d = 2$, see Morris Newman's book [**183**].

Example 5.5. In $\mathbb{R}^1$ we have the integer lattice $\mathbb{Z}$, but we also have lattices of the form $r\mathbb{Z}$, for any real number r. It is easy to show that any lattice in $\mathbb{R}^1$ is of this latter type (Exercise (5)). For example, if $r = \sqrt{2}$, then all integer multiples of $\sqrt{2}$ form a 1-dimensional lattice. □

Example 5.6. In $\mathbb{R}^2$ consider the lattice $\mathcal{L}$ generated by the two integer vectors $v_1 := \left(\begin{smallmatrix}-1\\3\end{smallmatrix}\right)$ and $v_2 := \left(\begin{smallmatrix}-4\\1\end{smallmatrix}\right)$, drawn in Figure 5.1. A different choice of basis for the same lattice $\mathcal{L}$ is $\{\left(\begin{smallmatrix}-3\\-2\end{smallmatrix}\right), \left(\begin{smallmatrix}-8\\-9\end{smallmatrix}\right)\}$, drawn in Figure 5.2. We note that $\det \mathcal{L} = 11$, and, indeed, the areas of both half-open parallelepipeds equals 11. □

Suppose we have a lattice $\mathcal{L}$ with a basis $\{v_1, \ldots, v_m\}$. A **fundamental parallelepiped** for $\mathcal{L}$ is defined by

$$(5.3) \qquad \Pi := \{\lambda_1 v_1 + \cdots + \lambda_m v_m \mid \text{ all } 0 \leq \lambda_k < 1\},$$

also known as a **half-open parallelepiped**. Any lattice $\mathcal{L}$ has infinitely many fundamental parallelepipeds and it is a nice fact of life that they are all images of one another by the unimodular group (Exercise (17)).

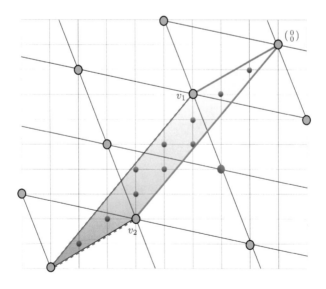

Figure 5.2. A second fundamental parallelepiped for the same lattice $\mathcal{L}$, as in Figure 5.1.

We have the pleasant property that Π tiles $\mathbb{R}^d$ by translations with vectors from $\mathcal{L}$ (with no overlaps). Let us make this intuition more precise in Lemma 5.7. We recall that for any real α,

$$\lfloor \alpha \rfloor \text{ is the greatest integer not exceeding } \alpha,$$

and

$$\{\alpha\} := \alpha - \lfloor \alpha \rfloor$$

is called the **fractional part** of α. Clearly $0 \le \{\alpha\} < 1$.

Lemma 5.7. *Suppose we are given a full rank lattice $\mathcal{L} \subset \mathbb{R}^d$, and a fundamental parallelepiped Π for $\mathcal{L}$, as in equation (5.3). Then any $x \in \mathbb{R}^d$ may be written uniquely as*

$$x = n + y$$

where $n \in \mathcal{L}$, and $y \in \Pi$. Consequently, Π tiles $\mathbb{R}^d$ by translations with $\mathcal{L}$.

Proof. We know that Π is formed by a basis for the lattice $\mathcal{L}$, and we can label the basis elements by $v_1, \ldots, v_d$. These d vectors also form a basis for $\mathbb{R}^d$, so, in particular, any $x \in \mathbb{R}^d$ may be written as

$$x = \sum_{j=1}^{d} \alpha_j v_j.$$

Writing each $\alpha_j := \lfloor \alpha_j \rfloor + \{\alpha_j\}$, we have

$$x = \sum_{j=1}^{d} \lfloor \alpha_j \rfloor v_j + \sum_{j=1}^{d} \{\alpha_j\} v_j := n + y,$$

where we have defined $n := \sum_{j=1}^{d} \lfloor \alpha_j \rfloor v_j$ and $y := \sum_{j=1}^{d} \{\alpha_j\} v_j$. Since $\lfloor \alpha_j \rfloor \in \mathbb{Z}$, we see that $n \in \mathcal{L}$. Since $0 \le \{\alpha_j\} < 1$, we see that $y \in \Pi$.

To prove uniqueness, suppose we are given $x := n_1 + y_1 = n_2 + y_2$, where $n_1, n_2 \in \mathcal{L}$ and $y_1, y_2 \in \Pi$. So, by definition, $y_1 = \sum_{j=1}^{d} \{\alpha_{j,1}\} v_j$ and $y_2 = \sum_{j=1}^{d} \{\alpha_{j,2}\} v_j$. Then $y_1 - y_2 = n_2 - n_1 \in \mathcal{L}$, which means that $\alpha_{j,1} - \alpha_{j,2} \in \mathbb{Z}$. But $0 \le \alpha_{j,1} < 1$ and $0 \le \alpha_{j,2} < 1$ implies that $\alpha_{j,1} - \alpha_{j,2} = 0$. Therefore, $y_1 = y_2$ and so $n_1 = n_2$. $\square$

It follows from the uniqueness statement of Lemma 5.7, for example, that the origin is the unique lattice point of $\mathcal{L}$ that lies in any fixed fundamental parallelepiped of $\mathcal{L}$.

How do we define the determinant of a "lower dimensional" lattice? Well, let us begin with a lattice $\mathcal{L} \subset \mathbb{R}^d$ of rank $r \le d$. We can observe how the squared lengths of vectors in $\mathcal{L}$ behave with respect to a given basis of $\mathcal{L}$:

$$(5.4) \quad \|x\|^2 = \left\langle \sum_{j=1}^{r} c_j v_j, \sum_{k=1}^{r} c_k v_k \right\rangle = \sum_{1 \leq j,k \leq r} c_j c_k \langle v_j, v_k \rangle := c^T M^T M c,$$

where $M^T M$ is an $r \times r$ matrix whose columns are basis vectors of $\mathcal{L}$. With this as motivation, we define

$$(5.5) \qquad\qquad \det \mathcal{L} := \sqrt{M^T M},$$

called the **determinant of the lattice** $\mathcal{L}$. This definition coincides, as it turns out, with the Lebesgue measure of any fundamental parallelepiped of $\mathcal{L}$ (Exercise (19)).

We may sometimes also use the following ubiquitous inequality of Hadamard, which gives a bound on the determinant of any invertible matrix, and hence on the determinant of a lattice. Hadamard's inequality can be intuitively visualized: if we keep all the lengths of the sides of a parallelepiped constant, and consider all possible parallelepipeds $\mathcal{P}$ with these fixed side lengths, then the volume of $\mathcal{P}$ is maximized exactly when $\mathcal{P}$ is rectangular.

Theorem 5.8 (Hadamard's inequality). *Given a nonsingular matrix M over the reals, whose column vectors are $v_1, \ldots, v_d$, we have*

$$|\det M| \leq \|v_1\| \|v_2\| \cdots \|v_d\|,$$

with equality if and only if all of the v_k are pairwise orthogonal.

Proof. We use the following matrix decomposition from linear algebra: $M = QR$, where Q is an orthogonal matrix, $R := [r_{i,j}]$ is an upper-triangular matrix, and $r_{kk} > 0$ (this decomposition is a well-known consequence of the Gram–Schmidt process applied to the columns of M). So now we know that $|\det Q| = 1$ and $\det R = \prod_{k=1}^{d} r_{kk}$, and it follows that

$$|\det M| = |\det Q \det R| = \det R = \prod_{k=1}^{d} r_{kk}.$$

Let us label the columns of Q by Q_k, and the columns of R by R_k. We now consider the matrix $M^T M = R^T Q^T Q R = R^T R$. Comparing the diagonal elements on both sides of $M^T M = R^T R$, we see that $\|Q_k\|^2 = \|R_K\|^2$. But we also have $\|R_K\|^2 \geq r_{kk}^2$, so that $\|Q_k\| \geq r_{kk}$. Altogether we have

$$(5.6) \qquad\qquad |\det M| = \prod_{k=1}^{d} r_{kk} \leq \prod_{k=1}^{d} \|Q_k\|.$$

The case of equality occurs if and only if $\|R_K\|^2 = r_{kk}^2$ for all $1 \leq k \leq d$, and this case of equality would mean that R is a diagonal matrix. Thus, we have equality in inequality (5.6) if and only if $M^T M = R^T R$ is a diagonal matrix, which means that the columns of M are mutually orthogonal. $\qquad\qquad\qquad\qquad\qquad\qquad\qquad\qquad\qquad\qquad\qquad\qquad\qquad\quad\square$

3. Sublattices

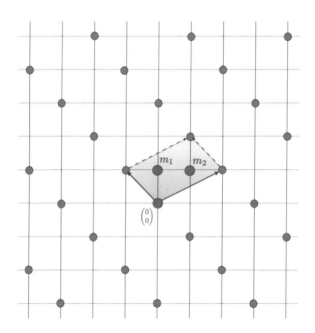

Figure 5.3. The sublattice $\mathcal{L}_0 \subset \mathbb{Z}^2$ of Example 5.9, drawn with the thickened green lattice points.

Given two lattices, $\mathcal{L}_0 \subset \mathbb{R}^d$ and $\mathcal{L} \subset \mathbb{R}^d$, such that $\mathcal{L}_0 \subseteq \mathcal{L}$, we say that $\mathcal{L}_0$ **is a sublattice of** $\mathcal{L}$. Sublattices that have the same rank are rather interesting, and extremely useful in applications. So we will usually focus on sublattices $\mathcal{L}_0 \subseteq \mathcal{L}$ such that $\text{rank}(\mathcal{L}) = \text{rank}(\mathcal{L}_0)$. In this context we sometimes call $\mathcal{L}_0$ a **coarser lattice**, and $\mathcal{L}$ a **finer lattice**. Given a sublattice $\mathcal{L}_0$ of $\mathcal{L}$, both of the same rank, a crucial idea is to think of all of the translates of $\mathcal{L}_0$ by an element of the finer lattice $\mathcal{L}$:

$$(5.7) \qquad \mathcal{L}/\mathcal{L}_0 := \{\mathcal{L}_0 + m \mid m \in \mathcal{L}\}.$$

Each such translate $\mathcal{L}_0 + m$ is called a **coset** of $\mathcal{L}_0$ in $\mathcal{L}$. The collection $\mathcal{L}/\mathcal{L}_0$ of all of these cosets is called a **quotient group**, and as we will see shortly, this is a very interesting finite set.

Example 5.9. Figure 5.3 shows a sublattice $\mathcal{L}_0$ of the integer lattice $\mathbb{Z}^2$ with a fundamental parallelepiped Π that is generated by the two vectors $\begin{pmatrix} -1 \\ 1 \end{pmatrix}$ and $\begin{pmatrix} 2 \\ 1 \end{pmatrix}$. Here, area$(\Pi) = 3$, and there are exactly 3 cosets of $\mathcal{L}_0$ in $\mathbb{Z}^2$ (not a coincidence, as we will see in Theorem 5.11). These 3 cosets are the trivial coset $\mathcal{L}_0$ and the two nontrivial cosets $\mathcal{L}_0 + m_1$ and $\mathcal{L}_0 + m_2$, drawn in Figure 5.4 with thickened blue points.   □

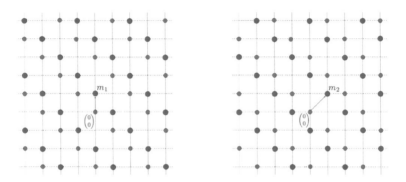

Figure 5.4. Left: the thickened blue points represent the nontrivial coset $\mathcal{L}_0 + m_1$ of the sublattice $\mathcal{L}_0$. Right: the thickened blue points represent the nontrivial coset $\mathcal{L}_0 + m_2$ of the sublattice $\mathcal{L}_0$. (see Example 5.9).

As an example of a lower-dimensional sublattice, Figure 5.5 shows a rank 1 sublattice of the integer lattice $\mathbb{Z}^2$ together with its determinant.

To better understand sublattices and some of their many subtleties, it is useful to first understand how many fundamental parallelpipeds of a lattice $\mathcal{L}$ are contained in a large ball asymptotically. Here we follow Barvinok's geometric approach [**17**, p. 287]. We define

$$B_\rho := \{x \in \mathbb{R}^d \mid \|x\| \leq \rho\} \subset \mathbb{R}^d,$$

the ball of radius ρ, centered at the origin.

Theorem 5.10. *Let $\mathcal{L} \subseteq \mathbb{R}^d$ be a full-rank lattice. Then:*

(1)

$$\lim_{\rho \to \infty} \frac{|\mathcal{L} \cap B_\rho|}{\text{vol } B_\rho} = \frac{1}{\det \mathcal{L}}.$$

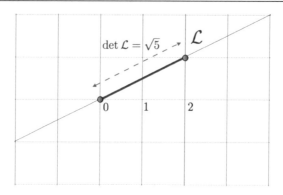

Figure 5.5. A sublattice $\mathcal{L} \subset \mathbb{Z}^2$ of rank 1, which has just one basis vector. Here, $\mathcal{L}$ has a 1-dimensional fundamental parallelepiped, showing that $\det \mathcal{L} = \sqrt{v^T v} = \sqrt{5}$, consistent with equation (5.5).

(2) *In general, for any $x \in \mathbb{R}^d$ we have*

$$\lim_{\rho \to \infty} \frac{\left| (\mathcal{L} + x) \cap B_\rho \right|}{\operatorname{vol} B_\rho} = \frac{1}{\det \mathcal{L}}.$$

Figure 5.6 may be helpful to the reader while digesting the proof.

Proof. We let Π be a fundamental parallelepiped of $\mathcal{L}$. Considering the set of all lattice points $n \in \mathcal{L}$ that are contained in the ball B_ρ of radius ρ, we may use each of these points to translate Π:

$$A_\rho := \bigcup_{n \in \mathcal{L} \cap B_\rho} (\Pi + n).$$

If we associate to each such lattice point $n \in \mathcal{L}$ the unique translate of Π that lies to its northeast direction, then we have the collection of fundamental parallelepipeds that are drawn with the shaded green squares in Figure 5.6. By Lemma 5.7 we know that the lattice translates of Π tile $\mathbb{R}^d$, so we have

$$\operatorname{vol} A_\rho = \left| \mathcal{L} \cap B_\rho \right| \operatorname{vol} \Pi.$$

Because Π is bounded, it is contained in some ball B_α, with radius $\alpha > 0$. For the construction of the proof, we will think of a "band" of diameter 4α placed around the perimeter of B_ρ, where the boundary of this band consists of the two large orange circles in Figure 5.6. While it is true that some portion of the translated copies of Π in $\bigcup_{n \in \mathcal{L} \cap B_\rho} (\Pi + n)$ leak out of the ball B_ρ, we can nevertheless cover them as well by taking the Minkowski sum of B_ρ with $B_{2\alpha}$, obtaining $B_{r+2\alpha}$. Therefore $A_\rho \subset B_{\rho+2\alpha}$.

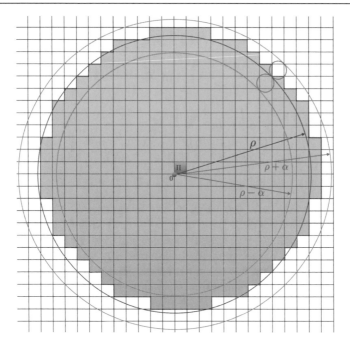

Figure 5.6. Here we use the integer lattice $\mathbb{Z}^2$ to illustrate the proof of Theorem 5.10. The shaded squares represent the number of integer points in a ball of radius ρ after identifying each integer point with its northeast square.

To see the inclusion $B_{\rho-2\alpha} \subset A_\rho$, we note that by using Lemma 5.7 again, we may conclude that each point of $B_{\rho-2\alpha}$ is contained in some translate $\Pi + n$, with $n \in B_\rho \cap \mathcal{L}$. Putting everything together, we therefore have

$$\operatorname{vol} B_{\rho-2\alpha} \leq \operatorname{vol} A_\rho = |\mathcal{L} \cap B_\rho| \operatorname{vol} \Pi \leq \operatorname{vol} B_{\rho+2\alpha},$$

which we will rewrite as

(5.8) $$\frac{\operatorname{vol} B_{\rho-2\alpha}}{\operatorname{vol} B_\rho} \leq \frac{|\mathcal{L} \cap B_\rho|}{\operatorname{vol} B_\rho} \operatorname{vol} \Pi \leq \frac{\operatorname{vol} B_{\rho+2\alpha}}{\operatorname{vol} B_\rho}.$$

So if we prove that $\lim_{\rho \to \infty} \frac{\operatorname{vol} B_{\rho-2\alpha}}{\operatorname{vol} B_\rho} = \lim_{\rho \to \infty} \frac{\operatorname{vol} B_{\rho+2\alpha}}{\operatorname{vol} B_\rho} = 1$, then by (5.8) we will have proved part (1). Recalling from (4.45) that $\operatorname{vol} B_\rho =$

$\dfrac{\pi^{\frac{d}{2}}}{\Gamma(\frac{d}{2}+1)}\rho^d$, we can finish the computation:

$$(5.9) \qquad \lim_{\rho\to\infty}\frac{\operatorname{vol}B_{\rho-2\alpha}}{\operatorname{vol}B_\rho} = \lim_{\rho\to\infty}\frac{(\rho-2\alpha)^d}{\rho^d} = 1,$$

and, similarly, $\lim_{\rho\to\infty}\frac{\operatorname{vol}B_{\rho+2\alpha}}{\operatorname{vol}B_\rho} = 1$.

To prove part (2), we first show that the following set inclusions hold:

$$(5.10) \qquad x + \left(\mathcal{L}\cap B_{\rho-\|x\|}\right) \subset (\mathcal{L}+x)\cap B_\rho \subset x + \left(\mathcal{L}\cap B_{\rho+\|x\|}\right).$$

To prove the left-hand inclusion, let $y = x + z$ with $z \in \mathcal{L}\cap B_{\rho-\|x\|}$. Then $\|y\| \le \|x\| + \|z\| \le \|x\| + (\rho - \|x\|) = \rho$, giving us $y \in B_\rho$. Also, $z \in \mathcal{L} \implies y \in \mathcal{L} + x$, which, together with $y \in B_\rho$ proves the first inclusion. To prove the second inclusion in (5.10), let $y \in (\mathcal{L}+x)\cap B_\rho$, so that by assumption $y = x + n$ with $n \in \mathcal{L}$ and $\|y\| \le \rho$. It remains to show that $\|n\| \le \rho + \|x\|$, but this follows from $\rho \ge \|y\| \ge \|n\| - \|x\|$.

From (5.10), we have

$$\left|\mathcal{L}\cap B_{\rho-\|x\|}\right| \le \left|(\mathcal{L}+x)\cap B_\rho\right| \le \left|\mathcal{L}\cap\left(B_{\rho+\|x\|}\right)\right|,$$

which we will rewrite as

$$\frac{\left|\mathcal{L}\cap B_{\rho-\|x\|}\right|}{\operatorname{vol}B_{\rho-\|x\|}}\frac{\operatorname{vol}B_{\rho-\|x\|}}{\operatorname{vol}B_\rho} \le \frac{\left|(\mathcal{L}+x)\cap B_\rho\right|}{\operatorname{vol}B_\rho} \le \frac{\left|\mathcal{L}\cap B_{\rho+\|x\|}\right|}{\operatorname{vol}B_{\rho+\|x\|}}\frac{\operatorname{vol}B_{\rho+\|x\|}}{\operatorname{vol}B_\rho}.$$

From part (1), we know that

$$\lim_{\rho\to\infty}\frac{\left|\mathcal{L}\cap B_{\rho-\|x\|}\right|}{\operatorname{vol}B_{\rho-\|x\|}} = \frac{1}{\det\mathcal{L}} = \lim_{\rho\to\infty}\frac{\left|\mathcal{L}\cap B_{\rho+\|x\|}\right|}{\operatorname{vol}B_{\rho+\|x\|}},$$

and from (5.9) we know that

$$\lim_{\rho\to\infty}\frac{\operatorname{vol}B_{\rho-\|x\|}}{\operatorname{vol}B_\rho} = 1 = \lim_{\rho\to\infty}\frac{\operatorname{vol}B_{\rho+\|x\|}}{\operatorname{vol}B_\rho},$$

finishing the proof. $\qquad\square$

Theorem 5.11. *Let $\mathcal{L}_0 \subseteq \mathcal{L}$ be any two lattices of the same rank, so, by definition, $\mathcal{L}_0$ is a sublattice of $\mathcal{L}$. Let Π be any fundamental parallelepiped for $\mathcal{L}_0$. Then:*

(1) *$\Pi\cap\mathcal{L}$ contains each coset representative of $\mathcal{L}/\mathcal{L}_0$ exactly once.*

(2) $\frac{\det \mathcal{L}_0}{\det \mathcal{L}}$ is a positive integer, and is equal to the number of cosets of $\mathcal{L}_0$ in $\mathcal{L}$. In other words, we have a finite abelian group $\mathcal{L}/\mathcal{L}_0$, whose size is

$$|\mathcal{L}/\mathcal{L}_0| = \frac{\det \mathcal{L}_0}{\det \mathcal{L}}.$$

(3) Consequently, $|\Pi \cap \mathcal{L}| = \frac{\det \mathcal{L}_0}{\det \mathcal{L}}$.

Proof. To prove part (1), we define $f : \Pi \cap \mathcal{L} \to \mathcal{L}/\mathcal{L}_0$ by $f(n) = \mathcal{L}_0 + n$. We must show that f is bijective. To show f is surjective, suppose that we are given any coset $\mathcal{L}_0 + n$. By Lemma 5.7, we know that $n = l_0 + x$, where $l_0 \in \mathcal{L}_0$ and $x \in \Pi$. Now $x = n - l_0$, and both $n, l_0 \in \mathcal{L}$ ($l_0 \in \mathcal{L}_0 \subset \mathcal{L}$), implying that $x \in \mathcal{L}$. This proves surjectivity because $x \in \Pi \cap \mathcal{L}$ and $f(x) := \mathcal{L}_0 + x = \mathcal{L}_0 + n - l_0 = \mathcal{L}_0 + n$.

For the injectivity of f, suppose that $f(n_1) = f(n_2)$ where $n_1, n_2 \in \Pi \cap \mathcal{L}$. Then $\mathcal{L}_0 + n_1 = \mathcal{L}_0 + n_2$ so that $n_1 - n_2 \in \mathcal{L}_0$. But the only element in Π that lies in $\mathcal{L}_0$ is the origin. Therefore $n_1 - n_2 = 0$.

To prove part (2), which is more interesting, we begin by letting $C := \Pi \cap \mathcal{L}$, a finite set of coset representatives for $\mathcal{L}/\mathcal{L}_0$. So, by definition, we have $\mathcal{L} = \bigcup_{x \in C} (\mathcal{L}_0 + x)$. Intersecting both sides of the latter identity with a ball B_ρ of radius ρ, it follows from the disjointness of the latter union that

(5.11) $$|\mathcal{L} \cap B_\rho| = \sum_{x \in C} |(\mathcal{L}_0 + x) \cap B_\rho|.$$

From Theorem 5.10, we know that

$$\lim_{\rho \to \infty} \frac{|\mathcal{L} \cap B_\rho|}{\text{vol } B_\rho} = \frac{1}{\det \mathcal{L}} \text{ and } \lim_{\rho \to \infty} \frac{|(\mathcal{L}_0 + x) \cap B_\rho|}{\text{vol } B_\rho} = \frac{1}{\det \mathcal{L}_0}$$

for any $x \in \mathbb{R}^d$. Dividing both sides of (5.11) by vol B_ρ and letting $\rho \to \infty$, we get

(5.12) $$\frac{1}{\det \mathcal{L}} = \frac{1}{\det \mathcal{L}_0} \sum_{x \in C} 1 = \frac{1}{\det \mathcal{L}_0} |\Pi \cap \mathcal{L}|,$$

which finished the proofs of Theorem 5.11(2) and (3). $\square$

Example 5.12. Let $\mathcal{L} := \mathbb{Z}^d$ and $\mathcal{L}_0 := 2\mathbb{Z}^d$, the sublattice consisting of vectors all of whose coordinates are even integers. So $\mathcal{L}_0 \subset \mathcal{L}$, and the quotient group $\mathcal{L}/\mathcal{L}_0$ consists of the cosets $\{2\mathbb{Z}^d + n \mid n \in \mathbb{Z}^d\}$. It is (almost) obvious that the number of elements of the latter set is exactly

2^d, and this observation is also a special case of Theorem 5.11:

(5.13) $$\mathbb{Z}^d / 2\mathbb{Z}^d = \frac{\det 2\mathbb{Z}^d}{\det \mathbb{Z}^d} = 2^d.$$

We may also think of this quotient group $\mathbb{Z}^d / 2\mathbb{Z}^d$ as the discrete unit cube, namely $\{0, 1\}^d$, a common object in theoretical computer science, for example. $\qquad\square$

4. Discrete subgroups: An alternate definition of a lattice

The goal here is to give another useful way to define a lattice. The reader does not need any background in group theory, because the ideas here are self-contained, given some background in basic linear algebra.

Definition 5.13. We define a **discrete subgroup** of $\mathbb{R}^d$ as a set $S \subset \mathbb{R}^d$, together with the operation of vector addition between all of its elements, which enjoys the following two properties.

(1) **[The subgroup property].** If $x, y \in S$, then $x - y \in S$.
(2) **[The discrete property].** There exists a positive real number $\delta > 0$, such that the distance between any two distinct points of S is at least δ.

In particular, it follows from Definition 5.13(1) that the zero vector must be in S, because for any $x \in S$, it must be the case that $x - x \in S$. The distance function that we alluded to in Definition 5.13(2) is the usual Euclidean distance function, which we denote here by

$$\|x - y\|_2 := \sqrt{\sum_{k=1}^{d} (x_k - y_k)^2}.$$

Example 5.14. The lattice $\mathbb{Z}^d$ is a discrete subgroup of $\mathbb{R}^d$. In dimension 1, the lattice $r\mathbb{Z}$ is a discrete subgroup of $\mathbb{R}$, for any fixed $r > 0$. Can we think of discrete subgroups that are not lattices? The answer is given by Lemma 5.15. $\qquad\square$

The magic here is the following useful way of going back and forth between this new notion of a discrete subgroup of $\mathbb{R}^d$, and equation (5.1) of a lattice. alternately, the idea of using Definition 5.13, as opposed to equation (5.1) of a lattice is that it gives us a **basis-free** way of discovering and proving facts about lattices.

Lemma 5.15. $\mathcal{L} \subset \mathbb{R}^d$ *is a lattice* $\iff$ $\mathcal{L}$ *is a discrete subgroup of* $\mathbb{R}^d$. *(For a proof, see* [98].) $\qquad\square$

Example 5.16. Given any two lattices $\mathcal{L}_1, \mathcal{L}_2 \subset \mathbb{R}^d$, let us show that $S := \mathcal{L}_1 \cap \mathcal{L}_2$ is also a lattice. First, any lattice contains the zero vector, and it may be the case that their intersection consists of only the zero vector. For any vectors $x, y \in S$, we also have $x, y \in \mathcal{L}_1$, and $x, y \in \mathcal{L}_2$, hence by the subgroup property of $\mathcal{L}_1$ and of $\mathcal{L}_2$, we know that both $x - y \in \mathcal{L}_1$ and $x - y \in \mathcal{L}_2$. In other words, $x - y \in \mathcal{L}_1 \cap \mathcal{L}_2 := S$. To see why the discrete property of Definition 5.13 holds here, we just notice that since $x - y \in \mathcal{L}_1$, we already know that $|x - y| > \delta_1$ for some $\delta_1 > 0$; similarly, because $x - y \in \mathcal{L}_2$, we know that $|x - y| > \delta_2$ for some $\delta_2 > 0$. So we let $\delta := \min(\delta_1, \delta_2)$, and we have shown that S is a discrete subgroup of $\mathbb{R}^d$. By Lemma 5.15, we see that S is a lattice.

If we had used equation (5.1) of a lattice to show that S is indeed a lattice, it would require us to work with bases, and this proof would be longer and less transparent. $\qquad\square$

Example 5.17. Consider the following discrete set of points in $\mathbb{R}^d$:

$$A_{d-1} := \left\{ x \in \mathbb{Z}^d \mid \sum_{k=1}^d x_k = 0 \right\},$$

for any $d \geq 2$, as depicted in Figure 5.7. Is A_d a lattice? Using the equation (5.1) of a lattice, it is not obvious that A_d is a lattice because we would have to exhibit a basis, but it turns out that the following set of vectors may be shown to be a basis $\{e_2 - e_1, e_3 - e_1, \cdots e_d - e_1\}$, and hence A_d is a sublattice of $\mathbb{Z}^d$, of rank $d - 1$ (Exercise (13)).

Just for fun, we will use Lemma 5.15 to show that A_d is indeed a lattice. To verify the subgroup property of Definition 5.13(1), suppose that $x, y \in A_d$. Then by definition we have $\sum_{k=1}^d x_k = 0$ and $\sum_{k=1}^d y_k = 0$. So $\sum_{k=1}^d (x_k - y_k) = 0$, implying that $x - y \in A_d$.

To verify the discrete property of Definition 5.13(2), suppose we are given two distinct points $x, y \in A_d$. We can first compute their "cab metric" distance function; in other words, the L^1-norm defined by

$$\|x - y\|_1 := |x_1 - y_1| + \cdots + |x_d - y_d|.$$

By assumption, there is at least one coordinate where x and y differ, say, the kth coordinate. Then $\|x - y\|_1 := |x_1 - y_1| + \cdots + |x_d - y_d| \geq 1$ because all of the coordinates are integers, and $x_k \neq y_k$ by assumption. Since the L^1-norm and the L^2-norm are only off by $\sqrt{d}$ (by Exercise (1)),

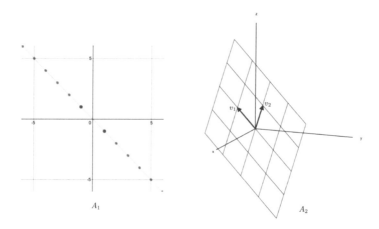

Figure 5.7. The lattice A_1, and the lattice A_2, with basis $\{v_1, v_2\}$.

we have

$$\sqrt{d}\|x - y\|_2 \geq \|x - y\|_1 \geq 1,$$

so Definition 5.13(2) is satisfied with $\delta := \frac{1}{\sqrt{d}}$, and we have shown that A_d is a lattice. $\qquad\square$

We note that the lattices A_d defined in Example 5.17 are very important in many fields of mathematics, including Lie algebras (root lattices), combinatorial geometry, and number theory.

5. Lattices defined by congruences

In this section we develop some of the theory in a concrete manner. A classic example of a lattice defined by an auxiliary algebraic construction is the following. Suppose we are given a constant integer vector $(c_1, \ldots, c_d) \in \mathbb{Z}^d$, where we further assume that $\gcd(c_1, \ldots, c_d) = 1$. Let

$$(5.14) \qquad C := \{x \in \mathbb{Z}^d \mid c_1 x_1 + \cdots + c_d x_d \equiv 0 \mod N\},$$

where N is a fixed positive integer.

Is C a lattice? Indeed, we can see that C is a lattice by first checking Definition 5.13(1). For any $x, y \in C$, we have $c_1 x_1 + \cdots + c_d x_d \equiv 0 \mod N$ and $c_1 y_1 + \cdots + c_d y_d \equiv 0 \mod N$. Subtracting these two congruences gives us $c_1(x_1 - y_1) + \cdots + c_d(x_d - y_d) \equiv 0 \mod N$, so that $x - y \in C$. The verification of Definition 5.13(2) and its logic, if left to the reader, is similar to Example 5.17.

There is even a simple formula for the volume of a fundamental parallelepiped for C:

$$(5.15) \qquad\qquad \det C = N,$$

as we prove in Lemma 5.21. But, perhaps, we can solve an easier problem first. Consider the **discrete hyperplane** defined by

$$H := \left\{x \in \mathbb{Z}^d \mid c_1 x_1 + \cdots + c_d x_d = 0\right\}.$$

Is H a lattice? We claim that H itself is indeed a sublattice of $\mathbb{Z}^d$ and has rank $d - 1$. Since this verification is quite similar to the arguments above, we leave this as Exercise (24).

The fundamental parallelepiped (which is $(d-1)$-dimensional) of H also has a wonderful formula, as follows. First, we recall a general fact (from calculus/analytic geometry) about hyperplanes, namely that the distance δ between any two parallel hyperplanes $c_1 x_1 + \cdots + c_d x_d = k_1$ and $c_1 x_1 + \cdots + c_d x_d = k_2$ is given by

$$(5.16) \qquad\qquad \delta = \frac{|k_1 - k_2|}{\sqrt{c_1^2 + \cdots + c_d^2}}.$$

See Exercise (4).

Lemma 5.18. *For any lattice defined by a discrete hyperplane*

$$H := \left\{x \in \mathbb{Z}^d \mid c_1 x_1 + \cdots + c_d x_d = 0\right\}$$

with $\gcd(c_1, \ldots, c_d) = 1$, *we have*

$$(5.17) \qquad\qquad \det H = \sqrt{c_1^2 + \cdots + c_d^2}.$$

Proof. We first fix a basis $\{v_1, \ldots, v_{d-1}\}$ for the $(d-1)$-dimensional sublattice defined by $H := \left\{x \in \mathbb{Z}^d \mid c_1 x_1 + \cdots + c_d x_d = 0\right\}$. We adjoin to this basis one new vector, namely, any integer vector w that translates H to its "hyperplane companion" $H + w$, which we define by

$$H + w := \left\{x \in \mathbb{Z}^d \mid c_1 x_1 + \cdots + c_d x_d = 1\right\}.$$

It iss easy—and fun—to see that there are no integer points strictly between these two hyperplanes H and $H + w$ (Exercise (25)), and so the parallelepiped $\mathcal{P}$ formed by the edge vectors $v_1, \ldots, v_{d-1}, w$ is a fundamental domain for $\mathbb{Z}^d$, hence has volume 1.

On the other hand, we may also calculate the volume of $\mathcal{P}$ by multiplying the volume of its base times its height using (5.16):

$$(5.18) \qquad 1 = \text{vol}\,\mathcal{P} = (\text{volume of the base of }\mathcal{P})(\text{height of }\mathcal{P})$$

$$(5.19) \qquad = (\det H)\cdot\delta$$

$$(5.20) \qquad = (\det H)\frac{1}{\sqrt{c_1^2 + \cdots + c_d^2}},$$

and so $\det H = \sqrt{c_1^2 + \cdots + c_d^2}$. □

It follows directly from equation (5.14) of C that we may write the lattice C as a countable, disjoint union of translates of H:

$$(5.21) \quad C := \{x \in \mathbb{Z}^d \mid c_1 x_1 + \cdots + c_d x_d = kN, \text{ where } k = 1, 2, 3, \ldots\}.$$

To be concrete, let us work out some examples.

Example 5.19. Using Lemma 5.18, we can easily compute the determinant of the A_d lattice from Example 5.17:

$$\det A_d = \sqrt{1 + 1 + \cdots + 1} = \sqrt{d}.$$ □

Example 5.20. As in Figure 5.8, consider the set of all integer points $(m, n) \in \mathbb{R}^2$ that satisfy

$$2m + 3n \equiv 0 \quad \text{mod } 4.$$

In this case, the related hyperplane is the line $2x + 3y = 0$ and the solutions to the latter congruence may be thought of as a union of discrete lines:

$$C = \left\{\begin{pmatrix} x \\ y \end{pmatrix} \in \mathbb{Z}^2 \mid 2x + 3y = 4k, \text{ and } k \in \mathbb{Z}\right\}.$$

In other words, our lattice C, a special case of (5.14), can, in this case, be visualized in Figure 5.8 as a disjoint union of discrete lines. If we denote the distance between any two of these adjacent discrete lines by δ, then by using (5.16) we have

$$(5.22) \qquad\qquad \delta = \frac{4}{\sqrt{3^2 + 2^2}}.$$

Finally, the determinant of our lattice C here is the area of the shaded parallelepiped:

$$(5.23) \qquad\qquad \det C = \delta\sqrt{3^2 + 2^2} = 4.$$ □

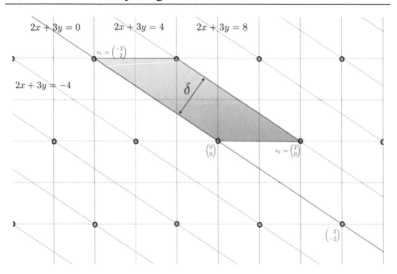

Figure 5.8. The lattice of Example 5.20.

Eager to prove the volume relation $\det C = N$, we can use the ideas of Example 5.20 as a springboard for this generalization. Indeed, Example 5.20 and the proof of Lemma 5.18 both suggest that we should compute the volume of a fundamental parallelepiped $\mathcal{P}$ for the lattice C (as opposed to the lattice $\mathbb{Z}^d$) by using a fundamental domain for its base, and then by multiplying its volume by the height of $\mathcal{P}$.

Lemma 5.21. *Given a constant integer vector* $(c_1, \dots, c_d) \in \mathbb{Z}^d$, *with* $\gcd(c_1, \dots, c_d) = 1$, *let*

$$(5.24) \qquad C := \left\{ x \in \mathbb{Z}^d \mid c_1 x_1 + \cdots + c_d x_d \equiv 0 \quad \mathrm{mod} \ N \right\},$$

where N is a fixed positive integer. Then C is a lattice, and

$$\det C = N.$$

Proof. We fix a basis $\{v_1, \dots, v_{d-1}\}$ for the $(d-1)$-dimensional sublattice defined by $H := \left\{ x \in \mathbb{Z}^d \mid c_1 x_1 + \cdots + c_d x_d = 0 \right\}$, and we adjoin to this basis one new vector, namely, any integer vector w that translates H to its nearest discrete hyperplane companion

$$H + w := \left\{ x \in \mathbb{Z}^d \mid c_1 x_1 + \cdots + c_d x_d = N \right\}.$$

Together, the set of vectors $\{v_1, \dots, v_{d-1}, w\}$ form the edge vectors of a fundamental parallelepiped $\mathcal{P}$ for the lattice C, whose height δ is the distance between these two parallel hyperplanes H and $H + w$. Using (5.16), we can may calculate the volume of $\mathcal{P}$ (which is, by definition, equal to $\det C$) by multiplying the volume of its "base" times its "height":

$$(5.25) \qquad \det C = (\text{volume of the base of } \mathcal{P})(\text{height of } \mathcal{P}) = (\det H)\delta$$

$$(5.26) \qquad = (\det H)\frac{N}{\sqrt{c_1^2 + \cdots + c_d^2}} = N,$$

using the fact that $\det H = \sqrt{c_1^2 + \cdots + c_d^2}$ from Lemma 5.18. $\square$

6. The Gram matrix

There is another very natural matrix that we may use to study lattices, which we can motivate as follows. Suppose we are given any basis for a lattice $\mathcal{L} \subset \mathbb{R}^d$, say $\beta := \{v_1, \ldots, v_r\}$, where $1 \leq r \leq d$. By definition $\mathcal{L} = M(\mathbb{Z}^d)$, and $\text{rank}(\mathcal{L}) = r$, where the columns of M are defined by the basis vectors from β, and so M is a $d \times r$ matrix. We can therefore represent any $x \in \mathbb{R}^d$ uniquely in terms of the basis β like this:

$$(5.27) \qquad x = c_1 v_1 + \cdots + c_r v_r,$$

and the squared length of x is

$$(5.28) \quad \|x\|^2 = \left\langle \sum_{j=1}^{r} c_j v_j, \sum_{k=1}^{r} c_k v_k \right\rangle = \sum_{1 \leq j,k \leq r} c_j c_k \langle v_j, v_k \rangle := c^T M^T M c,$$

where $c := (c_1, \ldots, c_r)^T$ is the coefficient vector defined by (5.27).

It is therefore very natural to focus on the matrix $M^T M$, whose entries are the inner products $\langle v_j, v_k \rangle$ of all the basis vectors of the lattice $\mathcal{L}$, so we define

$$G := M^T M,$$

a **Gram matrix** for $\mathcal{L}$. It is clear from the computation in (5.28) that G is positive definite. Although G does depend on which basis of $\mathcal{L}$ we choose, it is an elementary fact that $\det G$ is independent of the basis of $\mathcal{L}$.

Because we are always feeling the urge to learn more linear algebra, we would like to see why any real symmetric matrix B is the Gram matrix of some set of vectors. To see this, we apply the spectral theorem: $B = PDP^T$, for some orthogonal matrix P and a diagonal matrix D with nonnegative diagonal elements. So we can write $B = (P\sqrt{D})(P\sqrt{D})^T :=$ $M^T M$, where we defined the matrix $M := (P\sqrt{D})^T$, so that the columns of M are the vectors whose corresponding dot products form the symmetric matrix B, and now B is a Gram matrix.

To review some more linear algebra, suppose we are given a real symmetric matrix A. We recall that such a matrix is called **positive definite** if, in addition, we have the positivity condition

$$x^T A x > 0$$

for all $x \in \mathbb{R}^d$. Equivalently, all of the eigenvalues of A are positive. The reason is easy: $Ax = \lambda x$ for a nonzero vector $x \in \mathbb{R}^d$ implies that

$$x^T A x := \langle x, Ax \rangle = \langle x, \lambda x \rangle = \lambda \|x\|^2,$$

so that $x^T A x > 0$ if and only if $\lambda > 0$. In the sequel, if we only require a symmetric matrix A that enjoys the property $x^T A x \geq 0$ for all $x \in \mathbb{R}^d$, then we call such a matrix **positive semidefinite**.

Also, for a full-rank lattice $\mathcal{L} := M(\mathbb{Z}^d)$, we see that $B := M^T M$ will be positive definite if and only if M is invertible, so that the columns of M are a basis of $\mathcal{L}$. Since a positive definite matrix is symmetric by definition, we have proved Lemma 5.22.

Lemma 5.22. *Suppose we are given a real symmetric matrix B. Then:*

(1) *B is positive definite if and only if it is the Gram matrix of a full-rank lattice.*

(2) *B is positive semidefinite if and only if it is the Gram matrix of some set of vectors.* $\square$

What about reconstructing a lattice while knowing only one of its Gram matrices? This is almost possible to accomplish up to an orthogonal transformation, as follows.

Lemma 5.23. *Suppose that G is an invertible matrix, whose spectral decomposition is*

$$G = PDP^T.$$

Then

(5.29) $$G = X^T X \iff X = Q\sqrt{D}P^T,$$

for some orthogonal matrix Q.

Proof. The assumption $G = X^T X$ guarantees that G is symmetric and has positive eigenvalues, so by the spectral theorem we have

$$G = PDP^T,$$

where D is a diagonal matrix consisting of the positive eigenvalues of G, and P is an orthogonal matrix consisting of eigenvectors of G. Setting $X^T X = PDP^T$, we must have

$$(5.30) \qquad I = X^{-T} PDP^T X^{-1} = (X^{-T} P\sqrt{D})(X^{-T} P\sqrt{D})^T,$$

where we define $\sqrt{D}$ to be the diagonal matrix whose diagonal elements are the positive square roots of the eigenvalues of G. From (5.30), it follows that $X^{-T} P\sqrt{D}$ is an orthogonal matrix, which we will call Q^{-T}. Finally, $X^{-T} P\sqrt{D} = Q^{-T}$ implies that $X = Q\sqrt{D}P^T$. □

So, Lemma 5.23 allows us to reconstruct a lattice $\mathcal{L}$ up to an orthogonal transformation by only knowing one of its Gram matrices.

7. Dual lattices

Every lattice $\mathcal{L} := M(\mathbb{Z}^d)$ has a **dual lattice**, which we have already encountered in the Poisson summation formula for arbitrary lattices. The dual lattice of a full-rank lattice $\mathcal{L}$ was defined by

$$(5.31) \qquad \mathcal{L}^* = M^{-T}(\mathbb{Z}^d).$$

But there is another way to define the dual lattice of a lattice $\mathcal{L} \subset \mathbb{R}^d$ (of any rank), which is coordinate-free:

$$(5.32) \qquad \mathcal{L}^* := \left\{ x \in \mathbb{R}^d \mid \langle x, n \rangle \in \mathbb{Z}, \text{ for all } n \in \mathcal{L} \right\}.$$

Lemma 5.24. *The two definitions, (5.31) and (5.32), are equivalent.*

Proof. We let $A := \mathcal{L}^* := M^{-T}(\mathbb{Z}^d)$, and

$$B := \left\{ x \in \mathbb{R}^d \mid \langle x, n \rangle \in \mathbb{Z}, \text{ for all } n \in \mathcal{L} \right\}.$$

We first fix any $x \in A$. To show $x \in B$, we fix any $n \in \mathcal{L}$, and we now have to verify that $\langle x, n \rangle \in \mathbb{Z}$. By assumption, $x = M^{-T} m$ for some $m \in \mathbb{Z}^d$, and $n = Mk$ for some $k \in \mathbb{Z}^d$. Therefore,

$$\langle x, n \rangle = \langle M^{-T} m, n \rangle = \langle m, M^{-1} n \rangle = \langle m, k \rangle \in \mathbb{Z},$$

because both $m, k \in \mathbb{Z}^d$. So we have $A \subseteq B$.

For the other direction, suppose that $y \in B$, so, by definition,

$$\langle y, n \rangle \in \mathbb{Z}, \text{ for all } n \in \mathcal{L}.$$

We need to show that $y = M^{-T} k$ for some $k \in \mathbb{Z}^d$, which is equivalent to $M^T y \in \mathbb{Z}^d$. Noticing that the kth element of $M^T y$ is $\langle n, y \rangle$ with n belonging to a basis of $\mathcal{L}$, we are done. Therefore $A = B$. □

Example 5.25. Let $\mathcal{L} := r\mathbb{Z}^d$, the integer lattice dilated by a positive real number r. Its dual lattice is $\mathcal{L}^* = \frac{1}{r}\mathcal{L}$ because a basis for $\mathcal{L}$ is $M := rI$, implying that a basis matrix for $\mathcal{L}^*$ is $M^{-T} = \frac{1}{r}I$. We also notice that $\det \mathcal{L} = r^d$ while $\det \mathcal{L}^* = \frac{1}{r^d}$. $\qquad\square$

A fundamental relation between a full-rank lattice and its dual follows immediately from equation (5.31):

$$\det(\mathcal{L}^*) := \det(M^{-T}) = \frac{1}{\det M} = \frac{1}{\det \mathcal{L}},$$

which we record as

$$(5.33) \qquad\qquad (\det \mathcal{L})(\det \mathcal{L}^*) = 1.$$

If we consider any integer sublattice of $\mathbb{Z}^d$, say, $\mathcal{L} \subset \mathbb{Z}^d$, together with its dual lattice $\mathcal{L}^*$ in the same space, some interesting relations unfold between them. Let us consider an example.

Example 5.26. In $\mathbb{R}^2$, let $\mathcal{L} := \left\{ m \left(\begin{smallmatrix} 1 \\ 1 \end{smallmatrix} \right) + n \left(\begin{smallmatrix} 1 \\ 4 \end{smallmatrix} \right) \mid m, n \in \mathbb{Z} \right\}$, a lattice with $\det \mathcal{L} = 3$ that is depicted in Figure 5.9 by the larger green balls. Its dual lattice is

$$\mathcal{L}^* := \left\{ \frac{1}{3} \left(a \left(\begin{smallmatrix} 4 \\ -1 \end{smallmatrix} \right) + b \left(\begin{smallmatrix} -1 \\ 1 \end{smallmatrix} \right) \right) \mid a, b \in \mathbb{Z} \right\},$$

whose determinant equals $\frac{1}{3}$, and is depicted in Figure 5.9 by the smaller orange balls. So $\mathcal{L}$ is a coarser lattice than $\mathcal{L}^*$. That is, $\mathcal{L}^* \supseteq \mathcal{L}$.

We can verify the relation (5.33) here: $\det \mathcal{L}^* = \frac{1}{3} = \frac{1}{\det \mathcal{L}}$. We may notice that $\mathcal{L}^*/\mathcal{L}$ forms a finite group of order $9 = (\det \mathcal{L})^2$, which is equal to the number of cosets of the coarser lattice $\mathcal{L}$ in the finer lattice $\mathcal{L}^*$. $\qquad\square$

Question 5.27 (Rhetorical). When is it true that $\mathcal{L}^* \supseteq \mathcal{L}$? In other words, for which lattices is the dual lattice a refinement of the original lattice?

To study this phenomenon, a lattice $\mathcal{L} \subset \mathbb{R}^d$ is called an **integral lattice** if

$$\langle x, y \rangle \in \mathbb{Z} \text{ for all } x, y \in \mathcal{L}.$$

It follows directly from our definition of an integral lattice that

$$\mathcal{L}^* \supseteq \mathcal{L} \iff \mathcal{L} \text{ is an integral lattice,}$$

and in this case we have a finite abelian group $\mathcal{L}^*/\mathcal{L}$, called the **discriminant group**.

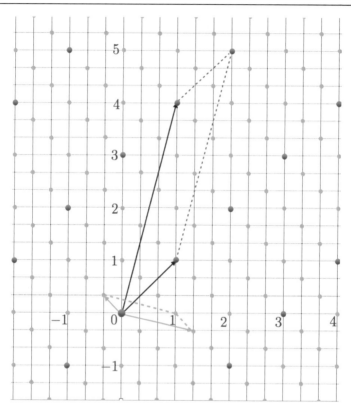

Figure 5.9. The lattice $\mathcal{L}$ of Example 5.26, depicted by the green points. Its dual lattice $\mathcal{L}^*$ is depicted by the orange points. Here $\mathcal{L}^* \supset \mathcal{L}$ and is therefore a finer lattice.

Lemma 5.28. *For a full-rank integral lattice $\mathcal{L}$, we have*

(5.34) $$|\mathcal{L}^*/\mathcal{L}| = (\det \mathcal{L})^2.$$

Proof. we recall Theorem 5.11:

$$|\mathcal{L}^*/\mathcal{L}| = \frac{\det \mathcal{L}}{\det \mathcal{L}^*} = \frac{\det \mathcal{L}}{(1/\det \mathcal{L})} = (\det \mathcal{L})^2. \qquad \square$$

Example 5.29. Clearly, any integer sublattice $\mathcal{L} \subseteq \mathbb{Z}^d$ is also an integral lattice. But there are others, as Example 5.30 shows. $\qquad \square$

Example 5.30. Here we will see infinite continuous families of integral lattices in $\mathbb{R}^2$ by considering orthogonal linear transformation of $\mathbb{Z}^2$. Let us fix an angle $0 < \theta < \frac{\pi}{2}$ with $\cos\theta$ and $\sin\theta$ irrationals and linearly independent over the rationals. We define:

$$M := \begin{pmatrix} \cos\theta & -\sin\theta \\ \sin\theta & \cos\theta \end{pmatrix}, \quad \mathcal{L} := \{ M\begin{pmatrix} a \\ b \end{pmatrix} \mid \begin{pmatrix} a \\ b \end{pmatrix} \in \mathbb{Z}^2 \}.$$

For any two lattice vectors $u, v \in \mathcal{L}$, we have

$$\langle u, v \rangle = \langle M\begin{pmatrix} a \\ b \end{pmatrix}, M\begin{pmatrix} c \\ d \end{pmatrix} \rangle = \langle M^T M \begin{pmatrix} a \\ b \end{pmatrix}, \begin{pmatrix} c \\ d \end{pmatrix} \rangle = \langle\!\langle \begin{pmatrix} a \\ b \end{pmatrix}, \begin{pmatrix} c \\ d \end{pmatrix} \rangle\!\rangle \in \mathbb{Z},$$

so that our lattice $\mathcal{L}$ is also an integral lattice. We notice that in this example $\mathcal{L}$ has no nonzero integer vectors at all!

Let us compute the dual lattice here: $\mathcal{L}^*$ is given by the matrix $M^{-T} = M$. In other words, we have $\mathcal{L}^* = \mathcal{L}$. Is this a coincidence? $\square$

Example 5.31. Continuing with Example 5.26, we have an integral lattice $\mathcal{L} \subset \mathbb{R}^2$ so that $\mathcal{L}^* \supseteq \mathcal{L}$. Here $\det \mathcal{L} = 3$, $\det \mathcal{L}^* = \frac{1}{3}$, confirming the claim from Lemma 5.28, namely that

$$|\mathcal{L}^*/\mathcal{L}| = \frac{3}{\left(\frac{1}{3}\right)} = 9 = (\det \mathcal{L})^2. \qquad \square$$

Next, we call $\mathcal{L} \subset \mathbb{R}^d$ a **unimodular lattice** if $\det \mathcal{L} = 1$. The collection of all unimodular lattices is quite important in number theory and, for example, in Siegel's mean value theorem. We say that a lattice $\mathcal{L}$ is **self dual** if $\mathcal{L}^* = \mathcal{L}$. Chasing these elementary ideas around, the following observation is immediate (Exercise (14)).

Lemma 5.32. *The following are equivalent:*

(1) $\mathcal{L}$ *is self-dual.*

(2) $\mathcal{L}$ *is an integral unimodular lattice.* $\square$

Example 5.33. Continuing with Example 5.30, we saw that the lattice defined by

$$\mathcal{L} := \{ M\begin{pmatrix} a \\ b \end{pmatrix} \mid \begin{pmatrix} a \\ b \end{pmatrix} \in \mathbb{Z}^2 \},$$

with $M := \begin{pmatrix} \cos\theta & -\sin\theta \\ \sin\theta & \cos\theta \end{pmatrix}$, was self-dual. According to Lemma 5.32, $\mathcal{L}$ should also be an integral unimodular lattice—and indeed it is. $\square$

8. Some important lattices

Throughout this section, we will fix the special vector

$$(5.35) \qquad\qquad w := \begin{pmatrix} \frac{1}{2} \\ \frac{1}{2} \\ \frac{1}{2} \\ \vdots \\ \frac{1}{2} \end{pmatrix} \in \mathbb{R}^d.$$

Example 5.34. The D_n lattice is defined by

$$D_n := \left\{ x \in \mathbb{Z}^n \mid \sum_{k=1}^{n} x_k \equiv 0 \mod 2 \right\}.$$

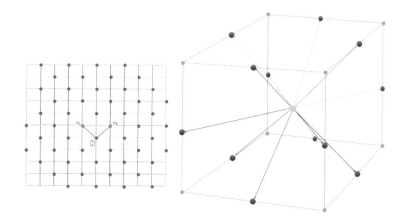

Figure 5.10. Left: the D_2 lattice. Right: the 12 shortest nonzero vectors of the D_3 lattice, inscribed in the cube $[-1,1]^3$.

In $\mathbb{R}^4$ the D_4 lattice turns out to be a fascinating object of study. The Voronoi cell $\mathrm{Vor}_0(D_4)$ is called the 24-**cell**, and is depicted in Figure 5.13. It is a 4-dimensional polytope with some incredible properties—for example, it is one of the few polytopes that is self-dual. It is also an example of a polytope $\mathcal{P}$ in the lowest possible dimension d (namely $d = 4$) such that $\mathcal{P}$ tiles $\mathbb{R}^d$ by translations, and yet $\mathcal{P}$ is not a zonotope.

By Lemma 5.21, we see that $\det D_n = 2$. The lattice D_n is often called the "checkerboard" lattice because $\det D_n = 2$ means there are exactly two cosets in $\mathbb{Z}^d / D_n$. Finally, the dual lattice D_n^* is equal to the lattice

$$\mathbb{Z}^d \cup \left(\mathbb{Z}^d + w \right),$$

which we leave for the pleasure of the reader (Exercise (8)). $\qquad\square$

Example 5.35. The E_8 lattice is defined by

$$E_8 := D_8 \cup (D_8 + w),$$

with w defined in (5.35). It is a nice exercise to show that the latter definition in fact gives us a lattice (Exercise (2)). It turns out that E_8 is a self-dual lattice (Exercise (3)). E_8 is also an even unimodular lattice. Moreover, it also turns out that E_8 gives the optimal solution to the sphere packing problem in $\mathbb{R}^8$. This lattice has amazing symmetries, and is important in the physics of string theory as well as data transmission. □

Example 5.36. We define the hyperplane $H := \{x \in \mathbb{Z}^8 \mid x_1 + \cdots + x_8 = 0\}$ in $\mathbb{R}^8$. Then we have the lattice

$$E_7 := E_8 \cap H,$$

which has rank 7. We also fix $V := \{x \in \mathbb{R}^8 \mid x_2 + x_3 + x_4 + x_5 + x_6 + x_7 = x_1 + x_8 = 0\} \subset \mathbb{R}^8$, a vector subspace of dimension 6, and we define

$$E_6 := E_8 \cap V,$$

a lattice of rank 6. Both E_6 and E_7 are, almost by definition, sublattices of E_8. □

Example 5.37. Last but not least is the famous Leech lattice in $\mathbb{R}^{24}$. It is the unique even unimodular lattice in $\mathbb{R}^{24}$ that has no vectors of length $\sqrt{2}$ (see [**55**] for a proof, among other constructions for the Leech lattice). There are many constructions of the Leech lattice, none of which are trivial, and one of which involves the important Golay binary code [**59**]. Coding theory, which is a discrete version of sphere packing, is a fascinating and important topic for another day. □

9. The Hermite normal form

If a lattice satisfies $\mathcal{L} \subset \mathbb{Z}^d$, we will call it an integer sublattice. We may recall that any lattice $\mathcal{L} \subset \mathbb{R}^d$ has infinitely many bases, so it may seem impossible at first to associate a single matrix with a given lattice. However, there is an elegant way to do this, as follows.

Example 5.38. Suppose we are given a lattice $\mathcal{L}$ as the integral span of the vectors

$$v_1 := \begin{pmatrix} 3 \\ 1 \end{pmatrix}, \quad v_2 := \begin{pmatrix} -2 \\ 2 \end{pmatrix},$$

which clearly has determinant 8. Then any integer linear combinations of v_1 and v_2 is still in $\mathcal{L}$. In particular, mimicking Gaussian elimination, we place v_1 and v_2 as rows of a matrix, and row-reduce over the integers

$$\begin{pmatrix} 3 & 1 \\ -2 & 2 \end{pmatrix} \rightarrow \begin{pmatrix} 3 & 1 \\ 1 & 3 \end{pmatrix} \rightarrow \begin{pmatrix} 0 & -8 \\ 1 & 3 \end{pmatrix} \rightarrow \begin{pmatrix} 1 & 3 \\ 0 & -8 \end{pmatrix} \rightarrow \begin{pmatrix} 1 & 3 \\ 0 & 8 \end{pmatrix},$$

where at each step we performed row operations (over $\mathbb{Z}$) that did not change the lattice. Hence we have a reduced basis for $\mathcal{L}$ consisting of $\begin{pmatrix} 1 \\ 3 \end{pmatrix}$ and $\begin{pmatrix} 0 \\ 8 \end{pmatrix}$.

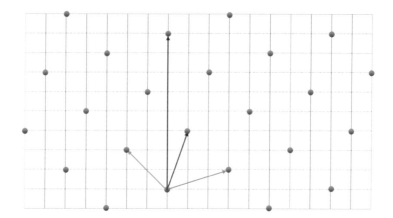

Figure 5.11. The lattice $\mathcal{L}$ of Example 5.38, depicted by the bold green points, showing the original basis $\{v_1, v_2\}$ of $\mathcal{L}$ and the Hermite-reduced basis of $\mathcal{L}$. Here it is geometrically clear that both are bases for the same lattice $\mathcal{L}$.

We notice that the resulting matrix is upper-triangular, with positive integers on the diagonal, nonnegative integers elsewhere, and in each column the diagonal element is the largest element in that column.

There is another way to interpret the above matrix reductions by using unimodular matrices, as follows. The first reduction step can be accomplished by the multiplication on the left by a unimodular matrix:

$$\begin{pmatrix} 1 & 0 \\ 1 & 1 \end{pmatrix} \begin{pmatrix} 3 & 1 \\ -2 & 2 \end{pmatrix} = \begin{pmatrix} 3 & 1 \\ 1 & 3 \end{pmatrix}.$$

Similarly, each step in the reduction process can be interpreted by multiplying on the left by some new unimodular matrix, so that at the end of the process we have a product of unimodular matrices times our original matrix

$$\begin{pmatrix} 3 & 1 \\ -2 & 2 \end{pmatrix}.$$

Because a product of unimodular matrices is yet another unimodular matrix, we can see that we arrived at a reduction of the form:

$$U \begin{pmatrix} 3 & 1 \\ -2 & 2 \end{pmatrix} = \begin{pmatrix} 1 & 3 \\ 0 & 8 \end{pmatrix},$$

where U is a unimodular matrix.   □

The point of Example 5.38 is that a similar matrix reduction persists for all integer lattices, culminating in the following result, which just hinges on the fact that $\mathbb{Z}$ has a division algorithm.

Theorem 5.39. *Given an invertible integer $d \times d$ matrix M, there exists a unimodular matrix U with $UM = H$, such that H satisfies the following conditions:*

(1) $[H]_{i,j} = 0$ *if* $i > j$.

(2) $[H]_{i,i} > 0$, *for each* $1 \leq i \leq d$.

(3) $0 \leq [H]_{i,j} < [H]_{i,i}$, *for each* $i > j$.

Property (3) *tells us that each diagonal element* $[H]_{i,i}$ *in the ith column of H is the largest element in the ith column.*

Moreover, the matrix H is the unique integer matrix that satisfies the above conditions. □

The matrix H in Theorem 5.39 is called the **Hermite normal form** of M. To associate a unique matrix to a given integral full-rank lattice $\mathcal{L} \subset \mathbb{R}^d$, we first choose any basis of $\mathcal{L}$, and we then construct a $d \times d$ integer matrix M whose rows are the basis vectors that we chose. We then apply Theorem 5.39 to M, arriving at an integer matrix H whose rows are another basis of $\mathcal{L}$, called the **Hermite-reduced basis**.

Corollary 5.40. *There is a one-to-one correspondence between full-rank integer sublattices in $\mathbb{R}^d$ and integer $d \times d$ matrices in their Hermite normal form.* □

Example 5.41. Given any 2-dimensional lattice $\mathcal{L} \subset \mathbb{Z}^2$, with a basis matrix M, we can use the Hermite-normal form of M to get the following basis for $\mathcal{L}$: $\{\left(\begin{smallmatrix}1\\0\end{smallmatrix}\right), \left(\begin{smallmatrix}p\\q\end{smallmatrix}\right)\}$, for some nonnegative integers p, q. □

10. The Voronoi cell of a lattice

The **Voronoi cell** of a lattice $\mathcal{L}$, at the origin, is defined by

$$(5.36) \qquad \mathrm{Vor}_0(\mathcal{L}) := \left\{ x \in \mathbb{R}^d \mid \|x\| \leq \|x - v\|, \text{ for all } v \in \mathcal{L} \right\}.$$

In other words, the Voronoi cell $\mathrm{Vor}_0(\mathcal{L})$ of a lattice $\mathcal{L}$ is the set of all point in space that are closer to the origin than to any other lattice point in $\mathcal{L}$. Because the origin wins the battle of minimizing this particular distance function, it is also possible to construct the Voronoi cell by using half-spaces. Namely, for each $v \in \mathcal{L}$, we define the half-space

$$H_v := \left\{ x \in \mathbb{R}^d \mid \langle x, v \rangle \leq \tfrac{1}{2}\|v\| \right\},$$

and we observe that the Voronoi cell may also be given by

$$\mathrm{Vor}_0(\mathcal{L}) = \bigcap_{v \in \mathcal{L}-\{0\}} H_v,$$

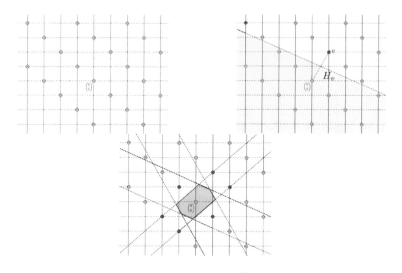

Figure 5.12. Top left: A sublattice $\mathcal{L}$ of $\mathbb{Z}^2$, of index 3. Top right: $v \in \mathcal{L}$ is one of the 6 relevant vectors with its corresponding half-plane H_v, helping to define the Voronoi cell at the origin. Bottom: The Voronoi cell $\mathrm{Vor}_0(\mathcal{L})$, a symmetric hexagon of area 3, with its 6 relevant (heavy blue) lattice points of $\mathcal{L}$.

as drawn in Figure 5.12. It is easy to observe that the Voronoi cell of a lattice is symmetric about the origin, convex, and compact. So we may expect that Minkowski's theorems apply to $\mathrm{Vor}_0(\mathcal{L})$, as we see in the proof of Lemma 5.42. It is also useful to define an analogous Voronoi cell located at each lattice point $m \in \mathcal{L}$:

$$(5.37) \qquad \mathrm{Vor}_m(\mathcal{L}) := \left\{ x \in \mathbb{R}^d \mid \|x - m\| \leq \|x - v\|, \text{ for all } v \in \mathcal{L} \right\}.$$

A moment's thought reveals that a translation of the Voronoi cell at the origin is exactly the Voronoi cell at another lattice point of $\mathcal{L}$, namely:

$$(5.38) \qquad \mathrm{Vor}_0(\mathcal{L}) + m = \mathrm{Vor}_m(\mathcal{L}).$$

Lemma 5.42. *Given a full-rank lattice $\mathcal{L} \subset \mathbb{R}^d$, whose Voronoi cell at the origin is K, we have:*

(1) *K tiles $\mathbb{R}^d$ by translations with $\mathcal{L}$.*

(2) $\operatorname{vol}(K) = \det \mathcal{L}$.

Proof. Part (1) follows from the observation that any $x \in \mathbb{R}^d$, there exists a lattice point $m \in \mathcal{L}$ that is at least as close to x as it is to any other lattice point of $\mathcal{L}$. In other words, $\|x - m\| \leq \|x - v\|, \forall v \in \mathcal{L}$, and so $x \in \operatorname{Vor}_m(\mathcal{L})$. From (5.38) we see that x is covered by the translate $\operatorname{Vor}_0(\mathcal{L}) + m$. It is also clear that as n varies over $\mathcal{L}$, all of the interiors of the translates $\operatorname{Vor}_0(\mathcal{L}) + n$ are disjoint, so that $K := \operatorname{Vor}_0(\mathcal{L})$ tiles $\mathbb{R}^d$ by translations with $\mathcal{L}$. To prove part (2), we let $B := 2K$. By Theorem 4.8 (regarding extremal bodies), we know that $\frac{1}{2}B = K$ tiles $\mathbb{R}^d$ with the lattice $\mathcal{L}$ if and only if $\operatorname{vol}(B) = 2^d \det \mathcal{L}$. Since (1) tells us that $K = \frac{1}{2}B$ tiles with the lattice $\mathcal{L}$, we see that $\operatorname{vol} K = \operatorname{vol}\left(\frac{1}{2}B\right) = \frac{1}{2^d} \operatorname{vol} B = \det \mathcal{L}$. $\qquad \square$

The proof above shows that the Voronoi cell of $\mathcal{L}$ is also an extremal body for $\mathcal{L}$ according to Theorem 4.8.

A fascinating open problem is the Voronoi conjecture, named after the Ukrainian mathematician Georgy Voronoi, who formulated it in 1908. Two polytopes $\mathcal{P}, Q$ are called **affinely equivalent** if $\mathcal{P} = M(Q) + v$, where $M \in GL_d(\mathbb{R})$, and $v \in \mathbb{R}^d$.

Question 5.43 (The Voronoi conjecture). Does a polytope $\mathcal{P}$ tile $\mathbb{R}^d$ by translations $\iff$ $\mathcal{P}$ is the Voronoi cell of some lattice $\mathcal{L}$, or $\mathcal{P}$ is affinely equivalent to such a Voronoi cell?

The main difficulty in the Voronoi conjecture appears to be the apriori search among all of the (infinitely many) possible affinely equivalent images of such a Voronoi cell.

Example 5.44. For the lattice $A_n \subset \mathbb{R}^{n+1}$, defined in Example 5.17, its Voronoi cell turns out to have beautiful and important properties: $\operatorname{Vor}(A_2) \subset \mathbb{R}^3$ is a hexagon, $\operatorname{Vor}(A_3) \subset \mathbb{R}^4$ is a truncated octahedron (one of the Fedorov solids), and so on (see Conway and Sloane [**59**]).

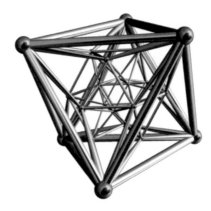

Figure 5.13. The Voronoi cell of the D_4 lattice in $\mathbb{R}^4$, known as the 24-cell.

11. Characters of lattices

For each lattice point $n \in \mathcal{L}$, we associate a function called a **character** of $\mathcal{L}$, which we define by:

$$(5.39) \qquad \chi_n(x) := e^{2\pi i \langle n, x \rangle}$$

for all $x \in \mathbb{R}^d$. If we multiply these characters together by defining $\chi_n \chi_m := \chi_{n+m}$, then

$$G_{\mathcal{L}} := \{\chi_n \mid n \in \mathcal{L}\}$$

forms a group under multiplication of functions, called the **group of characters** of $\mathcal{L}$. To see that this multiplication makes sense, we can compute

$$(5.40) \qquad (\chi_n \chi_m)(x) := e^{2\pi i \langle n, x \rangle} e^{2\pi i \langle m, x \rangle} = e^{2\pi i \langle n+m, x \rangle} := \chi_{n+m}(x).$$

But much more is true.

Theorem 5.45.

$$G_{\mathcal{L}} \simeq \mathcal{L},$$

an isomorphism of groups.

Proof. We consider the map $\Phi : \mathcal{L} \to G_{\mathcal{L}}$ defined by $\Phi(n) := \chi_n$. We will show that Φ is an isomorphism, so it is necessary to prove that ϕ is a bijective homomorphism by definition. By (5.40), the computation

$$\Phi(n + m) = \chi_{n+m} = \chi_n \chi_m = \Phi(n)\Phi(m)$$

already shows that Φ is a homomorphism. The surjectivity of Φ is clear from the definition of Φ. The more interesting direction is to show that

Φ is injective. First, $\Phi(n) = \Phi(m) \implies e^{2\pi i \langle n, x \rangle} = e^{2\pi i \langle m, x \rangle}$ for all $x \in \mathbb{R}^d \iff e^{2\pi i \langle n - m, x \rangle} = 1$ for all $x \in \mathbb{R}^d \iff$

$$\tag{5.41} \langle n - m, x \rangle \in \mathbb{Z}$$

for all $x \in \mathbb{R}^d$. Suppose to the contrary that $n - m \neq 0$. Consider the open ball

$$B := \left\{ x \in \mathbb{R}^d \mid \|x\| < \frac{1}{\|n - m\|} \right\},$$

and pick any $x \in B$. The Cauchy–Schwartz inequality gives us

$$|\langle n - m, x \rangle| \leq \|n - m\| \|x\| < \|n - m\| \frac{1}{\|n - m\|} = 1,$$

so that by (5.41) we now have $\langle n - m, x \rangle = 0$ for all $x \in B$. But this implies $n - m = 0$, a contradiction. $\qquad\qquad\square$

Intuitively, one of the huge benefits of group characters is that we can study d-dimensional lattices by simply using the magic of 2-dimensional complex numbers.

Example 5.46. For the integer lattice $\mathbb{Z}^d$, its group of characters comprises the following functions

$$\chi_n(x) := e^{2\pi i \langle n, x \rangle}$$

for each $n \in \mathbb{Z}^d$. $\qquad\qquad\square$

Now we allow ourselves the luxury of being slightly more general and free to think about any finite group. Although we focused thus far on discrete (sub)groups in $\mathbb{R}^d$, defined in (5.13), the reader may consult [118] for the definition of any group.

Lemma 5.47. *Let G be any finite group and $\chi : G \to \mathbb{C} \setminus \{0\}$ a nontrivial homomorphism of G.*

(1) *We have*

$$\sum_{g \in G} \chi(g) = 0.$$

(2) *For any two distinct homomorphisms $\chi, \psi : G \to \mathbb{C} \setminus \{0\}$, we have*

$$\sum_{g \in G} \chi(g)\overline{\psi(g)} = 0.$$

Proof. To prove part (1), we first note that because χ is nontrivial there exists a nonzero element $g_0 \in G$ such that $\chi(g_0) \neq 1$. We have

$$\chi(g_0) \sum_{g \in G} \chi(g) = \sum_{g \in G} \chi(g_0)\chi(g) = \sum_{g \in G} \chi(g_0 g) = \sum_{g \in G} \chi(g),$$

where the last step follows from the fact that multiplication by g_0 permutes all the elements of G (Exercise (15)). So we now have

$$(\chi(g_0) - 1) \sum_{g \in G} \chi(g) = 0,$$

and because $\chi(g_0) \neq 1$, we conclude that $\sum_{g \in G} \chi(g) = 0$.

To prove part (2), we define $\phi := \chi\psi^{-1}$, which is another character of G where we have $\phi(x) := \chi(x)\psi^{-1}(x) = \chi(x)\overline{\psi(x)}$, for all $x \in G$. Moreover, by assumption ϕ is not the trivial character (ϕ and ψ are distinct), so that part (1) applies to the character ϕ and we are done. $\qquad\square$

For some applications, it is useful to somehow transfer the problem of summing a function over a sublattice (or superlattice) of $\mathcal{L}$, to the problem of summing essentially the same function over $\mathcal{L}$. The following is the classical orthogonality relation for a finite abelian group $\mathbb{Z}^d/M\mathbb{Z}^d$, but we prefer to phrase it in terms of the lattice $\mathcal{L} := M(\mathbb{Z}^d)$ for future applications to lattices.

Corollary 5.48 (Orthogonality relations for characters of a lattice). *Let $\mathcal{L} \subset \mathbb{Z}^d$ be a full-rank integer sublattice, so we may write $\mathcal{L} := M(\mathbb{Z}^d)$, with M an invertible integer matrix. Then we have*

$$(5.42) \qquad \frac{1}{|\det M|} \sum_{g \in \mathbb{Z}^d/M\mathbb{Z}^d} e^{2\pi i \langle M^{-T}g, m \rangle} = \begin{cases} 1 & \text{if } m \in \mathcal{L} \\ 0 & \text{if } m \notin \mathcal{L} \end{cases}$$

for all $m \in \mathbb{Z}^d$.

Proof. If $m \in \mathcal{L}$, then $m = Mn$ for some $n \in \mathbb{Z}^d$. Therefore,

$$e^{2\pi i \langle M^{-T}g, m \rangle} = e^{2\pi i \langle g, M^{-1}Mn \rangle} = e^{2\pi i \langle g, n \rangle} = 1,$$

giving us

$$\sum_{g \in \mathbb{Z}^d/M\mathbb{Z}^d} e^{2\pi i \langle M^{-T}g, m \rangle} = \sum_{g \in \mathbb{Z}^d/M\mathbb{Z}^d} 1 = |\mathbb{Z}^d/M\mathbb{Z}^d| = |\det M|,$$

which proves the first part. On the other hand, if $m \notin \mathcal{L}$, then $m \to e^{2\pi i \langle M^{-T}g, m \rangle}$ is a nontrivial homomorphism of the finite group $G := \mathbb{Z}^d/M\mathbb{Z}^d$, so that we have the required vanishing by Lemma 5.47(1). $\qquad\square$

It is also very useful to think of Corollary 5.48 in the following way. The right-hand side of (5.42) is, by definition, $1_{\mathcal{L}}$, the indicator function of the lattice. So we have the alternate form

$$(5.43) \qquad 1_{\mathcal{L}}(m) = \frac{1}{|\det M|} \sum_{g \in \mathbb{Z}^d / M\mathbb{Z}^d} e^{2\pi i \langle M^{-T} g, m \rangle}$$

for all $m \in \mathbb{Z}^d$.

Finally, suppose we want to write a sum of a function f over a lattice $\mathcal{L}$ in terms of the sum of f over the integer lattice, with the small price of a multiplicative exponential.

Theorem 5.49. *Let $\mathcal{L} \subset \mathbb{Z}^d$ be a full-rank integer sublattice, so we may write $\mathcal{L} := M(\mathbb{Z}^d)$, with M an invertible integer matrix. Given an absolutely summable function $f : \mathbb{Z}^d \to \mathbb{C}$, we have*

$$(5.44) \qquad \sum_{n \in \mathcal{L}} f(n) = \frac{1}{\det M} \sum_{g \in \mathbb{Z}^d / M\mathbb{Z}^d} \sum_{n \in \mathbb{Z}^d} f(n) e^{2\pi i \langle M^{-T} g, n \rangle}.$$

Proof.

$$\sum_{n \in \mathcal{L}} f(n) = \sum_{n \in \mathbb{Z}^d} 1_{\mathcal{L}}(n) f(n)$$

$$= \frac{1}{|\det M|} \sum_{n \in \mathbb{Z}^d} \sum_{g \in \mathbb{Z}^d / M\mathbb{Z}^d} e^{2\pi i \langle M^{-T} g, n \rangle} f(n)$$

$$= \frac{1}{|\det M|} \sum_{g \in \mathbb{Z}^d / M\mathbb{Z}^d} \sum_{n \in \mathbb{Z}^d} e^{2\pi i \langle M^{-T} g, n \rangle} f(n),$$

where we used (5.43) in the penultimate equality. $\qquad \square$

Example 5.50. Suppose we consider the arithmetic progression

$$\mathcal{L} := \{n \in \mathbb{Z} \mid n \equiv 0 \pmod 7\} := 7\mathbb{Z},$$

which is, of course, a 1-dimensional integer sublattice of $\mathbb{Z}$. Here the finite group is $G = \mathbb{Z}/7\mathbb{Z}$, so that $|\det M| = 7$. Here we see that for any function $f : \mathbb{Z} \to \mathbb{C}$ such that $\sum_{n \in \mathbb{Z}} |f(n)| < \infty$, Theorem 5.49 gives us

$$\sum_{n \equiv 0 \pmod 7} f(n) = \frac{1}{7} \sum_{g \in \mathbb{Z}/7\mathbb{Z}} \sum_{n \in \mathbb{Z}} f(n) e^{\frac{2\pi i g n}{7}}. \qquad \square$$

Notes

(1) The important families of lattices A_n, B_n, C_n, $D_n \subset \mathbb{R}^n$ are called root lattices (in all dimensions $n \geq 1$). These lattices arise naturally in the classification of Lie algebras, the combinatorics of Weyl chambers, and representation theory. We have only glimpsed A_n and D_n in this chapter. The curious reader may consult Conway and Sloane's book [59] for more detail, which also gives more information about the five sporadic lattices E_6, E_7, E_8, F_4, G_2, as well as many properties of all the root lattices. Here, the index always signifies the dimension of the lattice.

(2) The special lattice D_4 is currently thought to be the correct candidate for the densest sphere packings in dimension 4.

(3) A lattice $\mathcal{L} \subset \mathbb{R}^d$ is called an **even** lattice if $\langle x, x \rangle \in 2\mathbb{Z}$ for all $x \in \mathcal{L}$, and $\langle x, y \rangle \in \mathbb{Z}$, for all $x, y \in \mathcal{L}$. It is a fact that the special lattice E_8 is the only even unimodular lattice in $\mathbb{R}^8$. A slightly deeper fact is that the only dimensions d for which there exists an even unimodular lattice are $d \equiv 0 \bmod 8$. This fact is closely tied to the theta function of such a lattice [59].

(4) The classic book by Martinet [167] develops many algebraic connections between lattices, semi-simple algebras, root systems, quaternions, and quadratic forms.

(5) The discriminant group $\mathcal{L}^*/\mathcal{L}$ arises naturally in the classification of lattices, but it also arises naturally in many different fields. For example, in the theory of chip-firing [135, Theorem 4.6.6], it is shown that for a finite graph G the discriminant groups of the cut and flow lattices of G are isomorphic.

(6) Theorem 5.11 is usually proved using the Hermite-normal form of an integer matrix. Here, we chose this geometric route partly because of its intrinsic beauty and partly because its philosophy matches the discrete geometric path of this book.

(7) We propose the following open question.

Question 5.51. Suppose a polytope $\mathcal{P}$ tiles $\mathbb{R}^d$ by translations with a lattice, and suppose that its dual polytope also tiles by some (possibly other) lattice. Must $\mathcal{P}$ be the 24-cell?

Exercises

"The only way to learn mathematics is to do mathematics."
  – Paul Halmos

(1) We recall that a lattice $\mathcal{L}$ is called self dual if $\mathcal{L}^* = \mathcal{L}$. Prove that for any lattice $\mathcal{L} \subset \mathbb{R}^d$ we have $(\mathcal{L}^*)^* = \mathcal{L}$.

(2) Show that E_8, defined in Example 5.35, is in fact a lattice.

(3) Show that E_8 is self-dual: $E_8^* = E_8$.

(4) ♣ Given any nonzero integer vector $c \in \mathbb{Z}^d$, we may define a countable sequence of discrete hyperplanes perpendicular to c, as follows:

$$H_k := \{x \in \mathbb{R}^d \mid c_1 x_1 + \cdots + c_d x_d = k\}$$

for each $k \in \mathbb{Z}$.

  (a) Show that the distance δ between any two of the hyperplanes H_{k_1} and H_{k_2} is given by

$$\delta = \frac{|k_1 - k_2|}{\sqrt{c_1^2 + \cdots + c_d^2}}.$$

  (b) Conclude that if we have two hyperplanes with no integer points strictly between them, then the distance between these hyperplanes must be $\dfrac{1}{\sqrt{c_1^2 + \cdots + c_d^2}}$.

  (c) Thus, we may always decompose $\mathbb{Z}^d$ into a countable union of disjoint discrete hyperplanes:

$$\mathbb{Z}^d = \bigcup_{k \in \mathbb{Z}} H_k.$$

(5) ♣ Let $\mathcal{L}$ be a lattice in $\mathbb{R}^1$. Show that $\mathcal{L} = r\mathbb{Z}$ for some real number r.

(6) Suppose we are given a rank k lattice $\mathcal{L} \subset \mathbb{R}^d$ with $1 \le k \le d$. If M is a basis matrix for $\mathcal{L}$, then prove that the matrix $M(M^T M)^{-1}$ gives a basis for the dual lattice $\mathcal{L}^*$.

(7) Show that for any two lattices $L, M \subset \mathbb{R}^d$, we have $L \subseteq M \iff M^* \subseteq L^*$.

(8) Prove that we have the following description for the dual lattice of D_n:

$$D_n^* = \mathbb{Z}^d \cup \left(\mathbb{Z}^d + \left(\tfrac{1}{2}, \cdots, \tfrac{1}{2}\right)^T\right).$$

(9) The **hexagonal lattice** is the 2-dimensional lattice defined by

$$\mathcal{L} := \{m + n\tau \mid m, n \in \mathbb{Z}\}, \text{ where } \tau := e^{2\pi i/3}.$$

Prove that $\det \mathcal{L} = \frac{\sqrt{3}}{2}$ and give a description of the dual lattice to the hexagonal lattice.

(10) (Hard). Show that the hexagonal lattice attains the minimal value for Hermite's constant in $\mathbb{R}^2$, namely $\gamma_2^2 = \frac{2}{\sqrt{3}}$.

(11) Let $\mathcal{L} \subset \mathbb{R}^2$ be any rank 2 lattice. Show that there exists a basis $\beta := \{v, w\}$ of $\mathcal{L}$ such that the angle θ_β between v and w satisfies

$$\frac{\pi}{3} \leq \theta_\beta \leq \frac{\pi}{2}.$$

(12) Suppose that M is a $d \times d$ matrix, all of whose d^2 elements are bounded by B. Show that

$$|\det M| \leq B d^{\frac{d}{2}}.$$

(Hint: consider Hadamard's inequality (Theorem 5.8).)

Notes. Let us consider matrices M such that all of their entries are ± 1, often called ± 1 matrices. Then if follows from this exercise that $|\det M| \leq d^{\frac{d}{2}}$. If it is still true that all of the rows of M are pairwise orthogonal, then M is called a **Hadamard matrix**. So we see from this exercise and Theorem 5.8 that for any ± 1 matrix M, M is a Hadamard matrix $\iff |\det M| = d^{\frac{d}{2}}$. Hadamard matrices are important in combinatorics. It is known that if $d > 2$, then Hadamard matrices can only possibly exist when $4 \mid d$. But for each $d = 4m$, it is not known whether a $d \times d$ Hadamard matrix exists, except for very small cases.

(13) ♣ Show that the following set of vectors is a basis for A_d

$$\{e_2 - e_1, e_3 - e_1, \cdots, e_d - e_1\},$$

where the e_j are the standard basis vectors. Hence A_d is a rank-$(d-1)$ sublattice of $\mathbb{Z}^d$.

(14) ♣ Prove Lemma 5.32, namely that the following are equivalent:
  (a) $\mathcal{L}$ is self-dual.
  (b) $\mathcal{L}$ is an integral unimodular lattice.

(15) Given a group G (finite or infinite), and an element $g \in G$, prove that $gG = G$, where $gG := \{gx \mid x \in G\}$.

(16) ♣ Here we prove the **orthogonality relations for characters of a lattice** $\mathcal{L}$. We will do it for any sublattice $\mathcal{L} \subset \mathbb{Z}^d$. Let D be a fundamental parallelepiped for $\mathcal{L}$. Prove that for any two characters $\chi_a, \chi_b \in G_\mathcal{L}$, we have

(5.45)
$$\frac{1}{\det \mathcal{L}} \sum_{n \in D \cap \mathbb{Z}^d} \chi_a(n)\overline{\chi_b(n)} = \begin{cases} 1 & \text{if } \chi_a = \chi_b \\ 0 & \text{if not.} \end{cases}$$

(17) ♣ Prove that any two fundamental parallelepipeds (as defined in the text) of $\mathcal{L}$, say, D_1 and D_2, must be related to each other by an element of the unimodular group
$$D_1 = M(D_2),$$
for some $M \in GL_d(\mathbb{Z})$.

(18) Let $f(n)$ be the number of distinct integer sublattices of index n in $\mathbb{Z}^2$. We recall from elementary number theory the function $\sigma(n) := \sum_{d|n} d$, the sum of the divisors of n (including $d = n$ itself). Show that
$$f(n) = \sigma(n).$$

(19) ♣ Given a sublattice $\mathcal{L} \subset \mathbb{R}^d$ of rank r, show that our definition of its determinant, namely $\det \mathcal{L} := \sqrt{M^T M}$, conincides with the Lebesgue measure of any of its fundamental parallelepipeds.
  (Here M is a $d \times r$ matrix whose columns are basis vectors of $\mathcal{L}$.)

(20) Show that a set of vectors $v_1, \ldots, v_m \in \mathbb{R}^d$, where $1 \le m \le d$, are linearly independent $\iff$ their Gram matrix is nonsingular.

(21) Prove that for any given lattice $\mathcal{L} \subset \mathbb{R}^2$, any two (nonzero) shortest linearly independent vectors for $\mathcal{L}$ generate the lattice $\mathcal{L}$.

  Notes. As a reminder, the first two shortest nonzero vectors of $\mathcal{L}$ may have equal length. We note that in dimensions $d \ge 5$, such a claim is false in general, as Exercise (22) shows.

(22) Find a lattice $\mathcal{L} \subset \mathbb{R}^5$ such that any set of five shortest nonzero vectors of $\mathcal{L}$ do not generate $\mathcal{L}$.

(23) Given any 2-dimensional lattice $\mathcal{L} := M(\mathbb{Z}^2)$, use the Hermite-normal form of M to prove that $\{\left(\begin{smallmatrix}1\\0\end{smallmatrix}\right), \left(\begin{smallmatrix}p\\q\end{smallmatrix}\right)\}$ is a basis for $\mathcal{L}$ for some nonnegative coprime integers p, q.

(24) ♣ Consider the **discrete hyperplane** defined by
$$H := \{x \in \mathbb{Z}^d \mid c_1 x_1 + \cdots + c_d x_d = 0\}.$$
Show that H is a sublattice of $\mathbb{Z}^d$ and has rank $d - 1$.

(25) ♣ Suppose we are given a discrete hyperplane H, as in Exercise (24).
   (a) Prove there exists a vector $x \in \mathbb{R}^d$ such that

$$\{H + kx \mid k \in \mathbb{Z}\} = \mathbb{Z}^d.$$

   (b) Prove that there are no integer points strictly between H and $H + x$.

Notes. You may assume Bezout's identity, which states that if $\gcd(c_1, \ldots, c_d) = 1$ then there exists an integer vector $(m_1, \ldots, m_d)$ such that $c_1 m_1 + \cdots + c_d m_d = 1$. This exercise shows that we can always tile the integer lattice $\mathbb{Z}^d$ with discrete translates of a discrete hyperplane H.

(26) We fix an orthonormal basis $\{b_1, \ldots, b_d\}$ for $\mathbb{R}^d$, and we define the following matrix:

$$M := \begin{pmatrix} | & | & \cdots & | \\ c_1 b_1 & c_2 b_2 & \cdots & c_d b_d \\ | & | & \cdots & | \end{pmatrix},$$

where all the c_k are positive scalars. We now apply the linear transformation M to the unit sphere $S^{d-1} := \{x \in \mathbb{R}^d \mid \|x\|^2 = 1\}$ in $\mathbb{R}^d$, and we recall what this entails. We define the Ellipsoid$_M :=$ $M(S^{d-1})$, a $(d-1)$-dimensional object. In the spirit of review, we recall that, by definition,

$$M(S^{d-1}) := \{u \in \mathbb{R}^d \mid u = Mx, x \in S^{d-1}\}.$$

   (a) Show that

(5.46) $$\text{Ellipsoid}_M = \left\{ x \in \mathbb{R}^d \mid \sum_{j=1}^{d} \frac{\langle x, b_j \rangle^2}{c_j^2} = 1 \right\}.$$

(27) We will use equation (5.46) as the definition of an ellipsoid. We can extend the previous exercise in the following way. Let A be **any** $d \times d$ real matrix and look at the action of A on the unit sphere $S^{d-1} \subset \mathbb{R}^d$. Show:
   (a) If $\text{rank}(A) = d$, then $A(S^{d-1})$ is a d-dimensional ellipsoid, defined by an equation of the form (5.46).
   (b) If $\text{rank}(A) := r < d$, then $A(S^{d-1})$ is an r-dimensional ellipsoid.

(28) Suppose that A is a positive definite real matrix. Solve for (i.e., characterize) all matrices X that are the "square roots" of A:

$$A = X^2.$$

(29) Suppose that a certain 2-dimensional lattice $\mathcal{L}$ has a Gram matrix

$$G := \begin{pmatrix} 2 & -1 \\ -1 & 2 \end{pmatrix}.$$

Reconstruct $\mathcal{L}$ (i.e., find a basis for $\mathcal{L}$) up to an orthogonal transformation.

(30) Find a 2 by 2 matrix M that enjoys one of the properties of a positive semidefinite matrix, namely that $x^T M x \geq 0$ for all $x \in \mathbb{R}^2$, but such that M is not symmetric.

(31) Given any three lattices with $L_1 \subseteq L_2 \subseteq L_3$, show that their indices are multiplicative in the following sense:

$$|L_3/L_1| = |L_3/L_2| \, |L_2/L_1|.$$

(32) To count the number of sublattices of a fixed index, let us define $N_d(k)$ to be the number of integer sublattices of $\mathbb{Z}^d$ that have a fixed index k for any given positive integer k.

(a) Using the notation above, $N_d(2)$ is the number of integer sublattices of $\mathbb{Z}^d$ which have index 2. Prove that

$$N_d(2) = 2^d - 1.$$

(b) Can you find a formula for $N_d(p)$ where p is prime?

Notes. Here, it may be useful to think about the Hermite-normal form. See [266] for a recent study of $N_d(k)$, and also of the number of sublattices of fixed index that are equivalent under the unimodular group $GL_d(\mathbb{Z})$.

(33) Suppose we are given a real 2 by 2 matrix A. Prove that

$$A \text{ is positive definite} \quad \Longleftrightarrow \quad \text{both trace}(A) > 0 \text{ and } \det A > 0.$$

(34) (Not trivial). Here we prove the existence of the (geometric) **Smith normal form** of a lattice. Namely, let $\mathcal{L}_0 \subset \mathcal{L}$ be a sublattice of $\mathcal{L}$. Then there exists a basis $\{v_1, \ldots, v_d\}$ of $\mathcal{L}$, and positive integers k_1, $\ldots, k_d$ such that:
(a) $\{k_1 v_1, \cdots, k_d v_d\}$ is a basis for $\mathcal{L}_0$.
(b) $k_j \mid k_{j+1}$ for $j = 1, \ldots, d-1$.

(35) (Assuming some background about finite abelian groups). Here we will assume the existence and notation of the **Smith normal form** from Exercise (34). Prove that for a full-rank lattice $\mathcal{L} \subset \mathbb{R}^d$ with $\mathcal{L} \subset \mathcal{L}^*$, we have the following explicit form for its discriminant group:

$$\mathcal{L}^*/\mathcal{L} = \mathbb{Z}/k_1\mathbb{Z} \times \cdots \times \mathbb{Z}/k_d\mathbb{Z}.$$

(36) Prove that for the lattice D_n, its discriminant group D_n^*/D_n has the following structure:
  (a) $D_n = \mathbb{Z}/2\mathbb{Z} \times \mathbb{Z}/2\mathbb{Z} \iff n$ is even.
  (b) $D_n = \mathbb{Z}/4\mathbb{Z} \iff n$ is odd.

(37) Prove that if we have two lattices $\mathcal{L}_1, \mathcal{L}_2 \subset \mathbb{R}^d$, then
  (a) $\mathcal{L}_1 \cap \mathcal{L}_2$ is a lattice.
  (b) If $\text{rank}(\mathcal{L}_1) + \text{rank}(\mathcal{L}_1) > d$, then
  $$\text{rank}(\mathcal{L}_1 \cap \mathcal{L}_2) \geq \text{rank}(\mathcal{L}_1) + \text{rank}(\mathcal{L}_1) - d.$$
  (c) Conclude that for any full-rank sublattice of the integer lattice, say $\mathcal{L} \subset \mathbb{Z}^d$, there is point of $\mathcal{L}$ on the x_1-axis (and similarly on each axis x_j).

Chapter 6

Geometry of numbers
Part II: Blichfeldt's
theorems

"Simplicity is the ultimate sophistication."
– Leonardo Da Vinci

Hans Blichfeldt

1. Intuition

There is a beautifully simple and powerful idea in the geometry of numbers due to Hans Blichfeldt, who discovered it in 1914. Here is a simple illustration of it—suppose we have a body $K \subset \mathbb{R}^2$, whose area is bigger than 1. Now, obviously K intersects each little integer square $[m, m+1] \times [n, n+1]$ in some little region $K_{m,n}$, as in Figure 6.1. After translating all of these little regions to the unit square $[0,1]^2$, it must be the case that there exists a point p in the interior of $[0,1]^2$ that is covered by at least 2 integer translates of the little regions $K_{m,n}$. Thinking through it over a fresh cup of coffee, we conclude that there are (at least) two points $x, y \in K$ that enjoy the property $x - y \in \mathbb{Z}^2$, as the overlapping regions in the unit square of Figure 6.1 suggest. This elegant conclusion, which we may call a geometric pigeon-hole principle, is part of a stronger phenomenon that was thoroughly developed by Blichfeldt. Corollary 6.2 gives another proof of this same fact but with more generality, including any full-rank lattice in dimension d.

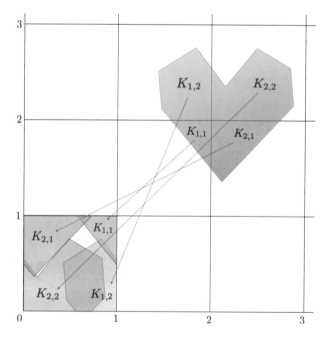

Figure 6.1. An outline of Blichfeldt's elementary argument, using a "broken heart". This result has enjoyed a lot of applications.

2. Blichfeldt's theorem

In this section we study a classical and powerful result of Blichfeldt, which will also give an alternate proof of Minkowski's first theorem. We begin with an elementary functional analysis fact (Theorem 6.1), and then we develop some straightforward number-theoretic consequences, such as a classical **pigeon-hole** geometric principle (Corollary 6.2), both of which have found many applications.

Robert Remak [207] further extended Blichfeldt's work (in a beautiful and elementary way), and we feel that it is very useful to follow his more general route. Namely, there is a dance between counting points and computing volumes. Proceeding more generally, we will begin with a simple function-analytic approach and end with the derivation of very concrete combinatorial consequences.

Theorem 6.1 (Remak, 1927). *Let $f \in L^1(\mathbb{R}^d)$ be a nonnegative function and let $\mathcal{L} \subset \mathbb{R}^d$ be a full-rank lattice.*

   (1) *There exists a point $y \in \mathbb{R}^d$ such that*

$$(6.1) \qquad (\det \mathcal{L}) \sum_{n \in \mathcal{L}} f(y + n) \geq \int_{\mathbb{R}^d} f(x) dx.$$

   (2) *On the other hand, there also exists a point $z \in \mathbb{R}^d$ such that*

$$(6.2) \qquad (\det \mathcal{L}) \sum_{n \in \mathcal{L}} f(z + n) \leq \int_{\mathbb{R}^d} f(x) dx.$$

Proof. We fix a basis $\{v_1, \ldots, v_d\}$ for the lattice $\mathcal{L}$, and we consider its fundamental parallelepiped

$$\Pi := \{\lambda_1 v_1 + \cdots + \lambda_m v_m \mid \text{all } 0 \leq \lambda_k < 1\}.$$

By Lemma 5.7, each $x \in \mathbb{R}^d$ can be written uniquely as $x = v + n$, with $v \in \Pi, n \in \mathcal{L}$. Therefore, we have

$$(6.3) \qquad \int_{\mathbb{R}^d} f(x) dx = \sum_{n \in \mathcal{L}} \int_{\Pi} f(v + n) dv = \int_{\Pi} \left(\sum_{n \in \mathcal{L}} f(v + n) \right) dv.$$

We may, of course, assume that f is not the zero function. Because f is nonnegative by the hypothesis of the theorem, we have $\int_{\mathbb{R}^d} f(x) dx > 0$, so there exists a positive constant $c > 0$ such that

$$(6.4) \qquad \int_{\mathbb{R}^d} f(x) dx = c \det \mathcal{L}.$$

To prove part (1), suppose it was true that $\sum_{n\in\mathcal{L}} f(v+n) < c$ for all $v \in \Pi$. Then using (6.3) we would obtain

$$\int_{\mathbb{R}^d} f(x)dx = \int_{\Pi}\left(\sum_{n\in\mathcal{L}} f(v+n)\right)dv < c\int_{\Pi} dv = c\det\mathcal{L},$$

contradicting (6.4). Therefore, there exists at least one point $y \in \Pi$, such that

$$\sum_{n\in\mathcal{L}} f(y+n) \geq c := \frac{1}{\det\mathcal{L}}\int_{\mathbb{R}^d} f(x)dx.$$

To prove part (2), suppose it was true that $\sum_{n\in\mathcal{L}} f(v+n) > c$ for all $v \in \Pi$. Then, using (6.3), we would obtain

$$\int_{\mathbb{R}^d} f(x)dx = \int_{\Pi}\left(\sum_{n\in\mathcal{L}} f(v+n)\right)dv > c\int_{\Pi} dv = c\det\mathcal{L},$$

again contradicting (6.4). Therefore there exists at least one point $z \in \Pi$, such that

$$\sum_{n\in\mathcal{L}} f(z+n) \leq c := \frac{1}{\det\mathcal{L}}\int_{\mathbb{R}^d} f(x)dx. \qquad \square$$

Next, we apply Theorem 6.1 to the indicator function of any set $S \subset \mathbb{R}^d$, arriving at the classical and useful result, known as "Blichfeldt's lemma" [**36**].

Corollary 6.2 (Blichfeldt's lemma, 1914). *Let $\mathcal{L} \subset \mathbb{R}^d$ be a full-rank lattice and let S be any subset of $\mathbb{R}^d$ whose volume $\mathrm{vol}(S)$ is also allowed to be ∞. We fix any positive integer m. If we have*

$$\mathrm{vol}(S) > m\det\mathcal{L},$$

then there exist $m+1$ distinct points $p_1, \ldots, p_{m+1} \in S$ such that their pairwise differences $p_i - p_j$ are all lattice points of $\mathcal{L}$.

Proof. Using the function 1_S in Remak's theorem (Theorem 6.1), we know there exists some $y \in \mathbb{R}^d$ such that

$$(6.5) \qquad (\det\mathcal{L})\sum_{n\in\mathcal{L}} 1_S(y+n) \geq \int_{\mathbb{R}^d} 1_S(x)dx = \mathrm{vol}(S) > m\det\mathcal{L},$$

where the second inequality above follows by assumption. So we arrive at

$$(6.6) \qquad \sum_{n\in\mathcal{L}} 1_S(y+n) > m,$$

which implies that $\sum_{n \in \mathcal{L}} 1_S(y + n) \geq m + 1$, since the left-hand side of (6.6) is an integer. But the latter inequality means that there are at least $m + 1$ distinct points $n_k \in \mathcal{L}$, such that $y + n_j \in S$, which is the desired conclusion (with $p_j := y + n_j \in S$). □

Even the case $m = 1$ of Corollary 6.2 is very useful, and we record it separately, as it is one of the best known results in the geometry of numbers.

Corollary 6.3 (Case $m = 1$ of Blichfeldt's lemma). *Suppose we are given a full-rank lattice $\mathcal{L} \subset \mathbb{R}^d$ and any subset $S \subset \mathbb{R}^d$ such that* $\operatorname{vol}(S) >$ det $\mathcal{L}$. *Then there exist (at least two) distinct points $a, b \in S$ such that*

$$a - b \in \mathcal{L}.$$

Now we can give another proof of Minkowski's first theorem (Theorem 4.3) as a quick consequence of Corollary 6.3.

Second proof of Minkowski's first theorem. We define $K := \frac{1}{2}B$, so we have

$$\operatorname{vol} K = \frac{1}{2^d} \operatorname{vol} B > \det \mathcal{L},$$

the latter inequality holding by the assumption of Theorem 4.3. Since vol $K >$ det $\mathcal{L}$, Corollary 6.3 tells us that there exist *distinct* points $a, b \in K$ such that $a - b \in \mathcal{L}$. If we show that $n := a - b$ is also in B, we are done. To this end, we notice that $2a \in B$ and $2b \in B$. Since B is centrally symmetric, we also have $-2b \in B$, so that

$$n = \tfrac{1}{2}(2a) + \tfrac{1}{2}(-2b) \in \tfrac{1}{2}B + \tfrac{1}{2}B = B,$$

where the latter equality holds because B is convex. □

There is another useful consequence of Remak's theorem (Theorem 6.1), originally due to Van der Corput.

Corollary 6.4 (Van der Corput). *Suppose we are given a full-rank lattice $\mathcal{L} \subset \mathbb{R}^d$, and any subset $S \subset \mathbb{R}^d$. Then there exists vectors $v_1, v_2 \in \mathbb{R}^d$ such that*

(6.7) $$|\mathcal{L} \cap (S + v_2)| \leq \frac{\operatorname{vol} S}{\det \mathcal{L}} \leq |\mathcal{L} \cap (S + v_1)|.$$

Proof. To prove the right-hand inequality in (6.7), we apply Theorem 6.1(1) to the indicator function 1_S, which gives us the existence of a $v_1 \in$

$\mathbb{R}^d$ such that

(6.8) $(\det \mathcal{L}) \sum_{n \in \mathcal{L}} 1_S(-v_1 + n) \geq \int_{\mathbb{R}^d} 1_S(x)dx := \text{vol } S.$

But we have

$$(\det \mathcal{L}) \sum_{n \in \mathcal{L}} 1_S(-v_1 + n) = (\det \mathcal{L}) \sum_{n \in \mathcal{L}} 1_{S+v_1}(n)$$

$$= (\det \mathcal{L}) |\mathcal{L} \cap (S + v_1)|,$$

and we are done. The left-hand side of inequality (6.7) is proved in exactly the same manner, this time applying Theorem 6.1(2) to the indicator function 1_S.   □

We note that in practice, the upper bound in Corollary 6.4 has found more applications.

3. Van der Corput's inequality for convex bodies

There is a natural extension of Minkowski's first theorem (Theorem 4.3) to convex centrally symmetric sets that contain any number of integer points, known as Van der Corput's inequality [255].

Corollary 6.5 (Van der Corput's inequality, 1936). *Let $\mathcal{L} \subset \mathbb{R}^d$ be a full-rank lattice, and let K be a centrally symmetric, convex d-dimensional set in $\mathbb{R}^d$, whose volume is also allowed to be ∞. We fix any positive integer m.*

(1) *If $\text{vol}(K) > m2^d \det \mathcal{L}$, then $|K \cap \mathcal{L}| \geq 2m + 1$.*

(2) *If $\text{vol}(K) = m2^d \det \mathcal{L}$, and we also assume that K is compact, then $|K \cap \mathcal{L}| \geq 2m + 1$.*

Proof. To prove (1), let us apply Blichfeldt's lemma (Lemma 6.2) to the set $\frac{1}{2}K$, whose volume equals $\frac{1}{2^d} \text{vol } K$. So there exist $m+1$ distinct points $\frac{1}{2}p_1, \ldots, \frac{1}{2}p_{m+1} \in \frac{1}{2}K$ with the property that all of their pairwise differences $\frac{1}{2}p_i - \frac{1}{2}p_j$ are distinct, and $\frac{1}{2}p_i - \frac{1}{2}p_j \in \mathcal{L}$. We define an ordering on $\mathbb{R}^d$ by saying that for any two points $x, y \in \mathbb{R}^d$, $x > y$ if the first coordinate of x is larger than the first coordinate of y. Without loss of generality we assume that $p_1 > p_2 > \cdots > p_{m+1}$. Defining $q_k := \frac{1}{2}p_k - \frac{1}{2}p_{m+1}$, we have already seen that $q_k \in \mathcal{L}$. With the ordering defined above, we also have $q_k > q_{k+1}$, and, in particular, the points $0, \pm q_1, \ldots, \pm q_m$ are all distinct.

So it suffices to show that the $2m + 1$ distinct points $0, \pm q_1, \ldots, \pm q_m$ all belong to K. But

$$q_k := \tfrac{1}{2} p_k - \tfrac{1}{2} p_1 \in \tfrac{1}{2} K - \tfrac{1}{2} K = K,$$

where we used the convexity and central symmetry of K in the last equality (recalling Exercise (5)). We leave part (2) as Exercise (7). $\qquad \square$

Example 6.6. We consider the long and thin box described by

$$K := \{x \in \mathbb{R}^d \mid |x_k| < 1, \text{ for } k = 1, 2, \ldots, d - 1, \text{ and } |x_d| < m\}$$

for any fixed positive integer m. Here, K contains precisely the integer points $(0, 0, \ldots, \pm k)$, for $k \in \{0, 1, \ldots, m - 1\}$. To summarize, K contains exactly $2m - 1$ integer points. Using the fact that $\operatorname{vol} K = m2^d$, we now see that Corollary 6.5(1) is sharp. $\qquad \square$

It is clear that the case $m = 1$ of Corollary 6.5(1) is Minkowski's theorem (Theorem 4.3); indeed when $m = 1$, the hypothesis $\operatorname{vol}(K) > 2^d \det \mathcal{L}$ tells us, via Minkowski's theorem, that K must contain at least one nonzero lattice point $p \in \mathcal{L}$. But by the central symmetry of K, we know that $-p \in \mathcal{L}$ as well, so that we have $K \cap \mathcal{L} \supset \{-p, 0, p\}$. This is equivalent to the conclusion of Corollary 6.5(1) for $m = 1$.

Sometimes it is useful to state Van der Corput's inequality (Corollary 6.5(1)) in its contrapositive form, using the (trivial) fact that the number of interior lattice points in a centrally symmetric body K is always an odd integer:

$$\text{If } |\operatorname{int} K \cap \mathcal{L}| \leq 2m - 1, \text{ then } \operatorname{vol} K \leq m2^d \det \mathcal{L}.$$

Interestingly, it was eighty-five years passed after the publication of Van der Corput's paper [255] before the equality cases of Corollary 6.5 were completely classified in Averkov's recent work [5].

Question 6.7 (Rhetorical). What about finding a Van der Corput–type inequality for bodies K that are not necessarily centrally symmetric?

There is an "easy fix" that gives us a positive answer to Question 6.7. We notice that the only time we used central symmetry in the proof of Corollary 6.5 was at the very end of the proof. So we get a more general conclusion for the body $\tfrac{1}{2} K - \tfrac{1}{2} K$ (instead of K) with precisely the same proof of Corollary 6.5.

Corollary 6.8. *Let $\mathcal{L} \subset \mathbb{R}^d$ be a full-rank lattice, and let K be a convex d-dimensional set in $\mathbb{R}^d$, whose volume is also allowed to be ∞. We fix any positive integer m.*

(1) *If* $\mathrm{vol}(K) > m2^d \det \mathcal{L}$, *then* $\left|\left(\frac{1}{2}K - \frac{1}{2}K\right) \cap \mathcal{L}\right| \geq 2m + 1$.

(2) *If* $\mathrm{vol}(K) = m2^d \det \mathcal{L}$ *and we also assume that K is compact, then*

$$\left|\left(\tfrac{1}{2}K - \tfrac{1}{2}K\right) \cap \mathcal{L}\right| \geq 2m + 1. \qquad \square$$

Example 6.9. Let us consider all convex integer polygons $K \subset \mathbb{R}^2$ with exactly one integer point in the interior of $\frac{1}{2}K - \frac{1}{2}K$, which we will assume to be the origin.

To begin, it is again useful to phrase Corollary 6.8(1) in its contrapositive form:

(6.9)   If $\left|\mathrm{int}\left(\frac{1}{2}K - \frac{1}{2}K\right) \cap \mathbb{Z}^2\right| \leq 2m - 1$, then $\mathrm{vol}\, K \leq m2^d := 4m$.

If $m = 1$, then by our assumption in (6.9) there is precisely 1 interior integer point belonging to the interior of $\frac{1}{2}K - \frac{1}{2}K$. The conclusion of (6.9) is that $\mathrm{vol}\, K \leq 4$. $\qquad \square$

Notes

(1) We mention another result of Blichfeldt, which goes in the other direction to the previous theorems, giving us a lower bound on the volume by assuming it contains enough integer points.

Theorem 6.10 (Blichfeldt, 1921). *Suppose that $K \subset \mathbb{R}^d$ is a d-dimensional convex body that contains at least d linearly independent integer points (possibly on its boundary). Then*

$$\mathrm{vol}\, K \geq \frac{1}{d!}\left(|K \cap \mathbb{Z}^d| - d\right). \qquad \square$$

Blichfeldt's latter bound is best-possible in the sense that equality is achieved, for example, by the following countable collection of integer simplices in each dimension:

(6.10) $\Delta_k := \mathrm{conv}\{0, k\,e_1, e_2, e_3, \ldots, e_d\},$

defined for each positive integer k. A moment's thought gives $\mathrm{vol}\, \Delta_k = \frac{k}{d!}$, as well as $|\Delta_k \cap \mathbb{Z}^d| = d + k$. For more information, see [**115**].

Exercises

"Math is dirty, if it is done right."
  – Günter Ziegler

(1) ♣ Let $K \subset \mathbb{R}^d$ be a convex set of finite volume (but not necessarily bounded).
   (a) Prove that if $\operatorname{vol} K > 1$, then K must contain an integer point of $\mathbb{Z}^d$.
   (b) Prove that if $\operatorname{vol} K > m$, for any positive integer m, then K must contain at least m distinct integer points of $\mathbb{Z}^d$.

(2) Suppose we have a convex and compact set $K \subset \mathbb{R}^d$ (but K is not necessarily centrally symmetric). We define $Q := \frac{1}{2}K - \frac{1}{2}K$. We already know the (trivial) fact that Q is centrally symmetric.
   Prove that $\frac{1}{2}Q - \frac{1}{2}Q = Q$.

(3) Suppose we are given a centrallly symmetric hexagon H in the plane with $\operatorname{vol} H = 8$. Prove that H contains at least five integer points (some of which might lie on its boundary as well).

(4) Prove the inequality
$$(x + y)^r \geq x^r + y^r$$
valid for all $r > 1$ and $x, y > 0$.

(5) With the usual norm $\|n\| := \sqrt{n_1^2 + \cdots + n_d^2}$, prove that if $r \in \mathbb{R}$, then
$$\sum_{n \in \mathbb{Z}^d} \frac{1}{\|n\|^r} < \infty \iff r > d.$$

(6) Given positive numbers $a_1, \ldots, a_d$ with $\prod_{k=1}^{d} a_k = 1$, prove that
$$(1 + a_1)(1 + a_2) \cdots (1 + a_d) \geq 2^d.$$

(7) ♣ Prove part (2) of Van der Corput's inequality (Corollary 6.5). Namely, we are given a full-rank lattice $\mathcal{L} \subset \mathbb{R}^d$ and a compact, convex, centrally symmetric d-dimensional set $K \subset \mathbb{R}^d$, together with any positive integer m. Prove that if $\operatorname{vol}(K) = m2^d \det \mathcal{L}$, then
$$|K \cap \mathcal{L}| \geq 2m + 1.$$

(8) Suppose $K \subset \mathbb{R}^d$ is a convex body. If there is exactly one integer point in the interior of $Q := \frac{1}{2}K - \frac{1}{2}K$, must there also exist at least one integer point in the interior of K?

(9) Suppose $K \subset \mathbb{R}^d$ is a convex body. If there is exactly one integer point in the interior of $Q := \frac{1}{2}K - \frac{1}{2}K$, must there also exist at least one integer point in the interior of K?

Suppose we are given n bounded sets $S_1, \ldots, S_n \subset \mathbb{R}^d$, and n positive numbers $c_1, \ldots, c_n$. Prove that there exists a single vector $y \in \mathbb{R}^d$ such that

$$c_1 \left| (S_1 + y) \cap \mathbb{Z}^d \right| + \cdots + c_1 \left| (S_1 + y) \cap \mathbb{Z}^d \right|$$
$$\geq c_1(\mathrm{vol}\, S_1) + \cdots + c_n(\mathrm{vol}\, S_n).$$

(Hint: Apply Theorem 6.1 to an appropriate linear combination of indicator functions.)

Chapter 7

The Fourier transform of a polytope via its vertex description: Brion's theorem

"See in **nature** the cylinder, the sphere, the cone."
– Paul Cézanne

Figure 7.1. The dodecahedron in $\mathbb{R}^3$, an example of a simple polytope. In Exercise (8), we compute its Fourier–Laplace transform by using Theorem 7.12.

1. Intuition

Here we introduce the basic tools for computing precise expressions for the Fourier transform of a polytope. To compute transforms here, we assume that we are given the vertices of a polytope $\mathcal{P}$, together with the local geometric information at each vertex of $\mathcal{P}$, namely its neighboring vertices in $\mathcal{P} \subset \mathbb{R}^d$. It turns out that computing the Fourier–Laplace transform of the tangent cone at each vertex of $\mathcal{P}$ completely characterizes the Fourier transform of $\mathcal{P}$.

Some basic families of polytopes are introduced, including simple polytopes and their polars, which are simplicial polytopes. These families of polytopes play an important role in the development of Fourier analysis on polytopes.

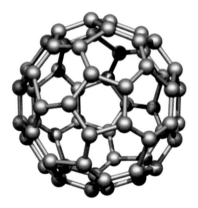

Figure 7.2. The C_{60} Carbon molecule, also known as a buckeyball, is another example of a simple polytope. The nickname "buckeyball" came from Buckminster Fuller, who used this molecule as a model for many other tensegrity structures. (the graphic is used with permission from Nanografi, at https://phys.org/news/2015-07-scientists-advance-tunable-carbon-capture-materials.html)

2. Cones, simple polytopes, and simplicial polytopes

One of the most important concepts in combinatorial geometry is the definition of a **cone** $\mathcal{K} \subset \mathbb{R}^d$, **with an apex** v, defined by

$$(7.1) \qquad \mathcal{K} := \left\{ v + \sum_{k=1}^{N} \lambda_k w_k \mid \lambda_k \geq 0 \right\}.$$

The **edge vectors** of $\mathcal{K}$ are those vectors among the $w_1, \ldots, w_N$ (not necessarily all of them) which belong to the boundary $\partial\mathcal{K}$ of $\mathcal{K}$. A fun exercise is to show that the following two conditions are equivalent:

(1) A cone $\mathcal{K}$ has an apex at the origin.

(2) $\mathcal{K}$ is a cone that enjoys the property $\lambda\mathcal{K} = \mathcal{K}$, for all $\lambda > 0$.

(See Exercise (11)).

We note that according to definition (7.1), an apex need not be unique—in Figure 7.3, the cone on the left has a unique apex, while the cone on the right has infinitely many apices. If the vectors $w_1, \ldots, w_N$ span a k-dimensional subspace of $\mathbb{R}^d$, we say that the cone $\mathcal{K}$ has **dimension** k. When a k-dimensional cone $\mathcal{K} \subset \mathbb{R}^d$ has exactly k linearly independent edge vectors $w_1, \ldots, w_k \in \mathbb{R}^d$, we call such a cone a **simplicial cone**.

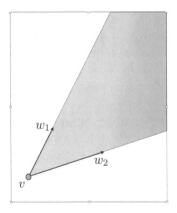 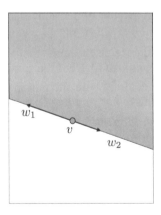

Figure 7.3. The cone on the left is pointed and has edges w_1, w_2. The cone on the right, with edges w_1, w_2, is not pointed, and in this case it is also a half-space.

A **pointed cone** is a cone $\mathcal{K} \subset \mathbb{R}^d$ with apex v, which enjoys the further property that there exists a hyperplane H with $H \cap \mathcal{K} = v$. The following four conditions give equivalent characterizations of a pointed cone $\mathcal{K}$:

(1) $\mathcal{K}$ has a unique apex.

(2) There does not exist a vector $u \in \mathbb{R}^d$ such that $\mathcal{K} + u = \mathcal{K}$.

(3) The translated cone $C := \mathcal{K} - v$, with apex at the origin, enjoys $C \cap (-C) = \{0\}$.

(4) $\mathcal{K}$ does not contain an entire line.

(See Exercise (14)).

We note that every cone has an apex, but the apex may not be unique, for example, when $\mathcal{K}$ is a half-space. All cones are unbounded regions, by definition, so some care will have to be taken when integrating over them. On the other hand, they are "almost linear", because for a cone with apex at the origin, we have

$$x, y \in \mathcal{K} \implies x + y \in \mathcal{K}.$$

This closure property, which does not exist for polytopes, makes cones extremely helpful in the analysis of polytopes (Section 4, for example).

An n-dimensional polytope $\mathcal{P} \subset \mathbb{R}^d$ is called a **simplicial polytope** if every facet of $\mathcal{P}$ is a simplex. Equivalently,

(1) Each facet of $\mathcal{P}$ has exactly n vertices.

(2) Each k-dimensional face of $\mathcal{P}$ has exactly $k + 1$ vertices, for $0 \leq k \leq n - 1$;

It is a fun exercise to show that any simplicial cone is always a pointed cone (Exercise (12)), but the converse is clearly false.

By contrast with the notion of a simplicial polytope, we have the following "polar" family of polytopes.

An n-dimensional polytope $\mathcal{P} \subset \mathbb{R}^d$ is called a **simple** polytope if every vertex is contained in exactly n edges of $\mathcal{P}$. Equivalently,

(1) Each vertex of $\mathcal{P}$ is contained in exactly n of its facets;

(2) Each k-dimensional face of $\mathcal{P}$ is contained in exactly $d - k$ facets, for all $k \geq 0$.

Example 7.1. Any d-dimensional simplex Δ is a simple polytope. In fact, any k-dimensional face of the simplex Δ is also a simplex, and hence a simple polytope of lower dimension.

The 3-dimensional dodecahedron in Figure 7.1 is also a simple polytope. Its edge graph, which is always a planar graph for a convex polytope, in this case consists of 20 vertices, 30 edges, and 12 faces. □

Example 7.2. A d-dimensional simplex also happens to be a simplicial polytope. The 3-dimensional icosahedron is a simplicial polytope. □

It is a nice exercise to show that the only polytopes which are both simple and simplicial are either simplices or 2-dimensional polygons (Exercise (15)).

Example 7.3. The d-dimensional cube $[0, 1]^d$ is a simple polytope. Its polar polytope, which is the cross-polytope $\Diamond$ (see equation (11)), is a simplicial polytope. □

One might ask whether the facets of a simple polytope necessarily simplicial polytopes. Again, an example helps here.

Example 7.4. The 120-cell is a 4-dimensional polytope whose 3-dimensional boundary is composed of 120 dodecahedra [**223**]. The 120-cell is a simple polytope, but because all of its facets are dodecahedra, it does not have any simplicial facets. □

As becomes apparent after comparing the notion of a simple polytope with that of a simplicial polytope, these two types of polytopes are indeed polar to each other, in the sense of polarity that we have already encountered in definition (2.66).

Lemma 7.5. $\mathcal{P} \subset \mathbb{R}^d$ is a simple polytope $\iff \mathcal{P}^o$ is a simplicial polytope.

See Grünbaum [**101**] for a thorough study of polarity. This polarity between simple and simplicial polytopes suggests a stronger connection between our geometric structures thus far, and the combinatorics inherent in the partially ordered set of faces of $\mathcal{P}$. Indeed, Grünbaum put it elegantly:

> "In my opinion, the most satisfying way to approach the definition of polyhedra is to distinguish between the combinatorial structure of a polyhedron, and the geometric realizations of this combinatorial structure." [**102**]

3. Tangent cones

An important step for us is to work with the Fourier–Laplace transform of a cone, and then build some theorems that allow us to simplify many geometric computations by using the frequency domain on the Fourier transform side.

We may define the **tangent cone** of each face $\mathcal{F} \subset \mathcal{P}$ as follows:

$$(7.2) \qquad \mathcal{K}_{\mathcal{F}} = \left\{ q + \lambda(p - q) \mid q \in \mathcal{F}, p \in \mathcal{P}, \lambda \in \mathbb{R}_{\geq 0} \right\}.$$

We note that, in general, $\mathcal{K}_{\mathcal{F}}$ does not necessarily contain the origin. The tangent cone is also known as the **cone of feasible directions**. Intuitively, we can imagine standing at the point $q \in \mathcal{F}$ and looking in the direction of all points that belong to P. Then we take the union of all of these directions.

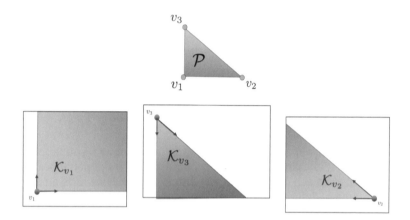

Figure 7.4. The triangle $\mathcal{P}$ has three vertex tangent cones: $\mathcal{K}_{v_1}, \mathcal{K}_{v_2}, \mathcal{K}_{v_3}$. The picture is meant to signify that these cones are, of course, unbounded.

In the very important case that the face F is a vertex of $\mathcal{P}$, we call this tangent cone a **vertex tangent cone**. Suppose we are given the neighboring vertices of v, say, $v_1, \ldots, v_N$. Then the vertex tangent cone $\mathcal{K}_v$, which is a cone with apex v, may also be generated by the edge vectors $v_k - v$:

$$(7.3) \qquad \mathcal{K}_v = \{ v + \sum_{k=1}^{N} \lambda_k(v_k - v) \mid \text{ all } \lambda_k \geq 0, \},$$

a construction we will often use in practice.

The tangent cone of an edge of a 3-dimensional convex polytope is an infinite wedge containing the whole line passing through that edge, while the tangent cone of a vertex (for a convex polytope) never contains a whole line (Exercise (13)). For nonconvex polytopes, there are many competing definition for the vertices, and not all of them agree.

One definition for the vertices of nonconvex polytopes appears in [12] using Fourier transforms of cones. But in this chapter we focus mainly on convex polytopes.

Example 7.6. For the unit cube $\square := [0,1]^d$, the tangent cone at the vertex $v = 0$ is

$$\mathcal{K}_0 = \{\lambda_1 \mathbf{e}_1 + \lambda_2 \mathbf{e}_2 + \lambda_3 \mathbf{e}_3 + \cdots + \lambda_d \mathbf{e}_d \mid \lambda_k \geq 0\},$$

which also happens to be the **positive orthant** $\mathbb{R}^d_{\geq 0}$. On the other hand, the tangent cone of $\square$ at the vertex $v = (1, 0, \ldots, 0)$ is

$$\mathcal{K}_v = v + \{\lambda_1(-\mathbf{e}_1) + \lambda_2 \mathbf{e}_2 + \lambda_3 \mathbf{e}_3 + \cdots + \lambda_d \mathbf{e}_d \mid \lambda_k \geq 0\},$$

where $\mathbf{e}_j$ is the standard unit vector along the jth axis. $\square$

Example 7.7. To relate some of these definitions, consider a d-dimensional simplex $\Delta \subset \mathbb{R}^d$. Located at each of its vertices $v \in \Delta$, we have a tangent cone K_v, as in (7.3), and here K_v is a simplicial cone. The simplex Δ is both a simple polytope and a simplicial polytope. $\square$

4. The Brianchon–Gram identity

The following combinatorial identity, called the Brianchon–Gram identity, may be thought of as a geometric inclusion-exclusion principle. This identity is quite general, holding true for any convex polytope, simple or not. For a proof of the following result see [18] or [25].

Theorem 7.8 (Brianchon–Gram identity). *Let $\mathcal{P}$ be any convex polytope. Then*

$$(7.4) \qquad 1_{\mathcal{P}} = \sum_{\mathcal{F} \subseteq \mathcal{P}} (-1)^{\dim \mathcal{F}} 1_{\mathcal{K}_F},$$

where the sum takes place over all faces of $\mathcal{P}$, including $\mathcal{P}$ itself. $\square$

It turns out that the Brianchon–Gram relations (7.4) can be shown to be equivalent (in the sense that one easily implies the other) to the **Euler–Poincare relation** (Exercise (21)) for the face-numbers of a convex polytope, which says that

$$(7.5) \qquad f_0 - f_1 + f_2 - \cdots + (-1)^{d-1} f_{d-1} + (-1)^d f_d = 1.$$

Here, f_k is the number of faces of $\mathcal{P}$ of dimension k.

Example 7.9. If we let $\mathcal{P}$ be a 2-dimensional polygon (including its interior of course) with V vertices, then if must also have V edges, and exactly 1 face, so that (7.5) tells us that $V - V + 1 = 1$, which is not very enlightening, but true. $\square$

Example 7.10. If we let $\mathcal{P}$ be a 3-dimensional polytope with V vertices, E edge, and F facets, then (7.5) tells us that $f_0 - f_1 + f_2 - f_3 = 1$, which means that $V - E + F - 1 = 1$. So we have retrieved Euler's well-known formula

$$(7.6) \qquad\qquad V - E + F = 2,$$

for the Euler characteristic of 3-dimensional polytopes. $\qquad\qquad\square$

To gain some facility with the Euler characteristic, we consider if it is possible to construct a polytope in $\mathbb{R}^3$ all of whose facets are hexagons (which are not necessarily regular). We claim that this is impossible.

Lemma 7.11. *There is no convex polytope $\mathcal{P} \subset \mathbb{R}^3$ with only hexagonal facets.*

Proof. Suppose to the contrary that all the facets of $\mathcal{P}$ are hexagons (not necessarily regular). By the assumption that $\mathcal{P}$ is a polytope, we know that each edge of $\mathcal{P}$ bounds exactly two facets. To relate the facets to the edges, consider that each facet contains exactly 6 edges, giving us $6F = 2E$. Combining this latter identity with Euler's formula (equation (7.6)), we obtain $V - E + F = V - 2F$.

Now, let us relate the facets to the vertices. Each vertex meets at least three facets, and each hexagonal facet contains exactly six vertices. From the perspective of the facets towards the vertices, we get $6F \geq 3V$, so that $V \leq 2F$. Putting things together, we arrive at

$$2 = V - E + F = V - 2F \leq 0,$$

a contradiction. $\qquad\qquad\square$

5. Brion's formula for the Fourier transform of a simple polytope

Brion proved the following extremely useful result, Theorem 7.12, concerning the Fourier–Laplace transform of a *simple polytope $\mathcal{P}$*. To describe the result, we consider each vertex v of $\mathcal{P}$, and we fix the d edge vectors $w_1(v), \ldots, w_d(v)$ that emanate from v. We recall that the nonnegative real span of the edge vectors $w_k(v)$ generate the vertex tangent cone $\mathcal{K}_v$, and that these edge vectors are not necessarily required to be unit vectors. Placing these edge vectors as columns of a matrix M_v, we define

$$\det \mathcal{K}_v := |\det M_v|,$$

the absolute value of the determinant of the ensuing matrix.

Theorem 7.12 (Brion's theorem—the continuous form, 1988). *Let $\mathcal{P} \subset \mathbb{R}^d$ be a simple, d-dimensional real polytope. Then*

$$(7.7) \qquad \int_{\mathcal{P}} e^{-2\pi i \langle u, \xi \rangle}\, du = \frac{1}{(2\pi i)^d} \sum_{v \text{ a vertex of } \mathcal{P}} \frac{e^{-2\pi i \langle v, \xi \rangle} \det \mathcal{K}_v}{\prod_{k=1}^{d} \langle w_k(v), \xi \rangle}$$

for all $\xi \in \mathbb{R}^d$ such that the denominators on the right-hand side do not vanish. □

Brion's theorem (Theorem 7.12) is one of the cornerstones of Fourier transforms of polytopes. Indeed, a similar formula to (7.7) exists for *any* polytope, namely in Theorem 7.15. We note that the determinant $\det \mathcal{K}_v$ clearly depends on our choice of edge vectors $w_1, \ldots, w_d$ for the cone $\mathcal{K}_v$, but it is straightforward (and interesting for applications) that the quotient

$$\frac{\det \mathcal{K}_v}{\prod_{k=1}^{d} \langle w_k(v), \xi \rangle}$$

does not depend on the choice of the lengths of the edge vectors (see Exercise (1)).

This new proof of Brion's theorem uses some of the Fourier techniques that we have developed so far. Because we promised a friendly approach, we first give a short outline of the relatively simple ideas of the proof.

Step 1. We begin with the Brianchon–Gram identity (a standard first step) involving the indicator functions of all of the tangent cones of $\mathcal{P}$.

Step 2. We now multiply both sides of the Brianchon–Gram identity (equation (7.4)) with the function $e^{2\pi i \langle x, \xi \rangle - \varepsilon \|x\|^2}$, where we fix an $\varepsilon > 0$, and then we will integrate over all $x \in \mathbb{R}^d$. Using these integrals, due to the damped Gaussians for each fixed $\varepsilon > 0$, we are able to keep the *same domain of convergence* for all of our ensuing functions.

Step 3. Now we let $\varepsilon \to 0$ and prove that the limit of each integral gives us something meaningful. Using integration by parts, we prove that for any vertex tangent cone $\mathcal{K}$ the corresponding integral

$$\int_{\mathcal{K}} e^{-2\pi i \langle x, \xi \rangle - \varepsilon \|x\|^2}\, dx$$

converges, as $\varepsilon \to 0$, to the desired exponential-rational function. In an analogous but easier manner, we will also prove that the corresponding integral over a nonpointed cone (which includes all faces of positive dimension) converges to zero, completing the proof.

In many of the traditional proofs of Theorem 7.12, the relevant Fourier–Laplace integrals over the vertex tangent cones have disjoint domains of convergence, lending the feeling that something magical is going on with the disjoint domains of convergence. Getting around this problem by defining functions that have the same domain of convergence (throughout the proof) was exactly the motivation for this proof. We favor a slightly longer but clearer expositional proof over a shorter, more obscure proof.

We also note that throughout the proof we will work over $\xi \in \mathbb{R}^d$, and we do not require any analytic continuation. On to the rigorous details of the proof.

Lemma 7.13. *The following limit holds*

$$(7.8) \qquad \lim_{\varepsilon \to 0} \int_0^\infty e^{-2\pi i x \xi - \varepsilon x^2} dx = \frac{1}{2\pi i \xi}$$

for all $\xi \in \mathbb{R} \setminus \{0\}$.

Proof. We proceed with integration by parts by letting $dv := e^{-2\pi i x \xi} dx$ and $u := e^{-\varepsilon x^2}$, to get

$$(7.9)$$
$$\int_0^\infty e^{-2\pi i x \xi - \varepsilon x^2} dx = e^{-\varepsilon x^2} \frac{e^{-2\pi i x \xi}}{-2\pi i \xi} \Big|_{x=0}^{x=+\infty} - \int_0^\infty \frac{e^{-2\pi i x \xi}}{-2\pi i \xi} (-2\varepsilon x) e^{-\varepsilon x^2} dx$$

$$(7.10) \qquad\qquad = \frac{1}{2\pi i \xi} - \frac{\varepsilon}{\pi i \xi} \int_0^\infty x e^{-2\pi i x \xi - \varepsilon x^2} dx$$

$$(7.11) \qquad\qquad = \frac{1}{2\pi i \xi} - \frac{1}{\pi i \xi} \int_0^\infty u e^{-2\pi i \frac{u}{\sqrt{\varepsilon}} \xi} e^{-u^2} du$$

where we have used the substitution $u := \sqrt{\varepsilon} x$ in the last equality (7.11). We now notice that

$$\lim_{\varepsilon \to 0} \int_0^\infty e^{-2\pi i \frac{u}{\sqrt{\varepsilon}} \xi} u e^{-u^2} du = \lim_{\varepsilon \to 0} \hat{g}\left(\frac{\xi}{\sqrt{\varepsilon}}\right),$$

where $g(u) := u e^{-u^2} 1_{[0,+\infty]}(u)$ is an absolutely integrable function. But we know by the Riemann–Lebesgue lemma (Lemma 3.13) that

$$\lim_{|w| \to \infty} \hat{g}(w) = 0,$$

finishing the proof. $\qquad\qquad\qquad\qquad\qquad\qquad\qquad\qquad\qquad\qquad\square$

Lemma 7.14. *Let $\mathcal{K}_v$ be a d-dimensional simplicial pointed cone, with apex v, and edge vectors $w_1, \ldots, w_d \in \mathbb{R}^d$. Then*

$$(7.12) \qquad \lim_{\varepsilon \to 0} \int_{\mathcal{K}_v} e^{-2\pi i \langle x, \xi \rangle - \varepsilon \|x\|^2} dx = \frac{1}{(2\pi i)^d} \frac{e^{-2\pi i \langle v, \xi \rangle} \det \mathcal{K}_v}{\prod_{k=1}^{d} \langle w_k(v), \xi \rangle},$$

for all $\xi \in \mathbb{R}^d$ such that $\prod_{k=1}^{d} \langle w_k(v), \xi \rangle \neq 0$.

Proof. We begin by noticing that we may prove the conclusion in the case that $v = 0$, the origin, and for simplicity write $\mathcal{K}_v := \mathcal{K}$ in this case.

The proof proceeds by induction on the dimension d. Lemma 7.13 was the $d = 1$ case. Now we map the simplicial cone $\mathcal{K}$ to the non-negative orthant $\mathbb{R}_{\geq 0}^d$ by the matrix M^{-1}, where M is the d by d matrix whose columns are the vectors w_k. Thus, in the integral of (7.12), we let $x := My$, with $y \in \mathbb{R}_{\geq 0}^d$, so that $dx = |\det M| dy$. Recalling the notation $\det \mathcal{K} := |\det M|$, we have

$$(7.13) \qquad \int_{\mathcal{K}} e^{-2\pi i \langle x, \xi \rangle - \varepsilon \|x\|^2} dx = |\det \mathcal{K}| \int_{\mathbb{R}_{\geq 0}^d} e^{-2\pi i \langle My, \xi \rangle - \varepsilon \|My\|^2} dy.$$

It suffices to therefore prove the following limiting identity:

$$(7.14) \qquad \lim_{\varepsilon \to 0} \int_{\mathbb{R}_{\geq 0}^d} e^{-\varepsilon \|My\|^2} e^{-2\pi i \langle My, \xi \rangle} dy = \frac{1}{(2\pi i)^d} \frac{1}{\prod_{k=1}^{d} \langle w_k(v), \xi \rangle}.$$

For the sake of clarity (and keeping in mind that this is a friendly book), let us see how the $d = 2$ case works.

Case $d = 2$. Although it is technically not necessary to include this case, we include it for extra clarity of exposition. We fix the variable y_2, and perform integration by parts on y_1. To this end we define

$$(7.15) \qquad dv_1 := e^{-2\pi i \langle My, \xi \rangle} dy_1 \quad \text{and} \quad u_1 := e^{-\varepsilon \|My\|^2},$$

both being considered as functions of y_1 alone. First, we have

$$(7.16) \qquad dv_1 := e^{-2\pi i \langle y, M^t \xi \rangle} dy_1 = e^{-2\pi i \left(y_1 \langle w_1, \xi \rangle + y_2 \langle w_2, \xi \rangle \right)} dy_1,$$

so we get

$$(7.17) \qquad v_1 = \frac{e^{-2\pi i \langle y, M^t \xi \rangle}}{-2\pi i \langle w_1, \xi \rangle}.$$

Next, we have

(7.18) $$\frac{du_1}{dy_1} := \frac{d}{dy_1}\left(e^{-\varepsilon\|My\|^2}\right)$$

$$= \frac{d}{dy_1}\left(e^{-\varepsilon y^T(M^TM)y}\right)$$

(7.19) $$= \frac{d}{dy_1}\left(e^{-\varepsilon\|w_1\|^2 y_1^2 - 2\varepsilon\langle w_1,w_2\rangle y_1 y_2 - \varepsilon\|w_2\|^2 y_2^2}\right)$$

(7.20) $$= \left(-2\varepsilon\|w_1\|^2 y_1 - 2\varepsilon\langle w_1,w_2\rangle y_2\right)e^{-\varepsilon\|My\|^2}.$$

Summarizing, the integral in (7.14) is now

$$\int_0^\infty \int_0^\infty e^{-\varepsilon\|My\|^2} e^{-2\pi i\langle My,\xi\rangle} dy$$

$$:= \int_0^\infty \int_0^\infty u_1 dv_1 dy_2$$

$$= \int_0^\infty \left(u_1 v_1\Big|_0^\infty - \int_0^\infty v_1 \frac{du_1}{dy_1} dy_1\right) dy_2$$

$$= \int_0^\infty \left(e^{-\varepsilon\|My\|^2} \frac{e^{-2\pi i\langle y,M^t\xi\rangle}}{-2\pi i\langle w_1,\xi\rangle}\Big|_{y_1=0}^{y_1=\infty} - \int_0^\infty v_1 \frac{du_1}{dy_1} dy_1\right) dy_2$$

$$= \int_0^\infty \left(0 + e^{-\varepsilon\|w_2\|^2 y_2^2 - 2\pi i y_2\langle w_2,\xi\rangle} \frac{1}{2\pi i\langle w_1,\xi\rangle} - \int_0^\infty v_1 \frac{du_1}{dy_1} dy_1\right) dy_2$$

$$= \frac{1}{2\pi i\langle w_1,\xi\rangle} \int_0^\infty e^{-\varepsilon\|w_2\|^2 y_2^2 - 2\pi i y_2\langle w_2,\xi\rangle} dy_2 - \int_0^\infty \int_0^\infty v_1 \frac{du_1}{dy_1} dy_1 dy_2$$

$$\rightarrow \frac{1}{(2\pi i)^2\langle w_1,\xi\rangle\langle w_2,\xi\rangle} - \lim_{\varepsilon\to 0} \int_0^\infty \int_0^\infty v_1 \frac{du_1}{dy_1} dy_1 dy_2,$$

as $\varepsilon \to 0$, where we have employed Lemma 7.13 in the last step above. So, by the statement we made in (7.14), it only remains to prove that

(7.21) $$\lim_{\varepsilon\to 0} \int_0^\infty \int_0^\infty v_1 \frac{du_1}{dy_1} dy_1 dy_2 = 0.$$

We have reduced the problem to computing the limit

$$\lim_{\varepsilon \to 0} \int_0^\infty \int_0^\infty v_1 \frac{du_1}{dy_1} dy_1 dy_2$$

$$= \lim_{\varepsilon \to 0} \int_0^\infty \int_0^\infty \frac{e^{-2\pi i \langle y, M^t \xi \rangle}}{2\pi i \langle w_1, \xi \rangle} \Big(2\varepsilon \|w_1\|^2 y_1 + 2\varepsilon \langle w_1, w_2 \rangle y_2 \Big)$$

$$\cdot e^{-\varepsilon \|My\|^2} dy_1 dy_2$$

$$:= I_1 + I_2,$$

where we have defined

$$I_1 := \frac{\|w_1\|^2}{\pi i \langle w_1, \xi \rangle} \lim_{\varepsilon \to 0} \varepsilon \int_0^\infty \int_0^\infty y_1 e^{-\varepsilon \|My\|^2 - 2\pi i \langle y, M^t \xi \rangle} dy_1 dy_2,$$

and

$$I_2 := \frac{\langle w_1, w_2 \rangle}{\pi i \langle w_1, \xi \rangle} \lim_{\varepsilon \to 0} \varepsilon \int_0^\infty \int_0^\infty y_2 e^{-\varepsilon \|My\|^2 - 2\pi i \langle y, M^t \xi \rangle} dy_1 dy_2.$$

By the symmetry of the two integrals in I_1 and I_2, it suffices to show $I_1 = 0$:

$$I_1 := \frac{\|w_1\|^2}{\pi i \langle w_1, \xi \rangle} \lim_{\varepsilon \to 0} \varepsilon \int_0^\infty \int_0^\infty y_1 e^{-\varepsilon \|My\|^2 - 2\pi i \langle y, M^t \xi \rangle} dy_1 dy_2$$

$$= \frac{\|w_1\|^2}{\pi i \langle w_1, \xi \rangle} \int_0^\infty \Big(\lim_{\varepsilon \to 0} \varepsilon \int_0^\infty y_1 e^{-\varepsilon \|My\|^2 - 2\pi i \langle y, M^t \xi \rangle} dy_1 \Big) dy_2$$

We will show that the limit of the inner 1-dimensional integral vanishes. We replace y_1 by $\frac{1}{\sqrt{\varepsilon}} y_1$ (hence dy_1 also gets replaced by $\frac{1}{\sqrt{\varepsilon}} dy_1$) in the innermost integral, to obtain

$$\lim_{\varepsilon \to 0} \varepsilon \int_0^\infty y_1 e^{-\varepsilon \|My\|^2 - 2\pi i \langle y, M^t \xi \rangle} dy_1$$

$$= \lim_{\varepsilon \to 0} \int_0^\infty y_1 e^{-\|My\|^2} e^{-2\pi i \frac{1}{\sqrt{\varepsilon}} \langle y, M^t \xi \rangle} dy_1$$

$$:= \lim_{\varepsilon \to 0} \hat{g} \Big(\frac{1}{\sqrt{\varepsilon}} M^t \xi \Big),$$

where $g(y_1) := y_1 e^{-\|My\|^2} 1_{[0,+\infty)}(y_1)$ is an absolutely integrable function. Finally, it follows from the Riemann–Lebesgue lemma (Lemma 3.13) that

$$\lim_{|w| \to \infty} \hat{g}(w) = 0,$$

finishing the proof for $d = 2$.

The general case. Now the proof of (7.14) for any dimension d will be identical in structure to the case $d = 2$. We fix the variables $y_2, \ldots, y_d$ and perform integration by parts on the variable y_1. We again use the same definitions as in the $d = 2$ case:

$$(7.22) \qquad dv_1 := e^{-2\pi i \langle My, \xi \rangle} dy_1 \quad \text{and} \quad u_1 := e^{-\varepsilon \|My\|^2},$$

both being considered as functions of y_1 alone. Similarly to the $d = 2$ case, we have

$$v_1 = \frac{e^{-2\pi i \langle y, M^t \xi \rangle}}{-2\pi i \langle w_1, \xi \rangle}.$$

and

$$(7.23) \qquad du_1 := \frac{d}{dy_1} \left(e^{-\varepsilon \|My\|^2} \right) dy_1$$

$$= \frac{d}{dy_1} \left(e^{-\varepsilon y^T (M^T M) y} \right) dy_1$$

$$(7.24) \qquad = \frac{d}{dy_1} \left(e^{-\varepsilon \|w_1\|^2 y_1^2 - 2\varepsilon \sum_{k=2}^{d} \langle w_1, w_k \rangle y_1 y_k - \varepsilon Q(y_2, \ldots, y_d)} \right) dy_1$$

$$(7.25) \qquad = -2\varepsilon \sum_{k=1}^{d} \langle w_1, w_k \rangle y_k e^{-\varepsilon \|My\|^2} dy_1,$$

where $Q := (0, y_2, \ldots, y_d) M^t M (0, y_2, \ldots, y_d)^t$ is the corresponding quadratic form in the variables $y_2, \ldots, y_d$. As in the $d = 2$ case, integrating by parts in the variable y_1, and using the notation $y := (y_1, z)$ with $z \in \mathbb{R}^{d-1}$, now gives us

$$\int_{\mathbb{R}^d_{\geq 0}} e^{-2\pi i \langle My, \xi \rangle - \varepsilon \|My\|^2} dy$$

$$:= \int_{\mathbb{R}^{d-1}_{\geq 0}} \left(\int_0^\infty u_1 dv_1 \right) dz$$

$$= \int_{\mathbb{R}^{d-1}_{\geq 0}} \left(u_1 v_1 \Big|_0^\infty - \int_0^\infty v_1 du_1 \right) dz$$

$$= \int_{\mathbb{R}^{d-1}_{\geq 0}} \left(e^{-\varepsilon \|My\|^2} \frac{e^{-2\pi i \langle y, M^t \xi \rangle}}{-2\pi i \langle w_1, \xi \rangle} \Big|_{y_1=0}^{y_1=\infty} - \int_0^\infty v_1 \frac{du_1}{dy_1} dy_1 \right) dz$$

$$= \int_{\mathbb{R}^{d-1}_{\geq 0}} \left(0 + \frac{e^{-\varepsilon Q(z) - 2\pi i \langle z, M^t \xi \rangle}}{2\pi i \langle w_1, \xi \rangle} - \int_0^\infty v_1 \frac{du_1}{dy_1} dy_1 \right) dz$$

$$= \frac{1}{2\pi i \langle w_1, \xi \rangle} \int_{\mathbb{R}^{d-1}_{\geq 0}} e^{-\varepsilon Q(z) - 2\pi i \langle z, M^t \xi \rangle} dz - \int_{\mathbb{R}^{d-1}_{\geq 0}} \int_0^\infty v_1 \frac{du_1}{dy_1} dy_1 dz$$

$$\longrightarrow \frac{1}{(2\pi i)^d \prod_{k=1}^d \langle w_k, \xi \rangle} - \lim_{\varepsilon \to 0} \int_{\mathbb{R}^{d-1}_{\geq 0}} \int_0^\infty v_1 \frac{du_1}{dy_1} dy_1 dz,$$

where we have used the induction hypothesis for $d - 1$ in the last step. The last step of the proof, namely showing that

$$\lim_{\varepsilon \to 0} \int_{\mathbb{R}^{d-1}_{\geq 0}} \int_0^\infty v_1 \frac{du_1}{dy_1} dy_1 dz = 0,$$

is now identical in reasoning to the case $d = 2$, and we are done. $\qquad \square$

6. Proof of Theorem 7.12, the Fourier transform of a simple polytope

Proof of Theorem 7.12. We begin with the Brianchon–Gram identity:

$$(7.26) \qquad 1_{\mathcal{P}} = \sum_{\mathcal{F} \subseteq \mathcal{P}} (-1)^{\dim \mathcal{F}} 1_{K_{\mathcal{F}}}.$$

We fix any $\xi \in \mathbb{R}^d$, and any $\varepsilon > 0$. Multiplying both sides of (7.26) by $e^{-2\pi i \langle x, \xi \rangle - \varepsilon \|x\|^2}$, and integrate over all $x \in \mathbb{R}^d$, we have

$$\int_{\mathbb{R}^d} 1_{\mathcal{P}}(x) e^{-2\pi i \langle x, \xi \rangle - \varepsilon \|x\|^2} dx$$

$$= \sum_{\mathcal{F} \subseteq \mathcal{P}} (-1)^{\dim \mathcal{F}} \int_{\mathbb{R}^d} 1_{K_F}(x) e^{-2\pi i \langle x, \xi \rangle - \varepsilon \|x\|^2} dx.$$

Equivalently,

$$(7.27) \qquad \int_{\mathcal{P}} e^{-2\pi i \langle x, \xi \rangle - \varepsilon \|x\|^2} dx = \sum_{\mathcal{F} \subseteq \mathcal{P}} (-1)^{\dim \mathcal{F}} \int_{K_F} e^{-2\pi i \langle x, \xi \rangle - \varepsilon \|x\|^2} dx.$$

For each fixed $\varepsilon > 0$, all integrands in (7.27) are Schwartz functions, and so all of the integrals in the latter identity now converge absolutely (and rapidly). We identify two types of tangent cones that may occur on the right-hand side of (7.27) for each face $\mathcal{F} \subseteq \mathcal{P}$.

Case 1. When $\mathcal{F} = v$, a vertex, we have the vertex tangent cone $\mathcal{K}_v$: these are the tangent cones that exist for each vertex of $\mathcal{P}$. It is a standard fact that all of these vertex tangent cones are pointed cones. By hypothesis, all of our vertex tangent cones are simplicial cones, so letting $\varepsilon \to 0$ and calling on Lemma 7.14, we obtain the required limit for $\int_{\mathcal{K}_v} e^{2\pi i \langle x, \xi \rangle - \varepsilon \|x\|^2} dx$.

Case 2. When $\mathcal{F}$ is not a vertex, we have the tangent cone $\mathcal{K}_{\mathcal{F}}$, and it is a standard fact that in this case $\mathcal{K}_{\mathcal{F}}$ always contains a line. Another standard fact in the land of polytopes is that each tangent cone in this case may be written as $\mathcal{K}_{\mathcal{F}} = \mathbb{R}^k \oplus \mathcal{K}_p$, the direct sum of a copy of Euclidean space with a pointed cone $\mathcal{K}_p$ for any point $p \in \mathcal{F}$. As a sidenote, it is also true that $\dim \mathcal{F} = k$.

We would like to show that for all faces $\mathcal{F}$ that are not vertices of $\mathcal{P}$, the associated integrals tend to 0:

$$\int_{\mathcal{K}_F} e^{-2\pi i \langle x, \xi \rangle - \varepsilon \|x\|^2} dx \to 0,$$

as $\varepsilon \to 0$. Indeed,

$$(7.28) \qquad \int_{\mathcal{K}_F} e^{-2\pi i \langle x, \xi \rangle - \varepsilon \|x\|^2} dx$$

$$(7.29) \qquad = \int_{\mathbb{R}^k \oplus \mathcal{K}_p} e^{-2\pi i \langle x, \xi \rangle - \varepsilon \|x\|^2} dx$$

$$(7.30) \qquad = \int_{\mathbb{R}^k} e^{-2\pi i \langle x, \xi \rangle - \varepsilon \|x\|^2} dx \int_{\mathcal{K}_p} e^{-2\pi i \langle x, \xi \rangle - \varepsilon \|x\|^2} dx.$$

The integral $\int_{\mathbb{R}^k} e^{-2\pi i \langle x, \xi \rangle - \varepsilon \|x\|^2} dx$ is precisely the usual Fourier transform of a Gaussian, which is known to be the Gaussian

$$G_\varepsilon(x) := \varepsilon^{-k/2} e^{-\frac{\pi}{\varepsilon} \|x\|^2}$$

by Exercise (18). It is apparent that for any fixed nonzero value of $x \in \mathbb{R}^k$, we have $\lim_{\varepsilon \to 0} G_\varepsilon(x) = 0$. Finally, by Lemma 7.14 again, the limit

$$\lim_{\varepsilon \to 0} \int_{\mathcal{K}_p} e^{-2\pi i \langle x, \xi \rangle - \varepsilon \|x\|^2} dx$$

is finite, because $\mathcal{K}_p$ is another pointed cone. Therefore the product of the integrals in (7.30) tends to zero, completing the proof. □

7. The Fourier transform of any real polytope

Brion's theorem, which holds for simple polytopes, is particularly useful whenever we are given a polytope in terms of its local data at the vertices—including the edge vectors for each vertex tangent cone. We can then easily write down the Fourier transform of a simple polytope, by Theorem 7.12. What happens, though, for nonsimple polytopes? There is the following natural extension of Brion's theorem (Theorem 7.12) to all real polytopes, which is now easy to prove.

Theorem 7.15 (Fourier transform of any real polytope). *Let $\mathcal{P} \subset \mathbb{R}^d$ be any d-dimensional polytope. Then*

$$(7.31) \qquad \int_{\mathcal{P}} e^{-2\pi i \langle u, \xi \rangle} \, du = \sum_{v \in V} \frac{e^{-2\pi i \langle v, \xi \rangle}}{(2\pi i)^d} \sum_{j=1}^{M(v)} \frac{\det \mathcal{K}_j(v)}{\prod_{k=1}^d \langle w_{j,k}(v), \xi \rangle},$$

for all $\xi \in \mathbb{R}^d$ such that none of the denominators vanish:

$$\prod_{k=1}^d \langle w_{j,k}(v), \xi \rangle \neq 0.$$

At each vertex vertex $v \in \mathcal{P}$, the vertex tangent cone $\mathcal{K}_v$ is triangulated into simplicial cones using the notation $\mathcal{K}_v = \mathcal{K}_1(v) \cup \cdots \cup \mathcal{K}_{M(v)}(v)$.

Proof. The proof here is identical in almost every aspect to the proof of Theorem 7.12, except for Case 1 of its proof. By contrast with the proof of Case 1, here our vertex tangent cones $\mathcal{K}_v$ need not be simplicial. However, we may triangulate each vertex tangent cone $\mathcal{K}_v$ into simplicial cones $\mathcal{K}_1(v), \ldots \mathcal{K}_{M(v)}(v)$, so that we have the disjoint union $\mathcal{K}_v = \mathcal{K}_1(v) \cup \cdots \cup \mathcal{K}_{M(v)}(v)$. Therefore,

$$\lim_{\varepsilon \to 0} \int_{\mathcal{K}_v} e^{-2\pi i \langle x, \xi \rangle - \varepsilon \|x\|^2} dx = \lim_{\varepsilon \to 0} \sum_{j=1}^{M(v)} \int_{\mathcal{K}_{j,v}} e^{-2\pi i \langle x, \xi \rangle - \varepsilon \|x\|^2} dx$$

$$= \sum_{j=1}^{M(v)} \lim_{\varepsilon \to 0} \int_{\mathcal{K}_{j,v}} e^{-2\pi i \langle x, \xi \rangle - \varepsilon \|x\|^2} dx$$

$$= \left(\frac{-1}{2\pi i} \right)^d \sum_{j=1}^{M(v)} \frac{e^{-2\pi i \langle v, \xi \rangle} \det \mathcal{K}_j(v)}{\prod_{k=1}^d \langle w_{j,k}(v), \xi \rangle},$$

where we have used Lemma 7.14 in the last equality, owing to the fact that all of the cones $\mathcal{K}_j(v)$ are simplicial. The calculation above is valid for each $\xi \in \mathbb{R}^d$ such that $\prod_{k=1}^d \langle w_{j,k}(v), \xi \rangle \neq 0$ for all vertices v and all $j = 1, \ldots, M(v)$. $\square$

The nonvanishing condition $\prod_{k=1}^{d} \langle w_{j,k}(v), \xi \rangle \neq 0$ may be restated more combinatorially as follows. Let $\mathcal{H}$ be the finite union of hyperplanes, where each hyperplane is defined by

$$(7.32) \qquad \mathcal{H} := \{\xi \in \mathbb{R}^d \mid \langle w_{j,k}(v), \xi \rangle = 0\}.$$

In other words, $\mathcal{H}$ is the union of all hyperplanes that are orthogonal to any edge of $\mathcal{P}$. So the only restriction in (7.31) is that $\xi \notin \mathcal{H}$. But again we emphasize that these "singularities" are removable singularities because after extending both sides to all $\xi \in \mathbb{C}^d$, the left-hand side of (7.31) is an entire function of $\xi \in \mathbb{C}^d$.

8. Fourier–Laplace transforms of cones

What about the Fourier transform of a cone? Well, if we naively try to use the same integrand over a cone, the integral will diverge. But there is a way to fix this divergence by replacing the real vector $\xi \in \mathbb{R}^d$ by a complex vector $z \in \mathbb{C}^d$. Let us consider what would happen if we formally replace the variable $\xi \in \mathbb{R}^d$ by a complex vector $z := x + iy \in \mathbb{C}^d$, to obtain the transform:

$$1_{\mathcal{P}}(z) := \int_{\mathcal{P}} e^{-2\pi i \langle u, z \rangle} \, du.$$

Our inner product $\langle u, z \rangle := u_1 z_1 + \cdots + u_d z_d$ is always the usual inner product on $\mathbb{R}^d$, defined without using the Hermitian inner product here. In other words, we simply use the usual inner product on $\mathbb{R}^d$, and then formally substitute complex numbers z_k into it. This means, by definition, that

$$(7.33) \qquad \int_{\mathcal{P}} e^{-2\pi i \langle u, z \rangle} \, du := \int_{\mathcal{P}} e^{-2\pi i \langle u, x + iy \rangle}$$

$$(7.34) \qquad \qquad := \int_{\mathcal{P}} e^{-2\pi i \langle u, x \rangle} e^{2\pi \langle u, y \rangle} \, du,$$

so that we have an extra useful real factor of $e^{2\pi \langle u, y \rangle}$ that makes the integral converge quite rapidly over unbounded domains, provided that $\langle u, y \rangle < 0$. If we set $y = 0$, then it is clear that we retrieve the usual Fourier transform of $\mathcal{P}$, while if we set $x = 0$, we get a new integral, which we call the **Laplace transform** of $\mathcal{P}$. Finally, the **Fourier–Laplace transform** of $\mathcal{P}$ is defined by

$$\hat{1}_{\mathcal{P}}(z) := \int_{\mathcal{P}} e^{-2\pi i \langle u, z \rangle} \, du,$$

valid for any $z \in \mathbb{C}^d$ for which the integral converges.

One clear reason for the use and flexibility of the full Fourier–Laplace transform (as opposed to just the Fourier transform) is the fact that for a cone $\mathcal{K}$, its usual Fourier transform diverges. But if we allow a complex variable $z \in \mathbb{C}^d$, then the integral does converge on a restricted domain. Namely, the Fourier–Laplace transform of a cone $\mathcal{K}$ is defined by

$$\hat{1}_{\mathcal{K}}(z) := \int_{\mathcal{K}} e^{-2\pi i \langle u, z \rangle} \, du,$$

for a certain set of $z \in \mathbb{C}^d$, but we can easily understand its precise domain of convergence. For an arbitrary cone $\mathcal{K} \subset \mathbb{R}^d$, we define its **dual cone** by

$$(7.35) \qquad \mathcal{K}^* := \{ y \in \mathbb{R}^d \mid \langle y, u \rangle < 0 \text{ for all } u \in \mathcal{K} \},$$

which is an open cone. As one might expect, there is an easy duality: $\mathcal{K}_1 \subset \mathcal{K}_2 \iff \mathcal{K}_2^* \subset \mathcal{K}_1^*$ (Exercise (16)).

Example 7.16. Given the 1-dimensional cone $\mathcal{K}_0 := \mathbb{R}_{\geq 0}$, we compute its Fourier–Laplace transform:

$$\int_{\mathcal{K}_0} e^{-2\pi i u z} \, du = \int_0^\infty e^{-2\pi i u z} \, du$$

$$= \frac{1}{-2\pi i z} e^{-2\pi i u (x+iy)} \Big|_{u=0}^{u=\infty}$$

$$= \frac{1}{-2\pi i z} e^{-2\pi i u x} e^{2\pi u y} \Big|_{u=0}^{u=\infty}$$

$$= \frac{1}{-2\pi i z} (0 - 1) = \frac{1}{2\pi i} \frac{1}{z},$$

valid for all $z := x + iy \in \mathbb{C}$ such that $y < 0$. We note that for such a fixed complex z, $|e^{-2\pi i u z}| = e^{2\pi u y}$ is a rapidly decreasing function of $u \in \mathbb{R}_{>0}$, because $y < 0$. $\qquad \square$

Now let us work out the Fourier–Laplace transform of a d-dimensional cone whose apex is the origin.

Lemma 7.17. *Let $\mathcal{K} \subset \mathbb{R}^d$ be a simplicial, d-dimensional cone, with apex at the origin. If the edges of $\mathcal{K}$ are labelled $w_1, \ldots, w_d$, then*

$$\hat{1}_K(z) := \int_{\mathcal{K}} e^{-2\pi i \langle u, z \rangle} \, du = \frac{1}{(2\pi i)^d} \frac{\det \mathcal{K}}{\prod_{k=1}^d \langle w_k, z \rangle}.$$

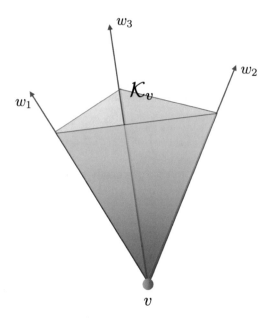

Figure 7.5. A simplicial pointed cone in $\mathbb{R}^3$, with apex v and edge vectors w_1, w_2, w_3.

*Furthermore, the **domain of convergence** for the latter integral is naturally associated with the dual cone, and it is given by*

$$\{z := x + iy \in \mathbb{C}^d \mid y \in \mathcal{K}^*\}.$$

Proof. We first compute the Fourier–Laplace transform of the positive orthant $\mathcal{K}_0 := \mathbb{R}^d_{\geq 0}$, with a complex vector $z = x + iy \in \mathbb{C}^d$:

$$(7.36) \qquad \hat{1}_{\mathcal{K}_0}(z) := \int_{\mathcal{K}_0} e^{-2\pi i \langle z, u \rangle} du$$

$$(7.37) \qquad = \int_{\mathbb{R}_{\geq 0}} e^{-2\pi i z_1 u_1} du_1 \cdots \int_{\mathbb{R}_{\geq 0}} e^{-2\pi i z_d u_d} du_d$$

$$(7.38) \qquad = \prod_{k=1}^{d} \frac{0 - 1}{-2\pi i z_k}$$

$$= \frac{1}{(2\pi i)^d} \frac{1}{z_1 z_2 \cdots z_d}.$$

Next, the positive orthant $\mathcal{K}_0$ may be mapped to the cone $\mathcal{K}$ by a linear transformation. Namely, we may use the matrix M whose columns are defined to be the edges of $\mathcal{K}$, so that by definition $\mathcal{K} = M(\mathcal{K}_0)$. Using this mapping, we have

$$\hat{1}_{\mathcal{K}}(z) := \int_{\mathcal{K}} e^{-2\pi i \langle z, u \rangle} du$$

$$= |\det M| \int_{\mathcal{K}_0} e^{-2\pi i \langle z, Mt \rangle} dt$$

$$= |\det M| \int_{\mathcal{K}_0} e^{-2\pi i \langle M^T z, t \rangle} dt$$

$$= \frac{1}{(2\pi i)^d} \frac{|\det M|}{\prod_{k=1}^{d} \langle w_k, z \rangle}.$$

where in the second equality we have made the substitution $u = Mt$, with $t \in \mathcal{K}_0, u \in \mathcal{K}$, and $du = |\det M| dt$. In the final equality, we used equation (7.38), noting that the kth element of the vector $M^T z$ is $\langle w_k, z \rangle$, and we note that by definition $|\det M| = \det \mathcal{K}$.

For the domain of convergence of the integral, we observe that

$$e^{-2\pi i \langle u, z \rangle} = e^{-2\pi i \langle u, x + iy \rangle} = e^{-2\pi i \langle u, x \rangle} e^{2\pi \langle u, y \rangle},$$

and because $\left| e^{-2\pi i \langle u, x \rangle} \right| = 1$, the integral $\int_{\mathcal{K}} e^{-2\pi i \langle u, z \rangle} du$ converges $\iff$ $\langle u, y \rangle < 0$ for all $u \in \mathcal{K}$. But by definition of the dual cone, this means that $y \in \mathcal{K}^*$. $\qquad \square$

Example 7.18. Given the 2-dimensional cone $\mathcal{K} := \{\lambda_1\left(\begin{smallmatrix}1\\5\end{smallmatrix}\right) + \lambda_2\left(\begin{smallmatrix}-3\\2\end{smallmatrix}\right) \mid \lambda_1, \lambda_2 \in \mathbb{R}_{\geq 0}\}$, we compute its Fourier–Laplace transform, and find its domain of convergence. By Lemma 7.17,

$$\hat{1}_{\mathcal{K}}(z) := \int_{\mathcal{K}} e^{-2\pi i \langle u, z \rangle} \, du = \frac{1}{(2\pi i)^2} \frac{17}{(z_1 + 5z_2)(-3z_1 + 2z_2)},$$

valid for all $z = \left(\begin{smallmatrix}z_1\\z_2\end{smallmatrix}\right) := x + iy$ such that $y \in \mathcal{K}^*$. Here the dual cone is given by

$$\mathcal{K}^* = \text{int}\{\lambda_1\left(\begin{smallmatrix}5\\-1\end{smallmatrix}\right) + \lambda_1\left(\begin{smallmatrix}-2\\-3\end{smallmatrix}\right) \mid \lambda_1, \lambda_2 \in \mathbb{R}_{\geq 0}\}. \qquad \square$$

To compute the Fourier–Laplace transform of a simplicial cone $\mathcal{K}$ whose apex is $v \in \mathbb{R}^d$, we may first compute the transform of the translated cone $\mathcal{K}_0 := \mathcal{K} - v$, whose apex is at the origin, using the previous lemma. We can then use the fact that the Fourier transform behaves in a simple way under translations, namely,

$$\hat{1}_{K+v}(z) = e^{2\pi i \langle z, v \rangle} \hat{1}_K(z),$$

to obtain the following result (Exercise (4)).

Corollary 7.19. *Let $\mathcal{K}_v \subset \mathbb{R}^d$ be a simplicial d-dimensional cone, whose apex is $v \in \mathbb{R}^d$. Then*

$$(7.39) \qquad \hat{1}_{\mathcal{K}_v}(z) := \int_{\mathcal{K}_v} e^{-2\pi i \langle u, z \rangle} \, du = \frac{1}{(2\pi i)^d} \frac{e^{-2\pi i \langle v, z \rangle} \det \mathcal{K}_v}{\prod_{k=1}^{d} \langle w_k, z \rangle},$$

a rational-exponential function. More generally, for any d-dimensional cone $\mathcal{K}_v \subset \mathbb{R}^d$ with apex v, we can always triangulate $\mathcal{K}_v$ into $M(v)$ simplicial subcones $\mathcal{K}_j(v)$ [67], and apply the previous result to each simplicial subcone, obtaining

$$(7.40) \quad \hat{1}_{\mathcal{K}_v}(z) := \int_{\mathcal{K}_v} e^{-2\pi i \langle u, z \rangle} \, du = \frac{e^{-2\pi i \langle v, z \rangle}}{(2\pi i)^d} \sum_{j=1}^{M(v)} \frac{\det \mathcal{K}_j(v)}{\prod_{k=1}^{d} \langle w_{j,k}(v), z \rangle},$$

a rational-exponential function. □

For a nonsimple polytope, the question of computing efficiently the Fourier–Laplace transforms of all of its tangent cones becomes unwieldy, as far as we know (this problem is related to the $P \neq NP$ problem). In fact, even computing the volume of a polytope is already known to be NP-hard in general, and the volume is just the Fourier transform evaluated at one point: vol $\mathcal{P} = 1_{\mathcal{P}}(0)$.

Example 7.20. Let us work out a 2-dimensional example of Brion's theorem (Theorem 7.12) using Fourier–Laplace transforms of tangent cones. We will find the rational-exponential function for the Fourier–Laplace transform of the triangle Δ, whose vertices are defined by $v_1 := \binom{0}{0}$, $v_2 := \binom{a}{0}$, and $v_3 := \binom{0}{b}$, with $a > 0, b > 0$.

First, the tangent cone at the vertex $v_1 := \binom{0}{0}$ is simply the nonnegative orthant in this case, with edge vectors $w_1 = \binom{1}{0}$ and $w_2 = \binom{0}{1}$. Its determinant, given these two edge vectors, is equal to 1. Its Fourier–Laplace transform is

$$(7.41) \qquad \int_{\mathcal{K}_{v_1}} e^{-2\pi i \langle x, z \rangle} \, dx = \frac{1}{(2\pi i)^2} \frac{1}{z_1 z_2},$$

and note that here we must have both $\mathfrak{I}(z_1) > 0$ and $\mathfrak{I}(z_2) > 0$ in order to make the integral converge. Here we use the standard notation $\mathfrak{I}(z)$ is the imaginary part of z.

The second tangent cone at vertex v_2 has edges $w_1 = \binom{-a}{b}$ and $w_2 = \binom{0}{-b}$ (recall that we do not have to normalize the edge vectors at all).

Its determinant has absolute value equal to ab, and its Fourier–Laplace transform is

$$(7.42) \qquad \int_{\mathcal{K}_{v_2}} e^{-2\pi i \langle x, z \rangle} \, dx = \left(\frac{1}{2\pi i}\right)^2 \frac{(ab)e^{-2\pi i a z_1}}{(-az_1 + bz_2)(-az_1)},$$

and here the integral converges only for those z for which $\mathfrak{I}(-az_1 + bz_2) > 0$ and $\mathfrak{I}(-az_1) > 0$.

Finally, the third tangent cone at vertex v_3 has edges $w_1 = \left(\begin{smallmatrix} a \\ -b \end{smallmatrix}\right)$ and $w_2 = \left(\begin{smallmatrix} 0 \\ -b \end{smallmatrix}\right)$. Its determinant has absolute value equal to ab, and its Fourier–Laplace transform is

$$(7.43) \qquad \int_{\mathcal{K}_{v_3}} e^{-2\pi i \langle x, z \rangle} \, dx = \left(\frac{1}{2\pi i}\right)^2 \frac{(ab)e^{-2\pi i b z_2}}{(az_1 - bz_2)(-bz_2)},$$

and here the integral converges only for those z for which $\mathfrak{I}(az_1 - bz_2) > 0$ and $\mathfrak{I}(-bz_2) > 0$.

We can again see quite explicitly the disjoint domains of convergence in this example, so that there is not even one value of $z \in \mathbb{C}^2$ for which all three Fourier–Laplace transforms of all the tangent cones converge simultaneously. Despite this apparent shortcoming, Brion's identity (Theorem (7.12)) still tells us that we may somehow still add these local contributions of the integrals at the vertices combine to give us a formula for the Fourier–Laplace transform of the triangle:

$$\hat{1}_\Delta(z) := \int_\Delta e^{-2\pi i \langle x, z \rangle} dx$$

$$= \left(\frac{1}{2\pi i}\right)^2 \left(\frac{1}{z_1 z_2} + \frac{-b \, e^{-2\pi i a z_1}}{(-az_1 + bz_2)z_1} + \frac{-a \, e^{-2\pi i b z_2}}{(az_1 - bz_2)z_2} \right),$$

which is *now* magically valid for all generic $(z_1, z_2) \in \mathbb{C}^2$; in other words, it is now valid for all $(z_1, z_2) \in \mathbb{C}^2$ except those values which make the denominators vanish. $\qquad \square$

9. The Fourier transform of a polygon

Here we give an efficient formula for the Fourier transform of any polygon, namely Corollary 7.22. Let us begin with a simple and natural question: What is the Fourier transform of a hexagon?

Example 7.21. Suppose we have a hexagon H that is symmetric about the origin. We know that its Fourier transform is real-valued by Lemma 4.16, so that it makes sense to form a 3-dimensional graph of the points $(x, y, \hat{1}_H(x, y))$, as in Figure 7.6.

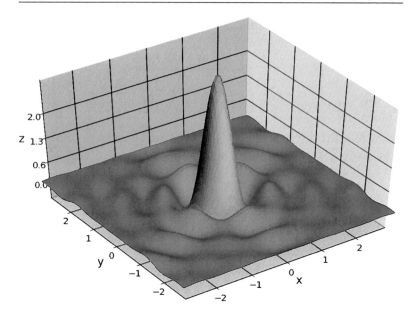

Figure 7.6. A graph of the Fourier transform $\hat{1}_H(x, y)$ of the symmetric hexagon H in Example 7.21. The graph suggests that the largest peak occurs at the origin, which indeed is always the case, by Exercise (26).

To be concrete, let us define a (parametrized) hexagon H with the following vertices:

$$v_1 = \left(\frac{2c}{\sqrt{3}}, 0\right), \quad v_2 = \left(\frac{c}{\sqrt{3}}, c\right), \quad v_3 = \left(\frac{-c}{\sqrt{3}}, c\right),$$
$$v_4 = -v_1, \quad v_5 = -v_2, \quad v_6 = -v_3,$$

for each fixed parameter $c > 0$. Just for fun, our hexagon is scaled so that it has an inscribed circle of radius c, which may be useful in future applications.

We first use Brion's theorem (Theorem 7.12) to compute the Fourier transforms of the six vertex tangent cones of H. For v_1, the two rays defining K_{v_1} are $w_1 := v_2 - v_1 = (-\frac{c}{\sqrt{3}}, c)$ and $w_2 := v_6 - v_1 = (-\frac{c}{\sqrt{3}}, -c)$, so the Fourier Transform of K_{v_1} is

$$\hat{1}_{K_{v_1}}(z) = \frac{e^{-2\pi i \frac{2c}{\sqrt{3}} z_1}}{(-2\pi i)^2} \frac{\frac{2c^2}{\sqrt{3}}}{(-\frac{c}{\sqrt{3}} z_1 + cz_2)(-\frac{c}{\sqrt{3}} z_1 - cz_2)}$$

$$= \frac{2\sqrt{3}}{(2\pi)^2} \frac{e^{-\frac{4\pi i c}{\sqrt{3}} z_1}}{(-z_1 + \sqrt{3} z_2)(z_1 + \sqrt{3} z_2)}.$$

For v_2, the two rays are $w_1 := v_3 - v_2 = (-\frac{2c}{\sqrt{3}}, 0)$ and $w_2 := v_1 - v_2 = (\frac{c}{\sqrt{3}}, -c)$, giving us

$$\hat{1}_{K_{v_2}}(z) = \frac{e^{-2\pi i(\frac{c}{\sqrt{3}} z_1 + cz_2)}}{(-2\pi i)^2} \frac{\frac{2c^2}{\sqrt{3}}}{\frac{-2c}{\sqrt{3}} z_1(\frac{c}{\sqrt{3}} z_1 - cz_2)} = \frac{\sqrt{3}}{(2\pi)^2} \frac{e^{-2\pi c i(\frac{1}{\sqrt{3}} z_1 + z_2)}}{z_1(z_1 - \sqrt{3} z_2)}.$$

For v_3, the two rays are $w_1 := v_4 - v_3 = (-\frac{c}{\sqrt{3}}, -c)$ and $w_2 := v_2 - v_3 = (\frac{2c}{\sqrt{3}}, 0)$, giving us

$$\hat{1}_{K_{v_3}}(z) = \frac{e^{-2\pi i(-\frac{c}{\sqrt{3}} z_1 + cz_2)}}{(-2\pi i)^2} \frac{\frac{c}{\sqrt{3}}}{(-\frac{c}{\sqrt{3}} z_1 - cz_2)\frac{2c}{\sqrt{3}} z_1}$$

$$= \frac{\sqrt{3}}{(2\pi)^2} \frac{e^{-2\pi c i(-\frac{1}{\sqrt{3}} z_1 + z_2)}}{z_1(z_1 + \sqrt{3} z_2)}.$$

By the inherent symmetry of our hexagon H, the computations for the other tangent cones are just $\hat{1}_{K_{-v}}(z) = 1_{K_v}(-z)$, so we have

$$\hat{1}_H(z_1, z_2)$$

$$:= \int_H e^{-2\pi i \langle \xi, z \rangle} d\xi$$

$$= \hat{1}_{K_{v_1}}(z) + \hat{1}_{K_{v_1}}(-z) + \hat{1}_{K_{v_2}}(z) + \hat{1}_{K_{v_2}}(-z) + \hat{1}_{K_{v_3}}(z) + \hat{1}_{K_{v_3}}(-z)$$

$$= \frac{\sqrt{3}}{2\pi^2} \left(\frac{2\cos(\frac{4\pi c}{\sqrt{3}} z_1)}{(-z_1 + \sqrt{3} z_2)(z_1 + \sqrt{3} z_2)} + \frac{\cos(\frac{2\pi c}{\sqrt{3}} z_1 + 2\pi c z_2)}{z_1(z_1 - \sqrt{3} z_2)} \right.$$

$$\left. + \frac{\cos(\frac{2\pi c}{\sqrt{3}} z_1 - 2\pi c z_2)}{z_1(z_1 + \sqrt{3} z_2)} \right). \quad \square$$

More generally, suppose we are given the vertices of a polygon $\mathcal{P} \subset \mathbb{R}^2$, so that

$$\mathcal{P} := \mathrm{conv}\{v_1, \dots, v_N\},$$

the convex hull of its vertices. Brion's theorem (Theorem 7.12) again gives us a closed form in terms of the Fourier transforms of its vertex tangent cones. To this end, we first compute the FT of each of its vertex tangent cones:

$$\hat{1}_{\mathcal{K}_{v_k}}(\xi) = \frac{e^{-2\pi i \langle v, \xi \rangle} \det \mathcal{K}_{v_k}}{\langle v_{k+1} - v_k, \xi \rangle \langle v_{k-1} - v_k, \xi \rangle},$$

where

$$\det \mathcal{K}_{v_k} = \begin{pmatrix} | & | \\ v_{k+1} - v_k & v_{k-1} - v_k \\ | & | \end{pmatrix}$$

is the invertible 2×2 real matrix whose columns are the edge vectors that are incident with the vertex v_k. For any real convex polygon, we may order its vertices in a counterclockwise orientation $v_1, \dots, v_N$, with the definition $v_{N+1} := v_1$.

With this notation we have obtained the following expression for the Fourier transform of a polygon as a direct consequence of Brion's theorem (Theorem 7.12).

Corollary 7.22. *Given any convex polygon $\mathcal{P} \subset \mathbb{R}^2$, its Fourier transform has the formula*

$$\int_{\mathcal{P}} e^{-2\pi i \langle u, \xi \rangle} \, du = -\frac{1}{4\pi^2} \sum_{k=1}^{N} \frac{e^{-2\pi i \langle v, \xi \rangle} \det \mathcal{K}_{v_k}}{\langle v_{k+1} - v_k, \xi \rangle \langle v_{k-1} - v_k, \xi \rangle}$$

for all $\xi \in \mathbb{R}^2$ such that ξ is not orthogonal to any edge of $\mathcal{P}$. □

10. Each polytope has its moments

The following somewhat surprising formula for the volume of a simple polytope gives us a very rapid algorithm for computing volumes of simple polytopes. We note that it is an NP-hard problem [11] to compute volumes of general polytopes without fixing the dimension. Nevertheless, there are various other families of polytopes whose volumes possess tractable algorithms.

Theorem 7.23 (Lawrence [153]). *Suppose $\mathcal{P} \subset \mathbb{R}^d$ is a simple d-dimensional polytope. For a vertex tangent cone $\mathcal{K}_v$ of $\mathcal{P}$, fix a set of edges of the* *cone, say, $w_1(v), w_2(v), \ldots, w_d(v) \in \mathbb{R}^d$. Then*

$$(7.44) \qquad \text{vol } \mathcal{P} = \frac{(-1)^d}{d!} \sum_{v \in \text{vertices}(\mathcal{P})} \frac{\langle v, z \rangle^d \det \mathcal{K}_v}{\prod_{k=1}^{d} \langle w_k(v), z \rangle}$$

for all $z \in \mathbb{C}^d$, such that z does not belong to the finite union of hyperplanes that are orthogonal to any edge of $\mathcal{P}$.

*More generally, for any integer $k \geq 0$, we have the **moment formulas**:*

$$(7.45) \qquad \int_{\mathcal{P}} \langle x, z \rangle^k dx = \frac{(-1)^d k!}{(k+d)!} \sum_{v \in \text{vertices}(\mathcal{P})} \frac{\langle v, z \rangle^{k+d} \det \mathcal{K}_v}{\prod_{m=1}^{d} \langle w_m(v), z \rangle}.$$

Proof. We begin with Brion's identity (equation (7.7)) and we substitute $z := t z_0$ for a fixed complex vector $z_0 \in \mathbb{C}^d$, and any positive real value of t:

$$\int_{\mathcal{P}} e^{-2\pi i \langle u, z_0 \rangle t} \, du = \left(\frac{1}{2\pi i} \right)^d \sum_{v \in \text{vertices}(\mathcal{P})} \frac{e^{-2\pi i \langle v, z_0 \rangle t} \det \mathcal{K}_v}{t^d \prod_{m=1}^{d} \langle w_m(v), z_0 \rangle}.$$

Now we expand both sides in their Taylor series about $t = 0$. The left-hand side becomes

$$\int_{\mathcal{P}} \sum_{k=0}^{\infty} \frac{1}{k!} \left(-2\pi i \langle u, z_0 \rangle t \right)^k \, du$$

$$= \left(\frac{1}{2\pi i} \right)^d \sum_{v \in \text{vertices}(\mathcal{P})} \frac{\sum_{j=0}^{\infty} \frac{1}{j!} \left(-2\pi i \langle v, z_0 \rangle t \right)^j \det \mathcal{K}_v}{t^d \prod_{m=1}^{d} \langle w_m(v), z_0 \rangle}$$

Integrating term by term on the left-hand side, we get

$$(7.46)$$
$$\sum_{k=0}^{\infty} \frac{t^k}{k!} (-2\pi i)^k \int_{\mathcal{P}} \langle u, z_0 \rangle^k \, du$$
$$(7.47)$$
$$= \left(\frac{1}{2\pi i} \right)^d \sum_{v \in \text{vertices}(\mathcal{P})} \frac{\det \mathcal{K}_v}{\prod_{m=1}^{d} \langle w_m(v), z_0 \rangle} \sum_{j=0}^{\infty} \frac{t^{j-d}}{j!} (-2\pi i)^j \langle v, z_0 \rangle^j.$$

Comparing the coefficients of t^k on both sides, we have

$$\frac{(-2\pi i)^k}{k!} \int_{\mathcal{P}} \langle u, z_0 \rangle^k \, du$$

$$= \left(\frac{1}{2\pi i}\right)^d \sum_{v \in \text{vertices}(\mathcal{P})} \frac{\det \mathcal{K}_v}{\prod_{m=1}^d \langle w_m(v), z_0 \rangle} \frac{1}{(k+d)!} (-2\pi i)^{k+d} \langle v, z_0 \rangle^{k+d}.$$

Simplifying, we arrive at the moment formulas for each $k \geq 0$:

$$\int_{\mathcal{P}} \langle u, z_0 \rangle^k \, du = (-1)^d \frac{k!}{(k+d)!} \sum_{v \text{ a vertex of } \mathcal{P}} \frac{\langle v, z_0 \rangle^{k+d} \det \mathcal{K}_v}{\prod_{m=1}^d \langle w_m(v), z_0 \rangle}.$$

In particular, when $k = 0$, we get the volume formula (7.44).   □

The following interesting identities are also consequences of the proof above, and were discovered by Brion and Vergne [49].

Corollary 7.24. *Suppose $\mathcal{P} \subset \mathbb{R}^d$ is a simple d-dimensional polytope. For each $0 \leq j \leq d - 1$, we have*

$$(7.48) \qquad \sum_{v \in \text{vertices}(\mathcal{P})} \frac{\langle v, z \rangle^j \det \mathcal{K}_v}{\prod_{m=1}^d \langle w_m(v), z \rangle} = 0,$$

for all $z \in \mathbb{C}^d$ such that z does not belong to the finite union of hyperplanes that are orthogonal to any edge of $\mathcal{P}$.

Proof. We may go back to (7.46) and stare at that Laurent series in t. We notice that the singular part in t contains exactly the required terms (7.48) as coefficients of t^j, for $j = 0, -1, \ldots, -(d-1)$. These coefficients must vanish because the left-hand side of the identity (7.46) does not contain any singular terms in t.   □

11. The zero set of the Fourier transform

Now we know enough to derive some new results regarding the real zero set of the Fourier transform: $Z_{\mathbb{R}}(\mathcal{P}) := \{x \in \mathbb{R}^d \mid \hat{1}_{\mathcal{P}}(\xi) = 0\}$.

Corollary 7.25. *Let $\mathcal{P} \subset \mathbb{R}^d$ be a d-dimensional integer polytope $\mathcal{P} \subset \mathbb{R}^d$. Then*

$$(7.49) \qquad\qquad \hat{1}_{\mathcal{P}}(\xi) = 0$$

for each integer point $\xi \in \mathbb{Z}^d$ that does not belong to the finite union of hyperplanes orthogonal to an edge of $\mathcal{P}$.

Proof. Any integer polytope may be triangulated into integer simplices (not necessarily unimodular simplices), and we will call such a collection of simplices T. We consider any of these integer simplices, say Δ. By Brion's theorem (Theorem 7.12) we have

$$
(7.50) \qquad \hat{1}_\Delta(\xi) = \left(\frac{1}{2\pi i}\right)^d \sum_{v \text{ a vertex of } \mathcal{P}} \frac{e^{-2\pi i \langle v, \xi \rangle} \det \mathcal{K}_v}{\prod_{k=1}^d \langle w_k(v), \xi \rangle}
$$

for all $\xi \in \mathbb{R}^d$ such that the denominators on the right-hand side do not vanish. Here we have used the fact that Δ is a simple polytope. In particular, for an integer point $\xi \in \mathbb{Z}^d$ (which does not belong to the finite union of hyperplanes that are orthogonal to any edge of $\mathcal{P}$), we have $\langle \xi, v \rangle \in \mathbb{Z}$ using the assumption that the vertices $v \in \mathcal{P}$ are integer points. Consequently, we have

$$
(7.51) \qquad \hat{1}_\Delta(\xi) = \frac{1}{(2\pi i)^d} \sum_{v \text{ a vertex of } \mathcal{P}} \frac{\det \mathcal{K}_v}{\prod_{k=1}^d \langle w_k(v), \xi \rangle} = 0
$$

by Corollary 7.24 (the $j = 0$ case). Summing all of the Fourier transforms of the simplices that belong to our triangulation (and ignoring their boundaries because the FT vanishes there), we arrive at

$$
(7.52) \qquad \hat{1}_\mathcal{P}(\xi) = \sum_{\Delta \in T} \hat{1}_\Delta(\xi) = 0. \qquad \square
$$

Given a polytope $\mathcal{P} \subset \mathbb{R}^d$, we call a vector $\xi \in \mathbb{R}^d$ a **generic frequency** (relative to $\mathcal{P}$) if ξ is not orthogonal to any edge of $\mathcal{P}$ (and hence not orthogonal to any other face of $\mathcal{P}$). All other $\xi \in \mathbb{R}^d$ are orthogonal to some edge of $\mathcal{P}$, and are called **special frequencies**.

We recall the hyperplane arrangement defined by the finite collection of hyperplanes orthogonal to any edge of $\mathcal{P}$:

$$
(7.53) \qquad \mathcal{H} := \{\xi \in \mathbb{R}^d \mid \langle \xi, E \rangle = 0, \text{ for any edge } E \text{ of } \mathcal{P}\}
$$

$$
(7.54) \qquad = \{\text{special frequencies}\},
$$

which came up naturally in the general formula for the Fourier transform of a polytope (Theorem 7.15). It is clear from the definitions above that the special frequencies are $\xi \in \mathcal{H}$, and the generic frequencies are $\xi \notin \mathcal{H}$.

Hence, Corollary 7.25 may be restated as follows. For an integer polytope $\mathcal{P} \subset \mathbb{R}^d$, we have

$$
(7.55) \qquad \hat{1}_\mathcal{P}(\xi) = 0
$$

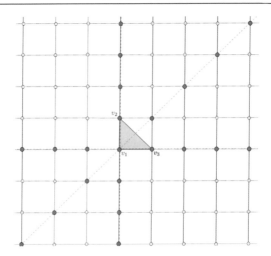

Figure 7.7. Here the green integer points depict the special integer frequencies of the Fourier transform $\hat{1}_\Delta(\xi)$, where Δ is the standard triangle. These special integer frequency vectors are orthogonal to the three sides of Δ. For all other nonzero integer points (the generic integer frequencies), $\hat{1}_\Delta(\xi) = 0$, according to Corollary 7.25.

for all generic frequencies $\xi \in \mathbb{Z}^d$. In other words,

$$\{\text{generic integer frequencies}\} \subset Z_{\mathbb{R}}(\mathcal{P}).$$

It is natural to wonder if the latter vanishing of the transform is sufficient to identify a polytope among the collection of all convex bodies, as follows.

Conjecture 7.26. Suppose we know that $\mathcal{P}$ is a convex body in $\mathbb{R}^d$. Suppose further that we are given the data

$$\hat{1}_\mathcal{P}(\xi) = 0, \text{ for all } \xi \in \mathbb{Z}^d \setminus \mathcal{H},$$

where $\mathcal{H}$ is some finite collection of hyperplanes passing through the origin. Then:

(1) $\mathcal{P}$ is a polytope.

(2) Moreover, $\mathcal{P}$ is an integer polytope, and $\mathcal{H}$ is precisely the collection of hyperplanes that are orthogonal to all of the edges of $\mathcal{P}$.

Although Conjecture 7.26 appears here for the first time, it highlights the importance of the zero set of the Fourier transform.

Kobayashi [**136**] asked the following question, which is still open.

Question 7.27. Given a convex body $\mathcal{P}$, does the complex zero set
$$Z_{\mathbb{C}}(\mathcal{P}) := \{\zeta \in \mathbb{C}^d \mid \hat{1}_{\mathcal{P}}(\zeta) = 0\}$$
uniquely determine $\mathcal{P}$ among all convex bodies, up to translations?

We have already seen, in Theorem 4.6 (Kolountzakis's vanishing criterion), that if we only assume that $\{\mathbb{Z}^d \setminus \{0\}\} \subset Z_{\mathbb{R}}(\mathcal{P})$, then even this very sparse assumption on the zero set is already equivalent to $\mathcal{P}$ multitiling Euclidean space.

We finish this section by reinterpreting Brion's theorem (Theorem 7.15) using the meromorphic continuing the real vector ξ, and the hyperplane arrangement $\mathcal{H}$ of (7.53). We may extend the Fourier transform $\hat{1}_{K_v}(z)$ of a rational cone to all of $\mathbb{C}^d$, using the bold-face notation $\hat{\mathbf{1}}_{K_v}(z)$, by using the fact that it is a rational function in several variables:

$$(7.56) \qquad \hat{\mathbf{1}}_{K_v}(z) := \frac{e^{-2\pi i \langle v, z \rangle}}{(2\pi i)^d} \sum_{j=1}^{M(v)} \frac{\det \mathcal{K}_j(v)}{\prod_{k=1}^{d} \langle w_{j,k}(v), z \rangle},$$

for all $z \notin \mathcal{H}$. With this notation we may rewrite Theorem 7.15, for any real polytope $\mathcal{P}$, as follows:

$$(7.57) \qquad \int_{\mathcal{P}} e^{-2\pi i \langle u, z \rangle}\, du = \sum_{v \in V} \hat{\mathbf{1}}_{K_v}(z),$$

valid for all $z \notin \mathcal{H}$.

Notes

(1) There is a lot more literature about the zero set of the Fourier transform of a convex body. For more information, we refer the reader to [**34**], [**136**], [**137**], [**140**].

(2) There is a lot of literature devoted to triangulations of cones, polytopes, and general point-sets, and the reader is invited to consult the excellent and encyclopedic book on triangulations by Jesús de Loera, Jörg Rambau, and Francisco Santos [**67**].

(3) There is growing literature on integration of functions over polytopes. In a forthcoming volume, we will see more of these topics; an early contribution was made by Jean B. Lasserre [**149**].

(4) The notion of a **random polytope** has literature as well, and although we do not go into this topic here, one classic survey paper is by Imre Bárány [**11**].

(5) The attempt to extend Ehrhart theory to nonrational polytopes, whose vertices have some irrational coordinates, is ongoing. The pioneering papers of Burton Randol ([**184**] and [**205**]) extended integer point counting to algebraic polytopes, meaning that their vertices are allowed to have coordinates that are algebraic numbers. Recently, a growing number of papers are considering all real dilates of a rational polytope, which is still rather close to the Ehrhart theory of rational polytopes.

In this direction, it is natural to ask how much more of the geometry of a given polytope $\mathcal{P}$ can be captured by counting integer points in all of its positive real dilates. Suppose we translate a d-dimensional integer polytope $\mathcal{P} \subset \mathbb{R}^d$ by an integer vector $n \in \mathbb{Z}^d$. The standard Ehrhart theory gives us an invariance principle, namely the equality of the Ehrhart polynomials for $\mathcal{P}$ and $\mathcal{P} + n$:

$$L_{\mathcal{P}+n}(t) = L_{\mathcal{P}}(t)$$

for all *integer* dilates $t > 0$.

However, when we allow t to be a positive *real* number, then it is in general **false** that

$$L_{\mathcal{P}+n}(t) = L_{\mathcal{P}}(t) \text{ for all } t > 0.$$

In fact, these two Ehrhart functions are so different in general, that by the breakthrough of Tiago Royer [**215**], it is even possible to uniquely reconstruct the polytope $\mathcal{P}$ if we know all the counting quasi-polynomials $L_{\mathcal{P}+n}(t)$ for all integer translates $n \in \mathbb{Z}^d$. In other words, the work of [**215**] shows that for two rational polytopes $\mathcal{P}, Q \subset \mathbb{R}^d$, we have

$$L_{\mathcal{P}+n}(t) = L_{Q+n}(t) \text{ for all } n \in \mathbb{Z}^d \text{ and all } t > 0 \iff \mathcal{P} = Q.$$

It is rather astounding that just by counting integer points in sufficiently many translates of $\mathcal{P}$, we may completely reconstruct the whole polytope $\mathcal{P}$ uniquely. Royer further demonstrated [**216**] that such an idea also works if we replace a polytope by any symmetric convex body. It is now natural to try to prove the following conjecture.

Conjecture 7.28. Suppose we are given polytopes $\mathcal{P}, Q \subset \mathbb{R}^d$. We can always find a finite subset $F \subset \mathbb{Z}^d$ (which may depend on $\mathcal{P}$ and Q) such that

(7.58) $L_{\mathcal{P}+n}(t) = L_{Q+n}(t)$ for all $n \in F$, and all $t > 0 \iff \mathcal{P} = Q$.

(6) Corollary 7.25 is due to Ricardo Diaz and Sinai Robins in an unpublished manuscript, so we decided to include it here.

(7) There is also a line integral formulation for the Fourier transform of a polytope, as given by Bence Borda [**43**, Theorem 2.4] in his work on enumerating lattice points in algebraic cross-polytopes and simplices.

Exercises

"It is better to solve one problem five different ways, than to solve five problems one way."
– George Pólya

(1) ♣ Although $\det \mathcal{K}_v$ depends on the choice of the length of each edge of $\mathcal{K}_v$, show that the ratio

$$\frac{|\det \mathcal{K}_v|}{\prod_{k=1}^{d} \langle w_k(v), z \rangle}$$

remains invariant if we replace each edge $w_k(v)$ of a simplicial cone by a constant positive multiple of it, say $\alpha_k w_k(v)$ with $\alpha_k > 0$.
   (Here z is any generic vector, meaning that $\langle w_k(v), z \rangle \neq 0$ for all $1 \leq k \leq d$).

(2) Consider the regular hexagon $\mathcal{P} \subset \mathbb{R}^2$, whose vertices are the sixth roots of unity.
   (a) Compute the area of $\mathcal{P}$ using Theorem 7.23.
   (b) Compute all of the moments of $\mathcal{P}$, as in Theorem 7.23.

(3) Compute the Fourier transform of the triangle Δ whose vertices are given by

$$(1, 0), (0, 1), (-c, -c),$$

where $c > 0$.

(4) ♣ Prove Corollary 7.19 for a simplicial cone $\mathcal{K}_v$, whose apex is v, by translating a cone whose vertex is at the origin, to get

$$\hat{1}_{\mathcal{K}_v}(z) := \int_{\mathcal{K}_v} e^{-2\pi i \langle u, z \rangle} \, du = \frac{1}{(2\pi i)^d} \frac{e^{-2\pi i \langle v, z \rangle} \det \mathcal{K}_v}{\prod_{k=1}^{d} \langle w_k, z \rangle}.$$

(5) Using some of the idea in Lemma 7.12, prove the following:

(a) For all nonzero $\alpha \in \mathbb{R}$,

$$\lim_{\varepsilon \to 0} \int_0^\infty \cos(\alpha x)\, e^{-\varepsilon |x|^2} dx = 0.$$

(b) For all nonzero $\alpha \in \mathbb{R}$,

$$\lim_{\varepsilon \to 0} \int_0^\infty \sin(\alpha x)\, e^{-\varepsilon |x|^2} dx = \frac{1}{\alpha}.$$

(6) Consider the following 3-dimensional polytope $\mathcal{P}$, whose vertices are as follows:

$$\{(0,0,0),\ (1,0,0),\ (0,1,0),\ (1,1,0),\ (0,0,1)\},$$

"a pyramid over a square". Compute its Fourier–Laplace transform $\hat{1}_{\mathcal{P}}(z)$.

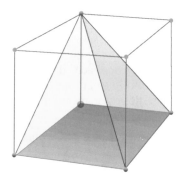

Figure 7.8. The pyramid over a square in Exercise (6).

(7) We recall that the 3-dimensional cross-polytope (also called an octahedron) was defined by

$$\lozenge := \{(x_1, x_2, x_3) \in \mathbb{R}^d \mid |x_1| + |x_2| + |x_3| \leq 1\}.$$

Compute the Fourier–Laplace transform of $\lozenge$ by using Theorem 7.15.

Notes. Here not all of the tangent cones are simplicial cones, so we may triangulate each vertex tangent cones into simplicial cones or you may try your own methods.

(8) (Hard-ish). Here we will find the Fourier transform of a dodeca-hedron $\mathcal{P}$, centered at the origin. Suppose we fix the following 20 vertices of $\mathcal{P}$:

$$\left\{(\pm 1, \pm 1, \pm 1), \left(0, \pm\phi, \pm\frac{1}{\phi}\right), \left(\pm\frac{1}{\phi}, 0, \pm\phi\right), \left(\pm\phi, \pm\frac{1}{\phi}, 0\right)\right\},$$

where $\phi := \frac{1+\sqrt{5}}{2}$. It turns out that $\mathcal{P}$ is a simple polytope. Compute its Fourier–Laplace transform using Theorem 7.12.

Notes. All of the vertices of $\mathcal{P}$ given here can easily be seen to lie on a sphere S of radius $\sqrt{3}$, and this is a regular embedding of the dodecahedron. It is also true (though a more difficult fact) that these 20 points maximize the volume of any polytope whose 20 vertices lie on the surface of this sphere S.

Figure 7.9. A climbing wall in Sweden made up of dodecahedrons, showing one of their real-life applications.

(9) Define the 3-dimensional polytope

$$\mathcal{P} := \operatorname{conv}\{(0,0,0), (1,0,0), (0,1,0), (0,0,1), (a,b,c)\},$$

where we fix real the positive real numbers a, b, c. Compute $\hat{1}_{\mathcal{P}}(z)$ by computing the Fourier–Laplace transforms of its tangent cones.

Notes. Here, not all of the tangent cones are simplicial cones.

(10) This exercise extends Exercise (6) to $\mathbb{R}^d$, as follows. Consider the d-dimensional polytope $\mathcal{P}$, called a "pyramid over a cube", defined by the convex hull of the unit cube $[0,1]^{d-1} \subset \mathbb{R}^{d-1}$, with the point $(0,0,\ldots,0,1) \in \mathbb{R}^d$. Compute its Fourier–Laplace transform $\hat{1}_{\mathcal{P}}(z)$.

(11) ♣ Show the following two conditions are equivalent:
    (a) A cone $\mathcal{K}$ has an apex at the origin.
    (b) $\mathcal{K}$ is a cone that enjoys the property $\lambda\mathcal{K} = \mathcal{K}$, for all $\lambda > 0$.

(12) ♣ Suppose we are given a d-dimensional simplicial cone $\mathcal{K} \subset \mathbb{R}^d$ (so be definition $\mathcal{K}$ has exactly d edges). Show that $\mathcal{K}$ must be pointed.

(13) ♣ Show that for any polytope $\mathcal{P} \subset \mathbb{R}^d$, a vertex tangent cone $\mathcal{K}_v$ never contains a whole line.

(14) ♣ Show that if $\mathcal{K}$ is a cone with an apex v (not necessarily a unique apex), the following conditions are equivalent:
    (a) $\mathcal{K}$ is a pointed cone.
    (b) There exists a hyperplane H such that $H \cap \mathcal{K} = v$.
    (c) The translated cone $C := \mathcal{K} - v$, with apex at the origin, enjoys $C \cap (-C) = \{0\}$.
    (d) $\mathcal{K}$ has a unique apex.
    (e) $\mathcal{K}$ does not contain an entire line.

(15) ♣ Show that the only polytopes that are both simple and simplicial are either simplices, or 2-dimensional polygons.

    For the next couple of problems, we recall—for the sake of disambiguation with the polar set below—that for any cone $\mathcal{K} \subset \mathbb{R}^d$, its dual cone $\mathcal{K}^*$ was defined (recalling (7.35)) by

$$\mathcal{K}^* := \{y \in \mathbb{R}^d \mid \langle y, u \rangle < 0 \text{ for all } u \in \mathcal{K}\}.$$

(16) ♣ Show that if we have reverse inclusions for dual cones. Namely,

$$\mathcal{K}_1 \subset \mathcal{K}_2 \iff \mathcal{K}_2^* \subset \mathcal{K}_1^*.$$

(17) Show that if we take the Minkowski sum $K_1 + K_2$ of two cones $\mathcal{K}_1, \mathcal{K}_2 \subset \mathbb{R}^d$, then polarity interacts with Minkowski sums in the following pleasant way:

$$(\mathcal{K}_1 + \mathcal{K}_2)^* = \mathcal{K}_1^* \cap \mathcal{K}_2^*.$$

    For problems 18–19, given any set $S \subset \mathbb{R}^d$, we define its **polar set** by

$$S^o := \{y \in \mathbb{R}^d \mid \langle y, z \rangle \leq 1 \text{ for all } z \in S\},$$

which may sometimes be unbounded. Note that this definition is consistent with our previous definition of the polar polytope in equation (2.66). We also note here the distinction between a polar set and the dual cone.

(18) Here are some elementary properties of polarity, applied to general sets.
   (a) If $A \subset B \subset \mathbb{R}^d$, show that $B^o \subset A^o$.
   (b) For $A \subset \mathbb{R}^d$, show that $A \subset (A^o)^o$.
   (c) If $A_1, \ldots, A_k \subset \mathbb{R}^d$, show that $\left(\cup_{j=1}^k A_j\right)^o = \cap_{j=1}^k A_j^o$.
   (d) For $A \subset \mathbb{R}^d$, we have $A = A^o \iff A = B_r$, a ball of radius r, centered at the origin.

(19) ♣ For any fixed translation vector $v \in \mathbb{R}^d$, prove that

(7.59) $$(S + v)^o = \left\{ \frac{1}{1 + \langle v, y \rangle} y \mid y \in S^o \right\}.$$

(20) Suppose we try to construct a polytope $\mathcal{P} \subset \mathbb{R}^3$, all of whose facets are pentagons (not necessarily regular). Show that $F \geq 12$, where F is the number of facets of $\mathcal{P}$.

(21) ♣
   (a) Show that the Brianchon–Gram relations (7.4) imply the Euler–Poincaré relation for the face-numbers of a convex polytope $\mathcal{P}$:

(7.60) $$f_0 - f_1 + f_2 - \cdots + (-1)^{d-1} f_{d-1} + (-1)^d f_d = 1,$$

   where f_k is the number of faces of $\mathcal{P}$ of dimension k.
   (b) (Hard). Conversely, suppose we are given a d-dimensional polytope $\mathcal{P} \subset \mathbb{R}^d$. Prove that the Euler–Poincaré relation above implies the Brianchon–Gram relations:

$$1_{\mathcal{P}}(x) = \sum_{\mathcal{F} \subset \mathcal{P}} (-1)^{\dim \mathcal{F}} 1_{\mathcal{K}_F}(x),$$

   for all $x \in \mathbb{R}^d$.

Notes. Interestingly, even though the above two conditions are equivalent, condition (21)(b) is often more useful in practice, because we have a free variable x, over which we may sum or integrate.

(22) Find a 2-dimensional integer polygon $\mathcal{P}$ such that, for any integer point $n \in \mathbb{Z}^2$ there exists $t > 0$ with

$$L_{\mathcal{P}+n}(t) \neq L_{\mathcal{P}}(t).$$

Notes. When t is restricted to be a positive integer, it is of course true that $L_{\mathcal{P}+n}(t) = L_{\mathcal{P}}(t)$. The point here is that when we work with *all* positive dilates, the distinction between integer polytopes and their integer translates becomes more pronounced.

Chapter 8

What is an angle in higher dimensions?

"Everyone else would climb a peak by looking for a
path somewhere in the mountain. Nash would climb
another mountain altogether and from that distant
peak would shine a searchlight back onto the first
peak."
– Donald Newman

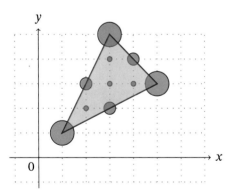

Figure 8.1. A discrete volume of the triangle $\mathcal{P}$ called the angle polynomial of $\mathcal{P}$. Here we sum local angle weights, relative to $\mathcal{P}$, at all
integer points.

1. Intuition

There are infinitely many ways to discretize the classical notion of volume, and here we offer a second path, using "local solid angles". Given a rational polytope $\mathcal{P}$, we will place small spheres at all integer points in $\mathbb{Z}^d$, and compute the proportion of the local intersection of each small sphere with $\mathcal{P}$. This discrete finite sum gives us a new method of discretizing the volume of a polytope, and it turns out to be a more symmetric way of doing so. To go forward, we first discuss how to extend the usual notion of "angle" to higher dimensions, and then use Poisson summation again to pursue the fine detail of this new discrete volume.

2. Defining an angle in higher dimensions

The question of how an angle in two dimensions extends to higher dimensions is a basic one in discrete geometry. A natural way to extend the notion of an angle is to consider a cone $\mathcal{K} \subset \mathbb{R}^d$, place a sphere centered at the apex of $\mathcal{K}$, and then compute the proportion of the sphere that intersects $\mathcal{K}$. This intuition is captured more rigorously by the following integral:

$$(8.1) \qquad\qquad \omega_{\mathcal{K}} = \int_{\mathcal{K}} e^{-\pi\|x\|^2} dx,$$

called the **solid angle of the cone** $\mathcal{K}$. The literature has other synonyms for solid angles, arising in different fields, including the **volumetric moduli** [97], and the **volume of a spherical polytope** [25], [68], [71].

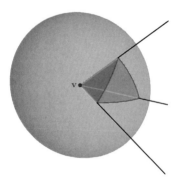

Figure 8.2. A solid angle in $\mathbb{R}^3$—note the equivalence with the area of the geodesic triangle on the sphere.

We can easily show that the latter definition of a solid angle is equivalent to the volume of a spherical polytope using polar coordinates in $\mathbb{R}^d$, as follows. We denote the unit sphere by $S^{d-1} := \{x \in \mathbb{R}^d \mid \|x\| = 1\}$. Then, using the fact that the Gaussians give a probability distribution, namely $\int_{\mathbb{R}^d} e^{-\pi\|x\|^2} dx = 1$ (which we know by Exercise (17)), we have

$$(8.2) \qquad \omega_{\mathcal{K}} = \frac{\int_{\mathcal{K}} e^{-\pi\|x\|^2} dx}{\int_{\mathbb{R}^d} e^{-\pi\|x\|^2} dx}$$

$$(8.3) \qquad = \frac{\int_0^\infty e^{-\pi r^2} r^{d-1} dr \int_{S^{d-1} \cap \mathcal{K}} d\theta}{\int_0^\infty e^{-\pi r^2} r^{d-1} dr \int_{S^{d-1}} d\theta}$$

$$(8.4) \qquad = \frac{\int_{S^{d-1} \cap \mathcal{K}} d\theta}{\int_{S^{d-1}} d\theta}$$

$$(8.5) \qquad = \frac{\mathrm{vol}_{d-1}\left(\mathcal{K} \cap S^{d-1}\right)}{\mathrm{vol}_{d-1}\left(S^{d-1}\right)},$$

where vol_{d-1} denotes the volume measure on the surface of the $(d-1)$-dimensional sphere S^{d-1}. We may think of (8.5) as the **normalized volume** of a spherical polytope defined by the intersection of the cone $\mathcal{K}$ with the unit sphere. Thus for any cone $\mathcal{K} \subset \mathbb{R}^d$, we have

$$0 \leq \omega_{\mathcal{K}} \leq 1.$$

We used polar coordinates in the second equality (8.2): $x = (r, \theta)$, with $r \geq 0$, $\theta \in x^{d-1}$. The Jacobian in the change of variables is $dx = r^{d-1} dr d\theta$.

We note that when $\mathcal{K} = \mathbb{R}^d$, so that here the cone is *all* of Euclidean space, the integral (8.1) becomes

$$\int_{\mathbb{R}^d} e^{-\pi\|x\|^2} dx = 1$$

by Exercise (17). This computation confirms that we do indeed have the proper normalization with $\omega_{\mathcal{K}} = 1$ if and only if $\mathcal{K} = \mathbb{R}^d$.

Example 8.1. If $\mathcal{K} \subset \mathbb{R}^d$ is a half-space, then $\omega_{\mathcal{K}} = \frac{1}{2}$. If $\mathcal{K} := \mathbb{R}^d_{\geq 0}$, the positive orthant, then

$$\omega_{\mathcal{K}} = \int_{\mathbb{R}^d_{\geq 0}} e^{-\pi\|x\|^2} dx = \left(\int_{\mathbb{R}_{\geq 0}} e^{-\pi u^2} du\right)^d = \frac{1}{2^d}.$$

So in the plane, the positive quadrant takes up $\frac{1}{4}$ of the whole plane. In $\mathbb{R}^3$, the positive octant takes up $\frac{1}{8}$ of the whole space, etc. $\square$

We might wonder: "Do we really need to use Gaussians to define these solid angles?" The clear answer is "no", as the following example shows. But one reason to favor Gaussians over other radially symmetric functions is that they behave beautifully under convolutions and Fourier transforms, as we will see in Lemma 8.4.

Example 8.2. Let $\mathcal{K} \subset \mathbb{R}^d$ be a d-dimensional polyhedral cone and fix $s > \frac{d}{2}$. Then we have

$$\omega_K = \frac{\pi^{\frac{d}{2}} \Gamma(s)}{\Gamma(s - \frac{d}{2})} \int_K \frac{dx}{(1 + \|x\|^2)^s}.$$

The reader may enjoy proving this from scratch in Exercise (9) [**200**, Proposition 2.3.2]. ☐

3. Local solid angles for a polytope and Gaussian smoothing

Here we want to define solid angles relative to a fixed polytope. So, given any polytope $\mathcal{P} \subset \mathbb{R}^d$, we fix any point $x \in \mathbb{R}^d$ and define a local solid angle relative to $\mathcal{P}$ as follows. The normalized **solid angle** fraction that a d-dimensional polytope $\mathcal{P}$ subtends at any point $x \in \mathbb{R}^d$ is defined by

$$(8.6) \qquad \omega_{\mathcal{P}}(x) = \lim_{\varepsilon \to 0} \frac{\mathrm{vol}(S^{d-1}(x, \varepsilon) \cap \mathcal{P})}{\mathrm{vol}(S^{d-1}(x, \varepsilon))}.$$

Here, $\omega_{\mathcal{P}}(x)$ measures the fraction of a small $(d-1)$-dimensional sphere $S^{d-1}(x, \varepsilon)$ centered at x, which intersects the polytope $\mathcal{P}$. We will use the standard notation for the interior of a convex body, namely, $\mathrm{int}(\mathcal{P})$, and for the boundary of a convex body $\partial\mathcal{P}$. As a side note, we mention that balls and spheres can be used interchangeably in this definition, meaning that the fractional weight given by (8.6) is the same using either method.

It follows from the definition of a solid angle that $0 \le \omega_{\mathcal{P}}(x) \le 1$, for all $x \in \mathbb{R}^d$, and that

$$(8.7) \qquad \omega_{\mathcal{P}}(x) = \begin{cases} 1 & \text{if } x \in \mathrm{int}(\mathcal{P}) \\ 0 & \text{if } x \notin \mathcal{P}. \end{cases}$$

But when $x \in \partial\mathcal{P}$, we have $0 < \omega_{\mathcal{P}}(x) < 1$. For example, if x lies on a codimension-two face of $\mathcal{P}$, then $\omega_{\mathcal{P}}(x)$ is the fractional dihedral angle subtended by $\mathcal{P}$ at x.

To define one type of discrete volume for any polytope $\mathcal{P} \subset \mathbb{R}^d$, we fix a positive integer t, and define the finite sum

$$(8.8) \qquad A_{\mathcal{P}}(t) := \sum_{n \in \mathbb{Z}^d} \omega_{t\mathcal{P}}(n),$$

where $t\mathcal{P} := \{tx \mid x \in \mathcal{P}\}$ is the tth dilation of the polytope $\mathcal{P}$. In other words, $A_{\mathcal{P}}(1)$ is, by definition, the discrete volume for $\mathcal{P}$ which is obtained by placing at each integer point $n \in \mathbb{Z}^d$ the weight $\omega_{\mathcal{P}}(n)$, and summing all of the weights over all $n \in \mathbb{Z}^d$.

Example 8.3. In Figure 8.1, the solid angle sum of the polygon $\mathcal{P}$ is

$$A_{\mathcal{P}}(1) = \theta_1 + \theta_2 + \theta_3 + 3\left(\tfrac{1}{2}\right) + 4 = 6.$$

Here the θ_j are the three angles at the vertices of $\mathcal{P}$. $\square$

Using purely combinatorial methods, Macdonald showed that for any integer polytope $\mathcal{P}$, and for **positive integer values** of t,

$$(8.9) \quad A_{\mathcal{P}}(t) = (\text{vol } \mathcal{P})t^d + a_{d-2}t^{d-2} + a_{d-4}t^{d-4} + \cdots + \begin{cases} a_1 t & \text{if } d \text{ is odd,} \\ a_2 t^2 & \text{if } d \text{ is even.} \end{cases}$$

We will call $A_{\mathcal{P}}(t)$ the **angle-polynomial** of $\mathcal{P}$, for integer polytopes $\mathcal{P}$ and positive integer dilations t. However, when these restrictions are lifted, the sum still captures crucial geometric information of $\mathcal{P}$, and we will simply call it the (solid) angle-sum of $\mathcal{P}$.

We define the **heat kernel** for each fixed positive ε, by

$$(8.10) \qquad G_\varepsilon(x) := \varepsilon^{-\frac{d}{2}} e^{-\frac{\pi}{\varepsilon}\|x\|^2}$$

for all $x \in \mathbb{R}^d$. By Exercises (17) and (18) we know that $\int_{\mathbb{R}^d} G_\varepsilon(x)dx = 1$ for each fixed ε, and that

$$(8.11) \qquad \hat{G}_\varepsilon(\xi) = e^{-\varepsilon\pi\|\xi\|^2}.$$

The convolution of the indicator function $1_{\mathcal{P}}$ by the heat kernel G_ε will be called the **Gaussian smoothing** of $1_{\mathcal{P}}$:

$$(8.12) \qquad (1_{\mathcal{P}} * G_\varepsilon)(x) := \int_{\mathbb{R}^d} 1_{\mathcal{P}}(y)G_\varepsilon(x-y)dy = \int_{\mathcal{P}} G_\varepsilon(y-x)dy$$

$$(8.13) \qquad = \varepsilon^{-\frac{d}{2}} \int_{\mathcal{P}} e^{-\frac{\pi}{\varepsilon}\|y-x\|^2}dy,$$

a C^∞ function of $x \in \mathbb{R}^d$, and in fact a Schwartz function.

The following Lemma provides a first crucial link between the discrete geometry of a local solid angle and the convolution of $1_{\mathcal{P}}$ with a Gaussian-based approximate identity.

Lemma 8.4. *Let $\mathcal{P}$ be a full-dimensional polytope in $\mathbb{R}^d$. Then for each point $x \in \mathbb{R}^d$, we have*

$$(8.14) \qquad \lim_{\varepsilon \to 0}(1_{\mathcal{P}} * G_\varepsilon)(x) = \omega_P(x).$$

Proof. We have

$$(1_{\mathcal{P}} * G_\varepsilon)(x) = \int_{\mathcal{P}} G_\varepsilon(y - x)dy$$

$$= \int_{u \in P - x} G_\varepsilon(u)du$$

$$= \varepsilon^{\frac{d}{2}} \int_{\frac{1}{\sqrt{\varepsilon}}(P - x)} G_1(v)dv.$$

In the calculation above we make use of the evenness of G_ε in the second equality. The substitution $v = u/\sqrt{\varepsilon}$ was used in the third equality. Following those substitutions, we change the domain of integration from P to the translated body $P - x$, and then to the dilation of $P - x$ by the factor $\frac{1}{\sqrt{\varepsilon}}$.

Finally, when ε approaches 0, $\frac{1}{\sqrt{\varepsilon}}(P - x)$ tends to a cone K with apex at the origin, subtended by $P - x$. This cone K is in fact a translation of the tangent cone of P, at x. We therefore arrive at

$$\lim_{\varepsilon \to 0}(1_{\mathcal{P}} * G_\varepsilon)(x) = \int_K G_1(v)dv = \omega_K(0) = \omega_P(x). \qquad \square$$

Putting things together, the definition (8.8) and Lemma 8.4 tell us that

$$(8.15) \qquad A_{\mathcal{P}}(t) = \sum_{n \in \mathbb{Z}^d} \omega_{tP}(x) = \sum_{n \in \mathbb{Z}^d} \lim_{\varepsilon \to 0}(1_{t\mathcal{P}} * G_\varepsilon)(n).$$

We would like to interchange a limit with an infinite sum over a lattice so that we may use Poisson summation, and although this is subtle in general, it is possible to carry out here because the summands are rapidly decreasing.

Lemma 8.5. *Let $\mathcal{P}$ be a full-dimensional polytope in $\mathbb{R}^d$. Then*

$$\sum_{n \in \mathbb{Z}^d} \lim_{\varepsilon \to 0} (1_{t\mathcal{P}} * G_\varepsilon)(n) = \lim_{\varepsilon \to 0} \sum_{n \in \mathbb{Z}^d} (1_{t\mathcal{P}} * G_\varepsilon)(n). \qquad \square$$

Lemma 8.5 is proved in Exercise (12). Next, we apply the Poisson summation formula to the Schwartz function $f(x) := (1_{t\mathcal{P}} * G_\varepsilon)(x)$:

$$(8.16) \qquad A_P(t) = \lim_{\varepsilon \to 0} \sum_{n \in \mathbb{Z}^d} (1_{t\mathcal{P}} * G_\varepsilon)(n)$$

$$(8.17) \qquad = \lim_{\varepsilon \to 0} \sum_{\xi \in \mathbb{Z}^d} \hat{1}_{t\mathcal{P}}(\xi) \hat{G}_\varepsilon(\xi)$$

$$(8.18) \qquad = \lim_{\varepsilon \to 0} \sum_{\xi \in \mathbb{Z}^d} \hat{1}_{t\mathcal{P}}(\xi) \, e^{-\varepsilon \pi \|\xi\|^2}$$

$$(8.19) \qquad = t^d \lim_{\varepsilon \to 0} \sum_{\xi \in \mathbb{Z}^d} \hat{1}_{\mathcal{P}}(t\xi) \, e^{-\varepsilon \pi \|\xi\|^2}$$

$$(8.20) \qquad = t^d \, \hat{1}_{\mathcal{P}}(0) + \lim_{\varepsilon \to 0} t^d \sum_{\xi \in \mathbb{Z}^d - \{0\}} \hat{1}_{\mathcal{P}}(t\xi) \, e^{-\varepsilon \pi \|\xi\|^2}$$

$$(8.21) \qquad = t^d (\text{vol}\, \mathcal{P}) + \lim_{\varepsilon \to 0} t^d \sum_{\xi \in \mathbb{Z}^d - \{0\}} \hat{1}_{\mathcal{P}}(t\xi) \, e^{-\varepsilon \pi \|\xi\|^2},$$

where we used the fact that Fourier transforms interact nicely with dilations of the domain:

$$\hat{1}_{t\mathcal{P}}(\xi) = \int_{t\mathcal{P}} e^{-2\pi i \langle \xi, x \rangle} dx$$

$$= t^d \int_{\mathcal{P}} e^{-2\pi i \langle \xi, ty \rangle} dy$$

$$= t^d \int_{\mathcal{P}} e^{-2\pi i \langle t\xi, y \rangle} dy$$

$$= t^d \hat{1}_{\mathcal{P}}(t\xi).$$

We also used the simple change of variable $x = ty$ with $y \in \mathcal{P}$, implying that $dx = t^d dy$ as well as the Fourier transform formula (8.11) for the heat kernel, in equation (8.18). So far, we have proved the following.

Lemma 8.6. *Given a real polytope $\mathcal{P} \subset \mathbb{R}^d$, its angle polynomial has the expression*

$$(8.22) \qquad A_{\mathcal{P}}(t) = t^d (\text{vol}\, \mathcal{P}) + t^d \lim_{\varepsilon \to 0} \sum_{n \in \mathbb{Z}^d - \{0\}} (\hat{1}_{\mathcal{P}}(t\xi) * G_\varepsilon)(n). \qquad \square$$

Lemma 8.6 suggests that $A_{\mathcal{P}}(t)$ possesses a polynomial-like behavior in t.

4. 1-dimensional polytopes: Their angle polynomial

Although this toy case is straightforward, we will still encounter some interesting formulae and ideas. We may use our knowledge of the Fourier transform of a 1-dimensional polytope $\mathcal{P}$, in the right-hand side of (8.22), namely a closed interval $P := [a, b]$.

Let us compute the angle polynomial of the 1-dimensional polytope $\mathcal{P} := [a, b]$, with $a, b \in \mathbb{R}$. We will use our knowledge of the 1-dimensional Fourier transform of an interval from Exercise (1), to compute

$$(8.23) \quad A_P(t) = (b-a)t + \lim_{\varepsilon \to 0} \sum_{\xi \in \mathbb{Z}-\{0\}} \hat{1}_{\mathcal{P}}(t\xi)\, e^{-\varepsilon\pi\xi^2}$$

$$(8.24) \quad = (b-a)t + \lim_{\varepsilon \to 0} \sum_{\xi \in \mathbb{Z}-\{0\}} \left(\frac{e^{-2\pi it\xi b} - e^{-2\pi it\xi a}}{-2\pi i\xi} \right) e^{-\varepsilon\pi\xi^2}$$

$$(8.25) \quad = (b-a)t - \lim_{\varepsilon \to 0} \sum_{\xi \in \mathbb{Z}-\{0\}} \frac{e^{-2\pi itb\xi - \varepsilon\pi\xi^2}}{2\pi i\xi}$$

$$+ \lim_{\varepsilon \to 0} \sum_{\xi \in \mathbb{Z}-\{0\}} \frac{e^{-2\pi ita\xi - \varepsilon\pi\xi^2}}{2\pi i\xi}$$

Throughout the latter computation, all series converge absolutely (and quite rapidly) due to the existence of the Gaussian damping factor $e^{-\varepsilon\pi\xi^2}$.

Let us see what happens when we specialize the vertices a or b—perhaps we can solve for one of these new limits? So we set $a = 0, b \in \mathbb{R}\backslash\mathbb{Z}, t \in \mathbb{R}_{>0}$. In this special case, one of the two series in (8.25) becomes

$$\sum_{\xi \in \mathbb{Z}-\{0\}} \frac{e^{-2\pi ita\xi} e^{-\varepsilon\pi\xi^2}}{-2\pi i\xi} = \sum_{\xi \in \mathbb{Z}-\{0\}} \frac{e^{-\varepsilon\pi\xi^2}}{-2\pi i\xi} = 0,$$

because the summand is an odd function of ξ. Since the solid angle at an integer vertex of an interval equals $\frac{1}{2}$, we already know by direct computation that in this case

$$A_{[0,b]}(t) = \begin{cases} \frac{1}{2} + \lfloor bt \rfloor & \text{if } bt \notin \mathbb{Z} \\ \lfloor bt \rfloor & \text{if } bt \in \mathbb{Z} \end{cases} = \frac{1}{2} - \frac{1}{2}1_{\mathbb{Z}}(bt) + \lfloor bt \rfloor$$

for all $t > 0$. Here we have used a handy definition for the indicator function of the integers:

$$1_{\mathbb{Z}}(x) := \begin{cases} 1 & \text{if } x \in \mathbb{Z} \\ 0 & \text{if } x \notin \mathbb{Z}. \end{cases}$$

Solving (8.25) for the other limit, we get

$$\frac{1}{2} - \frac{1}{2}1_{\mathbb{Z}}(bt) + \lfloor bt \rfloor = bt + \lim_{\varepsilon \to 0} \sum_{\xi \in \mathbb{Z} - \{0\}} \left(\frac{e^{-2\pi i t \xi b}}{-2\pi i \xi} \right) e^{-\varepsilon \pi \xi^2}$$

After relabelling $bt := x \in \mathbb{R}$, we have just proved the following.

Lemma 8.7. *For any $x \in \mathbb{R}$, we have*

$$\frac{1}{2\pi i} \lim_{\varepsilon \to 0} \sum_{\xi \in \mathbb{Z} - \{0\}} \frac{e^{-2\pi i x \xi - \varepsilon \pi \xi^2}}{\xi} = x - \lfloor x \rfloor - \frac{1}{2} + \frac{1}{2}1_{\mathbb{Z}}(x). \qquad \square$$

Now we can bootstrap our information from Lemma 8.7 by plugging its result back into equation (8.25):

$$(8.26) \qquad A_P(t) = (b - a)t - \left(bt - \lfloor bt \rfloor - \frac{1}{2} + \frac{1}{2}1_{\mathbb{Z}}(bt) \right)$$

$$(8.27) \qquad\qquad + \left(at - \lfloor at \rfloor - \frac{1}{2} + \frac{1}{2}1_{\mathbb{Z}}(at) \right)$$

$$(8.28) \qquad\qquad = \lfloor bt \rfloor - \frac{1}{2}1_{\mathbb{Z}}(bt) - \lfloor at \rfloor + \frac{1}{2}1_{\mathbb{Z}}(at),$$

and we have arrived at the angle polynomial for any 1-dimensional polytope $\mathcal{P} := [a, b]$, where $a, b \in \mathbb{R}$. Of course, (8.28) is easy to check directly from the definition of the angle polynomial for an interval, but note that we also recovered a nontrivial limit in the process, namely Lemma 8.7.

5. Pick's formula and Nosarzewska's inequality

A polygon $\mathcal{P}$ is called an **integer polygon** if all of its vertices belong to the integer lattice $\mathbb{Z}^2$. There is a wonderful relationship, discovered by George Pick in 1899, between the area of $\mathcal{P}$ and the number of integer points contained in $\mathcal{P}$ and on its boundary.

Theorem 8.8 (Pick's formula, 1899). *Let $\mathcal{P}$ be an integer polygon. Then*

$$(8.29) \qquad\qquad \text{Area } \mathcal{P} = I + \frac{1}{2}B - 1,$$

where I is the number of interior integer points in $\mathcal{P}$, and B is the number of boundary integer points in $\mathcal{P}$. $\qquad \square$

There is an equivalent formulation of Pick's theorem in terms of local solid angle weights at each integer point.

Theorem 8.9 (Pick's formula, reformulated with angle weights). *Let $\mathcal{P}$ be an integer polygon. Then*

$$\sum_{n\in\mathbb{Z}^2} \omega_{\mathcal{P}}(n) = \text{Area } \mathcal{P},$$

where $\omega_{\mathcal{P}}(n)$ is the 2-dimensional angle defined in (8.7). □

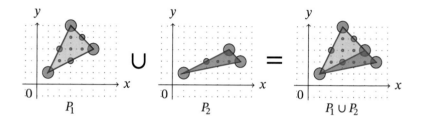

Figure 8.3. Additive property of the angle polynomial

Pick's formula, here formulated as Theorem 8.9, possesses a natural extension to higher dimensions (see [**212**]).

If we want to work with more general convex regions than polygons, there is a related and beautiful inequality for any 2-dimensional convex body, discovered in 1948 by Maria Nosarzewska [**186**].

Theorem 8.10 (Nosarzewska). *For a convex body $\mathcal{P} \subset \mathbb{R}^2$, whose perimeter has length S, we have*

$$(8.30) \qquad \text{Area } \mathcal{P} - \frac{1}{2}S < |\mathcal{P} \cap \mathbb{Z}^2| \leq \text{Area } \mathcal{P} + \frac{1}{2}S + 1. \qquad \Box$$

Proof. To prove the upper bound in (8.30), we will work with the convex hull $\mathcal{P}_0$ of the interior integer points of $\mathcal{P}$. Because $\mathcal{P}_0$ is an integer polygon, we may apply Pick's theorem to it. We let I_0 be the number of interior integer points of $\mathcal{P}_0$, B_0 be the number of boundary integer points of $\mathcal{P}_0$, and S_0 be the perimeter of $\mathcal{P}_0$, so that

$$\text{Area } \mathcal{P} + \frac{1}{2}S + 1 \geq \text{Area } \mathcal{P}_0 + \frac{1}{2}S_0 + 1$$

$$\geq \text{Area } \mathcal{P}_0 + \frac{1}{2}B_0 + 1$$

$$= I_0 + B_0$$

$$:= |\mathcal{P}_0 \cap \mathbb{Z}^2|$$

$$= |\mathcal{P} \cap \mathbb{Z}^2|.$$

The second inequality above uses the fact that each integer line segment in the plane has length at least 1, so that the perimeter of an integer polygon must be greater than or equal to the number of integer points on it. The equality Area $\mathcal{P}_0 + \frac{1}{2}B_0 + 1 = I_0 + B_0$ above is true by Pick's formula (8.29). For the lower bound, we refer the reader to [186]. □

For any convex body $\mathcal{P} \subset \mathbb{R}^2$, Nosarzewska's inequality (Theorem 8.10) is a refinement of Jarnik's inequality $|\text{Area } \mathcal{P} - |\mathcal{P} \cap \mathbb{Z}^2|| < S$. In 1972, Bokowski, Hadwiger, and Wills [41] extended the lower bound in (8.30) to all higher dimensions:

$$|\mathcal{P} \cap \mathbb{Z}^d| > \text{vol } \mathcal{P} - \frac{1}{2}S(\mathcal{P}),$$

where $S(\mathcal{P})$ is the surface area of the convex body $\mathcal{P} \subset \mathbb{R}^d$. We might wonder if the upper bound of Nosarzewska's inequality (8.30) also extends to higher dimensions directly. But a simple counter-example is an ε-neighborhood of a line segment along the first coordinate axis, for example, containing a fixed number of integer points, but whose surface area and volume are both arbitrarily small.

To discover a result that circumvents the latter counter-example, one might look for an extra assumption on the linear independence of integer points contained in $\mathcal{P}$. Such a result was given by Henk and Wills [114], as follows.

Theorem 8.11. *Let $\mathcal{P} \subset \mathbb{R}^3$ be a body that contains 3 linearly independent integer points. Then:*

$$|\mathcal{P} \cap \mathbb{Z}^d| < \text{vol } \mathcal{P} + 2S(\mathcal{P}).$$

6. The Gram relations for solid angles

Question 8.12 (Rhetorical). When we were kids, we learned that the sum of the angles of a triangle equals π radians. How does this theorem extend to higher dimensional polytopes?

We describe the extension here, mainly due to Gram (but has a colorful history). First, for each face F of a polytope $\mathcal{P} \subset \mathbb{R}^d$, we define the **solid angle** of F, as follows. Fix any $x_0 \in \text{int } F$, and let

$$\omega_F := \omega_P(x_0).$$

We notice that this definition is independent of x_0, as long as we restrict x_0 to the relative interior of F.

Example 8.13. If $\mathcal{P}$ is the d-dimensional cube $[0,1]^d$, then each of its facets F has $\omega_F = \frac{1}{2}$. Moreover, it is a fact that for the cube, each face F of dimension k has the same solid angle, namely,

$$\omega_F = \frac{1}{2^{d-k}}$$

for each $0 \le k \le d - 1$ (Exercise (13)). In particular, a vertex v of this cube, having dimension 0, has solid angle $\omega_v = \frac{1}{2^d}$. $\qquad\square$

Luckily, Question 8.12 has a beautifully simple answer, as follows.

Theorem 8.14 (Gram relations). *Given any d-dimensional polytope $P \subset \mathbb{R}^d$, we have*

$$\sum_{F \subset \mathcal{P}} (-1)^{\dim F} \omega_F = 0. \qquad\square$$

(For a proof of Theorem 8.14, see [25], for example.)

Example 8.15. Let us see what the Gram relations tell us in the case of a triangle Δ. For each edge E of Δ, placing a small sphere at a point in the interior of E means half of it is inside Δ and half of it is outside of Δ, so that $\omega_E = \frac{1}{2}$. Next, each vertex of Δ has a solid angle equal to the usual (normalized) angle $\theta(v)$ at that vertex. Finally, Δ itself has a solid angle of 1, because picking a point p in the interior of Δ and placing a small sphere centered at p, the whole sphere will be contained in Δ. Putting it all together, the Gram relations read

$$0 = \sum_{F \subset \Delta} (-1)^{\dim F} \omega_F$$

$$= (-1)^0 (\theta(v_1) + \theta(v_2) + \theta(v_3)) + (-1)^1 \left(\frac{1}{2} + \frac{1}{2} + \frac{1}{2} \right) + (-1)^2 \cdot 1$$

$$= \theta(v_1) + \theta(v_2) + \theta(v_3) - \frac{1}{2},$$

which looks familiar! We have retrieved our elementary school knowledge, namely that the three angles of a triangle sum to π radians. So the Gram relations really are an extension of this fact. $\qquad\square$

What about $\mathbb{R}^3$?

Example 8.16. Let us see what hidden secrets lie behind the Gram relations for the standard simplex $\Delta \subset \mathbb{R}^3$. At the origin $v_0 = 0$, the tangent cone is the positive orthant, so that $\omega(v_0) = \frac{1}{8}$. The other 3 vertices all "look alike", in the sense that their tangent cones are all isometric, and hence have the same solid angle ω_v. What about the edges? In general, it is a fact that the solid angle of an edge equals the dihedral angle between the planes of its two bounding facets (Exercise (14)). There are two types of edges here, as in the figure. For an edge E which lies on the boundary of the skew facet, we have the dihedral angle

$$\cos \phi = \left\langle \frac{1}{\sqrt{3}} \begin{pmatrix} 1 \\ 1 \\ 1 \end{pmatrix}, \begin{pmatrix} 0 \\ 1 \\ 0 \end{pmatrix} \right\rangle = \frac{1}{\sqrt{3}},$$

so that $\omega_E = \phi = \cos^{-1} \frac{1}{\sqrt{3}}$. It is straightforward that for the other type of edge, each of those 3 edges has a solid angle of $\frac{1}{4}$. Putting it all together, we see that

$$0 = \sum_{F \subset \Delta} (-1)^{\dim F} \omega_F$$

$$= (-1)^0 \left(\frac{1}{8} + 3\omega_v \right) + (-1)^1 \left(3\frac{1}{4} + 3 \cos^{-1} \frac{1}{\sqrt{3}} \right)$$

$$+ (-1)^2 \frac{1}{2} \cdot 4 + (-1)^3 \cdot 1.$$

Solving for ω_v, we get $\omega_v = \cos^{-1} \frac{1}{\sqrt{3}} - \frac{1}{8}$. So we were able to compute the solid angle of at a vertex of Δ in $\mathbb{R}^3$ using the Gram relations, together with a bit of symmetry.   □

Related to the topics above is the fact that the angle polynomial possesses the following fascinating functional equation (For a proof of Theorem 8.17, and an extension of it, see [68]).

Theorem 8.17 (Functional equation for the angle polynomial). *Given a d-dimensional rational polytope $\mathcal{P} \subset \mathbb{R}^d$, we may extend the domain of $A_{\mathcal{P}}(t)$ to all of $\mathbb{R}$ by using the expression (8.22). It follows that*

$$A_{\mathcal{P}}(-t) = A_{\mathcal{P}}(t)$$

for all $t \in \mathbb{R}$.   □

7. Bounds for solid angles

Throughout this section $\mathcal{K}$ is a d-dimensional, simplicial, pointed cone, with apex at the origin, and edge vectors $w_1, \ldots, w_d \in \mathbb{R}^d$. Let $M \in GL_{\mathbb{R}}(d)$ be the matrix whose columns are the edge vectors w_j. We will use the observation that M maps the positive orthant $\mathbb{R}^d_{\geq 0}$ bijectively onto $\mathcal{K}$.

Gourion and Seeger [97] gave some interesting bounds for the solid angle ω_K in terms of the singular value decomposition of M (Theorem 8.19). For the linear algebra definitions and applications of singular values, the reader may consult [35]. First, some of the many basic and easy facts that make singular values useful are the following upper and lower bounds on linear transformations.

Lemma 8.18. *Let $A \in \mathbb{R}^{m \times n}$, and $x \in \mathbb{R}^n$. Then*

$$(8.31) \qquad \sigma_{min}\|x\| \leq \|Ax\| \leq \sigma_{max}\|x\|,$$

where σ_{min} and σ_{min} are the smallest and largest singular values of A, respectively. □

(See [**96**] for a proof of Lemma 8.18.)

Theorem 8.19 (Gourion and Seeger, 2010). *Let σ_{min} be the smallest singular value of M, and let σ_{max} be the largest singular value of M. Then*

$$(8.32) \qquad \frac{|\det M|}{(2\sigma_{max})^d} \leq \omega_K \leq \frac{|\det M|}{(2\sigma_{min})^d}.$$

Proof.

$$(8.33) \qquad \omega_K := \int_K e^{-\pi\|x\|^2}\,dx$$

$$(8.34) \qquad = |\det M| \int_{\mathbb{R}^d_{\geq 0}} e^{-\pi\|Mu\|^2}\,du$$

$$(8.35) \qquad \leq |\det M| \int_{\mathbb{R}^d_{\geq 0}} e^{-\pi\sigma_{min}^2\|u\|^2}\,du$$

$$(8.36) \qquad = \frac{|\det M|}{\sigma_{min}^d} \int_{\mathbb{R}^d_{\geq 0}} e^{-\pi\|u\|^2}\,du$$

$$(8.37) \qquad = \frac{|\det M|}{2^d\sigma_{min}^d},$$

as claimed. The inequality above followed from the lower bound given by Lemma 8.18: $\|Mu\| \geq \sigma_{min}\|u\|$. The lower bound is proved in exactly the same manner using the upper bound of Lemma 8.18: $\|Mu\| \leq \sigma_{max}\|u\|$.   □

Example 8.20. Let us consider the 3-dimensional simplicial cone

$$K := \{\lambda_1 \begin{pmatrix} 1 \\ 0 \\ 0 \end{pmatrix} + \lambda_2 \begin{pmatrix} 1 \\ 1 \\ 0 \end{pmatrix} + \lambda_3 \begin{pmatrix} 1 \\ 1 \\ 1 \end{pmatrix} \mid \lambda_1, \lambda_2, \lambda_3 \geq 0\}.$$

It is not difficult to show that its solid angle is $\omega_K = \frac{1}{48}$, by tesellating all of $\mathbb{R}^d$ with isometric images of K (Exercise (1)). Computing (brute force) the minimum and maximum singular values for the matrix M whose columns are the edge vectors of K, and substituting them into Theorem 8.19, we get

$$0.01101 \leq \omega_K \leq 0.73135.$$

The latter lower bound gets much closer here to the true value $\omega_K = \frac{1}{48} \approx .02083$.   □

8. The classical Euler–Maclaurin summation formula

Here, we show yet another application of Poisson summation, which has found great applications in number theory and numerical analysis: the classical Euler–Maclaurin (EM) summation formula. We give Poisson's own proof here, which also appeared in G. H. Hardy's book *Divergent series* [**106**, page 330].

Theorem 8.21 (Euler–Maclaurin summation I). *Suppose $f : \mathbb{R} \to \mathbb{C}$ is infinitely smooth, compactly supported on $[a, b]$, and $f, \hat{f} \in L^1(\mathbb{R})$. Then we have:*
(8.38)

$$\sum_{a \leq n \leq b} f(n) - \int_a^b f(x)dx = f(b)P_1(b) - f(z)P_1(a) - \int_a^b f'(x)P_1(x)dx.$$

Proof. Applying Poisson summation to f, we have

$$\sum_{n \in \mathbb{Z}} f(n) = \sum_{\xi \in \mathbb{Z}} \hat{f}(\xi)$$

$$= \hat{f}(0) + \sum_{\xi \in \mathbb{Z} \setminus \{0\}} \hat{f}(\xi)$$

$$= \int_{\mathbb{R}} f(x)dx + \sum_{\xi \in \mathbb{Z} \setminus \{0\}} \hat{f}(\xi).$$

Because f is compactly supported on $[a, b]$, the latter equality becomes

$$(8.39) \qquad \sum_{a \le n \le b} f(n) - \int_a^b f(x)dx = \sum_{\xi \in \mathbb{Z} \setminus \{0\}} \hat{f}(\xi).$$

Now we use integration by parts:

$$(8.40) \qquad \hat{f}(\xi) := \int_{\mathbb{R}} f(x)e^{-2\pi i x \xi} dx$$

$$(8.41) \qquad = \int_a^b f(x)e^{-2\pi i x \xi} dx$$

$$(8.42) \qquad = f(b)\frac{e^{-2\pi i \xi b}}{-2\pi i \xi} - f(a)\frac{e^{-2\pi i \xi a}}{-2\pi i \xi} - \int_a^b f'(x)\frac{e^{-2\pi i \xi x}}{-2\pi i \xi}dx.$$

We would like to plug the latter formula into (8.39), but we will do it carefully, as follows:

$$(8.43) \quad \sum_{a \le n \le b} f(n) - \int_a^b f(x)dx = -f(b) \lim_{N \to \infty} \sum_{\substack{-N \le \xi \le N \\ \xi \ne 0}} \frac{e^{-2\pi i \xi b}}{2\pi i \xi}$$

$$(8.44) \qquad\qquad\qquad\qquad + f(a) \lim_{N \to \infty} \sum_{\substack{-N \le \xi \le N \\ \xi \ne 0}} \frac{e^{2\pi i \xi a}}{2\pi i \xi}$$

$$(8.45) \qquad\qquad\qquad\qquad - \lim_{N \to \infty} \int_a^b f'(x) \sum_{\substack{-N \le \xi \le N \\ \xi \ne 0}} \frac{e^{-2\pi i \xi x}}{2\pi i \xi}dx.$$

Because f is infinitely smooth, both $\hat{f}$ and $\hat{f}'$ are rapidly decreasing. By Corollary 3.26 we know that

$$- \lim_{N \to \infty} \sum_{\substack{-N \le \xi \le N \\ \xi \ne 0}} \frac{e^{-2\pi i \xi x}}{2\pi i \xi} = \{x\} - \frac{1}{2} := P_1(x),$$

for $x \notin \mathbb{Z}$. Therefore, the required identity follows from (8.45).   □

    The hypothesis in this initial version of Euler–Maclaurin summation formula may be weakened considerably, but this will suffice for now. Our proof above is not the easiest proof, but rather opens up a path to higher dimensions. Such an endeavor, in arbitrary dimension, entails a long and winding road, so here we will content ourselves with only a taste of it.

Historically, one of the first applications of EM summation to number theory was the asymptotic approximation for the tail of the Riemann zeta function:

$$\sum_{n>x} \frac{1}{n^s} = O(x^{1-s}),$$

for $s > 1$ (proved in [**3**, Theorem 3.2]).

9. Further topics

There is a fascinating conjecture related to bounding the smallest solid angle of any simplex, which was stated in [**127**].

Conjecture 8.22. Any d-dimensional simplex $\mathcal{P} \subset \mathbb{R}^d$ has a vertex solid angle not greater than the vertex solid angle of the d-dimensional regular simplex.

For dimension 2 the conjecture is trivial, but this problem becomes highly nontrivial in dimensions $d \geq 3$. It is known to be true (though nontrivial) in dimensions $d = 3$ and $d = 4$, as shown by Akopyan and Karasev [**1**]. For further details related to Conjecture 8.22 see [**127**]. In dimensions $d \geq 5$, Conjecture 8.22 is still open.

Notes

(1) Let us compare and contrast the two notions of discrete volumes that we have encountered so far. For a given rational polytope $\mathcal{P}$, we notice that the Ehrhart quasi-polynomial $L_{\mathcal{P}}(t)$ is invariant when we map $\mathcal{P}$ to any of its unimodular images. That is, any rational polytope in the whole orbit of the unimodular group $\mathrm{SL}_d(\mathbb{Z})(\mathcal{P})$ has the same discrete volume $L_{\mathcal{P}}(t)$. This is false for the second discrete volume $A_{\mathcal{P}}(t)$—it is not invariant under the modular group (Exercise (11)). But $A_{\mathcal{P}}(t)$ is invariant under the large finite group of the isometries of $\mathbb{R}^d$ that preserve the integer lattice (known as the hyperoctahedral group).

So we see that $A_{\mathcal{P}}(t)$ is more sensitive to the particular embedding of $\mathcal{P}$ in space because it is dependent upon a metric. It is reasonable to expect that it can distinguish between "more" rational polytopes, but such a question remains to be formalized.

The angle polynomial also has the advantage of being a much more symmetric polynomial, with half as many coefficients that occur in the Ehrhart polynomial of integer polytopes.

However, $L_{\mathcal{P}}(t)$ has its advantages as well—to compute a *local summand* for the angle polynomial $A_{\mathcal{P}}(t) := \sum_{n \in \mathbb{Z}^d} \omega_{tP}(x)$ requires finding the volume of a local spherical polytope, while to compute a *local summand* for the Ehrhart polynomial $L_{\mathcal{P}}(t) := \sum_{n \in t\mathcal{P} \cap \mathbb{Z}^d} 1$ is quite easy: it is equal to 1.

But as we have seen, computing the full global sum for $A_{\mathcal{P}}(t)$ turns out to have its simplifications.

(2) There are natural ways to associate probabilities with solid angles—see the work of Klain and Feldman [83].

(3) Nhat Le Quang developed a thorough analysis of solid angle sums in $\mathbb{R}^2$ for all rational polygons in his 2010 undergraduate dissertation [154].

(4) The recent work of Gervásio [200] gives an online implementation for the calculation of solid angles in any dimension with open source code. In fact, the thesis [200] contains extensive numerical computations that give empirical distributions for the bounds of Theorem 8.19 on random integer cones.

(5) In [71], there is an explicit description for some of the coefficients of the solid angle polynomial $A_{\mathcal{P}}(t)$ of a d-dimensional polytope for all positive real dilations $t > 0$. Indeed, the approach in [71] uses the Fourier analytic landscape.

(6) There is also a characterization of k-tiling $\mathbb{R}^d$ by using solid angle sums [100, Theorem 6.1], as follows.

Lemma 8.23 (Gravin, Robins, and Shiryaev). *A polytope P k-tiles $\mathbb{R}^d$ by integer translations if and only if*

$$\sum_{n \in \mathbb{Z}^d} \omega_{P+v}(n) = k$$

for every $v \in \mathbb{R}^d$.   □

Exercises

"I haven't failed, I have just successfully found $10,000$ ways that won't work."
      – Thomas Edison

(1) Let $\mathcal{K} = \{\lambda_1 \begin{pmatrix} 1 \\ 0 \\ 0 \end{pmatrix} + \lambda_2 \begin{pmatrix} 1 \\ 1 \\ 0 \end{pmatrix} + \lambda_3 \begin{pmatrix} 1 \\ 1 \\ 1 \end{pmatrix} \mid \lambda_1, \lambda_2, \lambda_3 \geq 0\}$, a simplicial cone. Show that the solid angle of $\mathcal{K}$ is $\omega_{\mathcal{K}} = \frac{1}{48}$.

(2) We recall the 2-dimensional cross-polytope
$$\Diamond := \{(x_1, x_2) \in \mathbb{R}^2 \mid |x_1| + |x_2| \le 1\}.$$
Find, from first principles, the angle quasi-polynomial for the rational polygon $\mathcal{P} := \frac{1}{3}\Diamond$, for all integer dilations of $\mathcal{P}$.

(3) We recall that the 3-dimensional cross-polytope was defined by
$$\Diamond := \{(x_1, x_2, x_3) \in \mathbb{R}^3 \mid |x_1| + |x_2| + |x_3| \le 1\}.$$
Compute the angle polynomial of $A_\Diamond(t)$.

(4) We recall that the d-dimensional cross-polytope was defined by
$$\Diamond := \{(x_1, x_2, \ldots, x_d) \in \mathbb{R}^d \mid |x_1| + |x_2| + \cdots + |x_d| \le 1\}.$$
Compute the angle polynomial of $A_\Diamond(t)$.

(5) Let $\mathcal{P}$ be an integer zonotope. Prove that the angle polynomial of $\mathcal{P}$ is
$$A_{\mathcal{P}}(t) = (\text{vol } \mathcal{P})t^d,$$
valid for all positive integers t.

(6) Using (8.28), find the angle quasi-polynomial $A_{\mathcal{P}}(t)$ for the 1-dimensional polytope $\mathcal{P} := [\frac{1}{2}, \frac{2}{3}]$.

(7) Generalizing the previous exercise using (8.28), compute the angle quasi-polynomial $A_{\mathcal{P}}(t)$ for any rational 1-dimensional polytope $\mathcal{P} := [\frac{a}{c}, \frac{b}{d}]$.

(8) Define the rational triangle Δ whose vertices are $(0, 0), (1, \frac{N-1}{N})$, and $(N, 0)$, where $N \ge 2$ is a fixed integer. Find the angle quasi-polynomial $A_\Delta(t)$.

(9) ♣ Let $\mathcal{K} \subset \mathbb{R}^d$ be a d-dimensional polyhedral cone and fix $s > \frac{d}{2}$. Prove that the solid angle ω_K has the alternate expression
$$\omega_K = \frac{\pi^{\frac{d}{2}} \Gamma(s)}{\Gamma(s - \frac{d}{2})} \int_K \frac{dx}{(1 + \|x\|^2)^s}.$$

(10) ♣ Given a nonnegative function $f : \mathbb{R}^d \to \mathbb{R}_{\ge 0}$, we call f radially symmetric if $f(x) = f(\|x\|)$, for all $x \in \mathbb{R}^d$. Prove that the following are equivalent:
   (a) (Radially symmetric probability distribution). f is radially symmetric and
$$\int_{\mathbb{R}^d} f(x)dx = 1.$$

(b) (Solid angle integral). $\int_K f(x)dx = \omega_K$ for all d-dimensional polyhedral cones $\mathcal{K} \subset \mathbb{R}^d$ with apex at the origin.

(11) ♣ For each dimension d, find an example of an integer polytope $\mathcal{P} \subset \mathbb{R}^d$ and a unimodular matrix $U \in GL_d(\mathbb{Z})$, such that the angle quasi-polynomials $A_{\mathcal{P}}(t)$ and $A_{U(\mathcal{P})}(t)$ are not equal to each other for all $t \in \mathbb{Z}_{>0}$.

(12) (Proof of Lemma 8.5). Let $C \subset \mathbb{R}^d$ be a compact set. Prove that

$$\lim_{\varepsilon \to 0} \sum_{n \in \mathbb{Z}^d} (1_C * G_\varepsilon)(n) = \sum_{n \in \mathbb{Z}^d} \lim_{\varepsilon \to 0} (1_C * G_\varepsilon)(n).$$

(13) ♣ For the cube $\square := [0,1]^d$, show that any k-dimensional face $F \subset \square$ has the solid angle

$$\omega_F = \frac{1}{2^{d-k}}.$$

(14) ♣ Show that the solid angle ω_E of an edge E (1-dimensional face) of a polytope equals the dihedral angle between the hyperplanes defined by its two bounding facets.

(Hint: Use the unit normal vectors for both of the bounding facets.)

(15) Using the Gram relations, namely Theorem 8.14, compute the solid angle at a vertex of the following regular tetrahedron:

$$T := \mathrm{conv}\left\{ \begin{pmatrix}1\\1\\0\end{pmatrix} \begin{pmatrix}1\\0\\1\end{pmatrix}, \begin{pmatrix}0\\1\\1\end{pmatrix}, \begin{pmatrix}1\\1\\1\end{pmatrix} \right\}.$$

(16) Can you find a convex body $\mathcal{P} \subset \mathbb{R}^2$ that achieves the equality case in the upper bound of Nosarzewska's inequality (8.30)?

Appendix A

Solutions and hints to selected problems

> "There are no problems—just pauses between ideas."
> – David Morrell, Brotherhood of the Rose

Solutions to Chapter 1

Exercise 1. By Euler, we have $1 = e^{i\theta} = \cos\theta + i\sin\theta$, which holds if and only if $\cos\theta = 1$ and $\sin\theta = 0$. The latter two conditions hold simultaneously if and only if $\theta \in 2\pi k$, with $k \in \mathbb{Z}$.

Exercise 2. Let $z := a + bi$, so that $|e^z| = |e^{a+bi}| = |e^a||e^{bi}| = e^a \cdot 1 \leq e^{\sqrt{a^2+b^2}} = e^{|z|}$, using the fact that $|e^{bi}| = 1$ for all $b \in \mathbb{R}$.

Exercise 3. In case $a \neq b$, we have

$$\int_0^1 e_a(x)\overline{e_b(x)}dx = \int_0^1 e^{2\pi i(a-b)x}dx = \frac{e^{2\pi i(a-b)}}{2\pi i(a-b)} - 1 = 0,$$

because we know that $a - b \in \mathbb{Z}$. In case $a = b$, we have

$$\int_0^1 e_a(x)\overline{e_a(x)}dx = \int_0^1 dx = 1.$$

Exercise 4. By definition,

$$
\begin{aligned}
\int_{[0,1]} e^{-2\pi i \xi x} dx &:= \int_{[0,1]} \cos(2\pi\xi x) dx + i \int_{[0,1]} \sin(2\pi\xi x) dx \\
&= \frac{\sin(2\pi\xi)}{2\pi\xi} + i\frac{-\cos(2\pi\xi)+1}{2\pi\xi} \\
&= \frac{i\sin(2\pi\xi)}{2\pi i\xi} + \frac{\cos(2\pi\xi)-1}{2\pi i\xi} \\
&= \frac{e^{2\pi i\xi} - 1}{2\pi i\xi}.
\end{aligned}
$$

Exercise 5. Let $S := \sum_{k=0}^{N-1} e^{\frac{2\pi i k}{N}}$, and note that we may write

$$
S = \sum_{k \bmod N} e^{\frac{2\pi i k}{N}}.
$$

Now, pick any m such that $e^{\frac{2\pi i m}{N}} \neq 1$. Consider

$$
\begin{aligned}
e^{\frac{2\pi i m}{N}} S &= \sum_{k \bmod N} e^{\frac{2\pi i (k+m)}{N}} \\
&= \sum_{n \bmod N} e^{\frac{2\pi i n}{N}} = S,
\end{aligned}
$$

so that $0 = (e^{\frac{2\pi i m}{N}} - 1)S$, and since by assumption $e^{\frac{2\pi i m}{N}} \neq 1$, we have $S = 0$.

Exercise 6. We use the finite geometric series $1 + x + x^2 + \cdots + x^{N-1} = \frac{x^N - 1}{x-1}$. Now, if $N \nmid M$, then $x := e^{\frac{2\pi i M}{N}} \neq 1$, so we may substitute this value of x into the finite geometric series to get

$$
\begin{aligned}
\frac{1}{N} \sum_{k=0}^{N-1} e^{\frac{2\pi i k M}{N}} &= \frac{e^{\frac{2\pi i M N}{N}} - 1}{e^{\frac{2\pi i M}{N}} - 1} \\
&= \frac{0}{e^{\frac{2\pi i M}{N}} - 1} = 0.
\end{aligned}
$$

On the other hand, if $N \mid M$, then $\frac{1}{N} \sum_{k=0}^{N-1} e^{\frac{2\pi i k M}{N}} = \frac{1}{N} \sum_{k=0}^{N-1} 1 = 1$.

Exercise 7.

$$
\frac{1}{N} \sum_{k=0}^{N-1} e^{\frac{2\pi i k a}{N}} e^{-\frac{2\pi i k b}{N}} = \frac{1}{N} \sum_{k=0}^{N-1} e^{\frac{2\pi i k (a-b)}{N}}.
$$

Therefore, using Exercise (6), we see that the latter sum equals 1 exactly when $N \mid a - b$, and vanishes otherwise.

Exercise 8. We begin with the factorization of the polynomial $x^n - 1 = \prod_{k=1}^{n}(x - \zeta^k)$, with $\zeta := e^{2\pi i/n}$. Dividing both sides by $x - 1$, we obtain $1 + x + x^2 + \cdots + x^{n-1} = \prod_{k=1}^{n-1}(x - \zeta^k)$. Now substituting $x = 1$, we have $n = \prod_{k=1}^{n-1}(1 - \zeta^k)$.

Exercise 9. Suppose, to the contrary, that a primitive Nth root of unity is of the form $e^{2\pi i m/N}$, where $\gcd(m, N) > 1$. Let $m_1 := \frac{m}{\gcd(m,N)}$, and $k := \frac{N}{\gcd(m,N)}$, so that by assumption both m_1 and k are integers. Thus $e^{2\pi i m/N} = e^{2\pi i m_1/k}$, a kth root of unity, with $k < N$, a contradiction.

Exercise 11. We begin with the definition of the complex exponential, which converges absolutely for all $z \in \mathbb{C}$:

$$e^{iz} := \sum_{n=0}^{\infty} \frac{1}{n!}(iz)^n = \sum_{n=0}^{\infty} \frac{1}{n!} i^n z^n$$
$$= \left(1 - \frac{1}{2!}z^2 + \frac{1}{4!}z^4 - \cdots\right) + i\left(z - \frac{1}{3!}z^3 + \frac{1}{5!}z^5 - \cdots\right)$$
$$:= \cos z + i \sin z,$$

where the last line follows from the definition of $\cos z$ and $\sin z$, valid for all $z \in \mathbb{C}$.

Exercise 14. We recall Euler's identity:

$$e^{iw} = \cos w + i \sin w,$$

which is valid for all $w \in \mathbb{C}$. Using Euler's identity first with $w := \pi z$, and then with $w := -\pi z$, we have the two identities $e^{\pi i z} = \cos \pi z + i \sin \pi z$ and $e^{-\pi i z} = \cos \pi z - i \sin \pi z$. Subtracting the second identity from the first, we have

$$\sin(\pi z) = \frac{1}{2i}\left(e^{\pi i z} - e^{-\pi i z}\right).$$

Now it is clear that $\sin(\pi z) = 0 \iff e^{\pi i z} = e^{-\pi i z} \iff e^{2\pi i z} = 1 \iff z \in \mathbb{Z}$, by Exercise (1).

Exercise 16. We will assume, to the contrary, that we only have one arithmetic progression with a common difference of a_N, the largest of the common differences. We hope to obtain a contradiction. To each arithmetic progression $\{a_k n + b_k \mid n \in \mathbb{Z}\}$, we associate the generating function

$$f_k(q) := \sum_{a_k n + b_k \geq 0, \ n \in \mathbb{Z}} q^{a_k n + b_k},$$

where $|q| < 1$, in order to make the series converge. The hypothesis that we have a tiling of the integers by these N arithmetic progressions translates directly into an identity among these generating functions:

$$\sum_{a_1 n + b_1 \geq 0, \, n \in \mathbb{Z}} q^{a_1 n + b_1} + \cdots + \sum_{a_N n + b_N \geq 0, \, n \in \mathbb{Z}} q^{a_N n + b_N} = \sum_{n=0}^{\infty} q^n.$$

Next, we use the fact that we may rewrite each generating function in a "closed form" of the following kind, because they are geometric series:

$$f_k(q) := \sum_{a_k n + b_k \geq 0, \, n \in \mathbb{Z}} q^{a_k n + b_k} = \frac{q^{b_k}}{1 - q^{a_k}}. \text{ Thus, we have:}$$

$$\frac{q^{b_1}}{1 - q^{a_1}} + \cdots + \frac{q^{b_N}}{1 - q^{a_N}} = \frac{1}{1 - q}.$$

Now we make a "pole analysis" by observing that each rational function $f_k(q)$ has poles at precisely all of the k'th roots of unity. The final idea is that the "deepest" pole, namely $e^{\frac{2\pi i}{N}}$, cannot cancel with any of the other poles. To make this idea precise, we isolate the only rational function that has this pole (by assumption):

$$\frac{q^{b_N}}{1 - q^{a_N}} = \frac{1}{1 - q} - \left(\frac{q^{b_1}}{1 - q^{a_1}} + \cdots + \frac{q^{b_{N-1}}}{1 - q^{a_{N-1}}} \right).$$

Finally, we let $q \to e^{\frac{2\pi i}{N}}$, to get a finite number on the right-hand side, and infinity on the left-hand side of the latter identity, a contradiction.

Solutions to Chapter 2

Exercise 1. If $\xi = 0$, we have $\hat{1}_{[a,b]}(0) := \int_a^b e^0 dx = b - a$. If $\xi \neq 0$, we can compute the integral:

$$\hat{1}_{[a,b]}(\xi) := \int_a^b e^{-2\pi i \xi x} dx$$

$$= \frac{e^{-2\pi i \xi b} - e^{-2\pi i \xi a}}{-2\pi i \xi}.$$

Exercise 2. Beginning with the definition of the Fourier transform of the unit cube $[0, 1]^d$, we have

$$\hat{1}_\square(\xi) = \int_\square e^{2\pi i \langle x, \xi \rangle} dx$$

$$= \int_0^1 e^{2\pi i \xi_1 x_1} dx_1 \int_0^1 e^{2\pi i \xi_2 x_2} dx_2 \cdots \int_0^1 e^{2\pi i \xi_d x_d} dx_d$$

$$= \frac{1}{(-2\pi i)^d} \prod_{k=1}^d \frac{e^{-2\pi i \xi_k} - 1}{\xi_k},$$

valid for all $\xi \in \mathbb{R}^d$, except for the finite union of hyperplanes defined by

$$H := \{x \in \mathbb{R}^d \mid \xi_1 = 0 \text{ or } \xi_2 = 0 \dots \text{ or } \xi_d = 0\}.$$

Exercise 4. To see that the generating function definition of the Bernoulli polynomials in fact gives polynomials, we first write the Taylor series of the following two analytic functions:

$$\frac{t}{e^t - 1} = \sum_{k=0}^\infty \frac{B_k}{k!} t^k,$$

$$e^{xt} = \sum_{j=0}^\infty \frac{x^j t^j}{j!}.$$

Multiplying these series together by brute force gives us

(A.1)
$$\frac{t}{e^t - 1} e^{xt} = \left(\sum_{k=0}^\infty \frac{B_k}{k!} t^k \right) \left(\sum_{j=0}^\infty \frac{x^j}{j!} t^j \right)$$

(A.2)
$$= \sum_{n=0}^\infty \left(\sum_{j+k=n} \frac{B_k}{k!} \frac{x^j}{j!} \right) t^n$$

(A.3)
$$= \sum_{n=0}^\infty \left(\sum_{k=0}^n \frac{B_k}{k!} \frac{x^{n-k}}{(n-k)!} \right) t^n.$$

The coefficient of t^n on the LHS is, by definition, $\frac{1}{n!} B_n(x)$, and by uniqueness of Taylor series, this must also be the coefficient on the RHS, which is seen here to be a polynomial in x. In fact, we see more, namely that

$$\frac{1}{n!} B_n(x) = \sum_{k=0}^n \frac{B_k}{k!} \frac{x^{n-k}}{(n-k)!},$$

which can be written more cleanly as $B_n(x) = \sum_{k=0}^{n} \binom{n}{k} B_k x^{n-k}$.

Exercise 5. Commencing with the generating function definition of the Bernoulli polynomials (equation (2.13)) we replace x with $1 - x$ in order to observe the coefficients $B_k(1 - x)$:

$$\sum_{k=0}^{\infty} \frac{B_k(1-x)}{k!} t^k = \frac{te^{t(1-x)}}{e^t - 1}$$

$$= \frac{te^t e^{-tx}}{e^t - 1}$$

$$= \frac{te^{-tx}}{1 - e^{-t}}$$

$$= \frac{-te^{-tx}}{e^{-t} - 1}$$

$$= \sum_{k=0}^{\infty} \frac{B_k(x)}{k!}(-t)^k,$$

where the last equality follows from the definition of the same generating function, namely equation (2.13), but with the variable t replaced by $-t$. Comparing the coefficient of t^k on both sides, we have $B_k(1 - x) = (-1)^k B_k(x)$.

Exercise 6. To show that $B_n(x + 1) - B_n(x) = nx^{n-1}$, we play with

$$\sum_{k=0}^{\infty} \left(\frac{B_k(x+1)}{k!} t^k - \frac{B_k(x)}{k!} t^k \right)$$

$$= \frac{te^{t(x+1)}}{e^t - 1} - \frac{te^{t(x)}}{e^t - 1}$$

$$= e^t \frac{te^{tx}}{e^t - 1} - \frac{te^{t(x)}}{e^t - 1}$$

$$= (e^t - 1)\frac{te^{tx}}{e^t - 1}$$

$$= te^{tx} = \sum_{k=0}^{\infty} \frac{x^k}{k!} t^{k+1}$$

$$= \sum_{k=1}^{\infty} \frac{x^{k-1}}{(k-1)!} t^k$$

$$= \sum_{k=1}^{\infty} \frac{kx^{k-1}}{k!} t^k.$$

Comparing the coefficients of t^k on both sides, we arrive at the required identity.

Exercise 7.   We need to show that $\frac{d}{dx}B_n(x) = nB_{n-1}(x)$. Well,

$$\sum_{k=0}^{\infty} \frac{d}{dx}\frac{B_k(x)}{k!}t^k = \frac{d}{dx}\frac{te^{tx}}{e^t-1}$$

$$= t\sum_{k=0}^{\infty}\frac{B_k(x)}{k!}t^k$$

$$= \sum_{k=0}^{\infty}\frac{B_k(x)}{k!}t^{k+1}$$

$$= \sum_{k=1}^{\infty}\frac{B_{k-1}(x)}{(k-1)!}t^k$$

$$= \sum_{k=1}^{\infty}k\frac{B_{k-1}(x)}{k!}t^k,$$

and by comparing the coefficient of t^n on both sides, we are done.

Exercise 22.   We will prove part (22b). To begin, we have

$$\left|e^{i\theta} - 1\right|^2 = \left|\cos\theta - 1 + i\sin\theta\right|^2$$

$$= (\cos\theta - 1)^2 + \sin^2\theta$$

$$= 2 - 2\cos\theta$$

$$= 4\sin^2\left(\frac{\theta}{2}\right).$$

So it suffices to show that $4\sin^2\left(\frac{\theta}{2}\right) \leq \theta^2$ for all $0 \leq \theta \leq 2\pi$. In other words, the problem is reduced to the calculus problem of showing that $\sin\left(\frac{\theta}{2}\right) \leq \frac{\theta}{2}$, for $\theta \in [0, 2\pi]$. To prove this, we let $y(x) = x - \sin x$, so that it suffices to prove that $y \geq 0$ on $[0, \pi]$. Computing its derivative, $y'(x) = 1 - \cos x \geq 0$ on $[0, \pi]$, and since $y(0) = 0$, we conclude that y is an increasing function. This proves $y \geq 0$ on $[0, \pi]$.

Exercise 27.   For part (a), suppose, to the contrary, that none of the vertices of $\mathcal{P}$ have degree 4. Because each of its vertices must have degree at least 3, then all of vertices have degree 3. By the "handshanking lemma" of elementary graph theory, we have

$$2|E| = \sum_{\text{vertices } v \in \mathcal{P}} \deg(v) = 3 \cdot 5,$$

a contradiction. To prove part (b), consider the unit cube in $\mathbb{R}^3$, and take 4 vertices that belong to one facet, with one vertex from an oppostive facet. It is clear that all of its vertices have degree 4.

Exercise 31.   Considering the partial sum $S_n := \sum_{k=1}^n a_k b_k$, we know by Abel summation that

$$S_n = a_n B_n + \sum_{k=1}^{n-1} B_k(a_k - a_{k+1}),$$

for each $n \geq 2$, where $B_n := \sum_{k=1}^n b_k$. By assumption, $|B_n| := |\sum_{k=1}^n b_k| \leq M$, and the a_k are going to 0, so we see that the first part of the right-hand side approaches zero, namely, $|a_n B_n| := |a_n| |\sum_{k+1}^n b_k| \to 0$, as $n \to \infty$.

Next, we have

$$|\sum_{k=1}^{n-1} B_k(a_k - a_{k+1})| \leq \sum_{k=1}^{n-1} |B_k||a_k - a_{k+1}|$$

$$\leq M \sum_{k=1}^{n-1} |a_k - a_{k+1}|$$

$$= M \sum_{k=1}^{n-1} (a_k - a_{k+1}),$$

where the last equality holds because, by assumption, the a_k are decreasing. But the last finite sum equals $-Ma_n + Ma_1$, and we have $\lim_{n \to \infty}(-Ma_n + Ma_1) = Ma_1$, a finite limit.

Therefore $\sum_{k=1}^{n-1} B_k(a_k - a_{k+1})$ converges absolutely, and so S_n converges, as desired.

Exercise 32.   Fix $x \in \mathbb{R} - \mathbb{Z}$. Notice that the Dirichlet kernel is a finite geometric sum:

$$\sum_{k=-n}^n e^{2\pi i k x} = \frac{e^{2\pi i (n+1)x} - e^{-2\pi i n x}}{e^{2\pi i x} - 1}$$

$$= \frac{e^{\pi i x(2n+1)} - e^{-\pi i x(2n+1)}}{e^{\pi i x} - e^{-\pi i x}}$$

$$= \frac{\sin(\pi x(2n + 1))}{\sin(\pi x)}.$$

Exercise 33. We fix $x \in \mathbb{R} - \mathbb{Z}$ and let $z := e^{2\pi ix}$, which lies on the unit circle, and by assumption $z \neq 1$. Then

(A.4)
$$\left| \sum_{k=1}^{n} e^{2\pi ikx} \right| = \left| \sum_{k=1}^{n} z^k \right| = \left| \frac{z^{n+1} - 1}{z - 1} \right| \leq \frac{2}{z - 1},$$

because $|z^{n+1} - 1| \leq |z^{n+1}| + 1 = 2$. We also have

$$|z - 1|^2 = |e^{2\pi ix} - 1||e^{-2\pi ix} - 1| = |2 - 2\cos(2\pi x)| = 4\sin^2(\pi x),$$

so that we have the equality $\left| \frac{2}{z-1} \right| = \left| \frac{1}{\sin(\pi x)} \right|$. Altogether, we see that

(A.5)
$$\left| \sum_{k=1}^{n} e^{2\pi ikx} \right| \leq \frac{1}{|\sin(\pi x)|}.$$

Exercise 34. We fix $a \in \mathbb{R} - \mathbb{Z}$ and need to prove that

$$\sum_{m=1}^{\infty} \frac{e^{2\pi ima}}{m}$$

converges. Abel's summation formula (equation (2.78)) gives us

$$\sum_{k=1}^{n} \frac{e^{2\pi ika}}{k} = \frac{1}{n} \sum_{r=1}^{n} e^{2\pi ira} + \sum_{k=1}^{n-1} \left(\sum_{r=1}^{k} e^{2\pi ira} \right) \frac{1}{k(k+1)},$$

so that

$$\sum_{k=1}^{\infty} \frac{e^{2\pi ika}}{k} = \sum_{k=1}^{\infty} \left(\sum_{r=1}^{k} e^{2\pi ira} \right) \frac{1}{k(k+1)},$$

and the latter series converges absolutely.

Solutions to Chapter 3

Exercise 1. For all four inequalities, we will use an arbitrary vector $a \in \mathbb{R}^d$. For the first inequality,

$$a_1^2 + \cdots + a_d^2 \geq \max\{|a_1|, \ldots, |a_d|\}^2 := \|a\|_\infty^2.$$

The second inequality $\|a\|_2 \leq \|a\|_1$ means that

$$\sqrt{a_1^2 + \cdots + a_d^2} \leq |a_1| + \cdots + |a_d|,$$

which is clear by squaring both sides.

To prove the third and most interesting inequality here, we use the Cauchy–Schwartz inequality, with the two vectors $x := (a_1, \ldots, a_d)$ and $(1, 1, \ldots, 1)$:

$$\|a\|_1 := |a_1| \cdot 1 + \cdots + |a_d| \cdot 1 \leq \sqrt{a_1^2 + \cdots + a_d^2}\sqrt{1 + \cdots + 1} = \sqrt{d}\|a\|_2,$$

which also shows that we obtain equality if and only if $(a_1, \ldots, a_d)$ is a scalar multiple of $(1, 1, \ldots, 1)$.

For the fourth inequality, we have

$$\sqrt{a_1^2 + \cdots + a_d^2} \leq \sqrt{d \max\{|a_1|, \ldots, |a_d|\}^2} := \sqrt{d}\|a\|_\infty.$$

Exercise 2. To prove part (a), we compute

$$\left(\frac{e^t + e^{-t}}{2}\right)^2 - \left(\frac{e^t - e^{-t}}{2}\right)^2 = \frac{e^{2t} + 2 + e^{-2t} - (e^{2t} - 2 + e^{-2t})}{4} = 1.$$

To prove part (b), we begin with the definition of the hyperbolic cotangent:

$$t \coth t = t\frac{e^t + e^{-t}}{e^t - e^{-t}}$$

$$= t\frac{e^t}{e^t - e^{-t}} + t\frac{e^{-t}}{e^t - e^{-t}}$$

$$= \frac{t}{1 - e^{-2t}} + \frac{t}{e^{2t} - 1}.$$

Recalling the definition of the Bernoulli numbers, namely,

$$\frac{t}{e^t - 1} = \sum_{k=0}^\infty B_k \frac{t^k}{k!},$$

we see that

$$t \coth t = \frac{1}{2}\left(\frac{-2t}{e^{-2t} - 1}\right) + \frac{1}{2}\left(\frac{2t}{e^{2t} - 1}\right)$$

$$= \frac{1}{2}\sum_{k=0}^\infty B_k \frac{(-2t)^k}{k!} + \frac{1}{2}\sum_{k=0}^\infty B_k \frac{(2t)^k}{k!}$$

$$= \sum_{k=0}^\infty \frac{1}{2}((-1)^k + 1) B_k \frac{(2t)^k}{k!},$$

so the only surviving terms in the latter series are the terms whose index k is an even integer. This yields $t \coth t = \sum_{n=0}^\infty \frac{2^{2n}}{(2n)!} B_{2n} t^{2n}$.

Exercise 3. We know, by equation (3.48), that the Fourier transform of $f(x) := e^{-2\pi t|x|}$ is equal to $\hat{f}(\xi) = \frac{t}{\pi(t^2+\xi^2)}$. So using Poisson summation, we have

$$\sum_{n\in\mathbb{Z}} e^{-2\pi t|n|} = \sum_{n\in\mathbb{Z}} f(n) = \sum_{\xi\in\mathbb{Z}} \hat{f}(\xi) = \frac{t}{\pi} \sum_{\xi\in\mathbb{Z}} \frac{1}{\xi^2+t^2}.$$

Exercise 21. We are given $f, g \in L^2(\mathbb{R}^d)$, and we wish to prove that $f * g$ is always continuous on $\mathbb{R}^d$. By definition, we need to show that $\lim_{h\to 0} \int_{\mathbb{R}^d} f(x-h-y)g(y)dy = (f*g)(x)$.

To prove part (21a), we fix any sequence of functions $f_n \in L^2(\mathbb{R}^d)$ with the property that $f_n \to f$ in $L^2(\mathbb{R}^d)$. We will prove that $\lim_{n\to\infty} ((f_n - f) * g)(x) = 0$ for each $x \in \mathbb{R}^d$. Well, we have

(A.6) $$\left| ((f_n - f) * g)(x) \right|$$

(A.7) $$\leq \int_{\mathbb{R}^d} |f_n(x-y) - f(x-y)|\, |g(y)|dy$$

(A.8) $$\leq \int_{\mathbb{R}^d} |f_n(x-u) - f(x-u)|^2\, du \int_{\mathbb{R}^d} |g(v)|^2 dv$$

(A.9) $$= \int_{\mathbb{R}^d} |f_n(u) - f(u)|^2\, du \int_{\mathbb{R}^d} |g(v)|^2 dv,$$

using the triangle inequality for integrals in (A.7), and the Cauchy–Schwartz inequality in (A.8). Since $f_n \to f$ in $L^2(\mathbb{R}^d)$, we are done. For part (21b), we must show that

$$\int_{\mathbb{R}^d} |T_h f(x) - f(x)|^2 dx := \int_{\mathbb{R}^d} |f(x-h) - f(x)|^2 dx \to 0,$$

as $h \to 0$. First we will show that the latter integral converges for each fixed nonzero vector h:

$$\int_{\mathbb{R}^d} |f(x-h) - f(x)|^2 dx$$

$$\leq \int_{\mathbb{R}^d} |f(x-h)|^2 dx + 2\int_{\mathbb{R}^d} |f(x-h)f(x)|\, dx + \int_{\mathbb{R}^d} |f(x)|^2 dx$$

$$\leq 2\|f\|_{L^2(\mathbb{R}^d)}^2 + 2\left(\int_{\mathbb{R}^d} |f(x-h)|^2 dx \right)^{\frac{1}{2}} \left(\int_{\mathbb{R}^d} |f(x)|^2 dx \right)^{\frac{1}{2}}$$

$$\leq 4\|f\|_{L^2(\mathbb{R}^d)}^2,$$

using $\int_{\mathbb{R}^d} |f(x-h)|^2 \, dx = \int_{\mathbb{R}^d} |f(x)|^2 \, dx := \|f\|_{L^2(\mathbb{R}^d)} < \infty$, and the Cauchy–Schwartz inequality for $\int_{\mathbb{R}^d} |f(x-h)f(x)| \, dx$. Therefore, we have convergence of the integral for each nonzero h. Next, we will separate the integral into two pieces, one of which is a "neighborhood of infinity":

$$\int_{\mathbb{R}^d} |f(x-h) - f(x)|^2 dx$$

$$= \int_{\|x\|>R} |f(x-h) - f(x)|^2 dx + \int_{\|x\|\leq R} |f(x-h) - f(x)|^2 dx.$$

By the convergence of the integral, we know that given any $\varepsilon > 0$, there exists $R > 0$ such that

$$\int_{\|x\|>R} |f(x-h) - f(x)|^2 dx < \frac{\varepsilon}{2}.$$

It remains to handle the remaining integral, where we will label the remaining compact set $E := \{x \in \mathbb{R}^d \mid \|x\| \leq R\}$:

$$\int_E |f(x-h) - f(x)|^2 dx < \text{vol } E \cdot \sup_{x \in E}\{|f(x-h) - f(x)|^2\}.$$

Although f may not necessarily be continuous, we may still conclude that as $h \to 0$, the latter expression tends to 0 (otherwise the integral would diverge), finishing part (21b).

To prove part (21c), we must show that $\lim_{h\to 0}(T_h f * g)(x) = (f * g)(x)$, for each $x \in \mathbb{R}^d$. We pick the sequence of functions $f_n := T_{h_n} f$, with some sequence of vectors $h_n \to 0$. By part (21b) we know that $T_{h_n} f \to f$ in $L^2(\mathbb{R}^d)$. So $f_n \to f$ in $L^2(\mathbb{R}^d)$. Now we may invoke part (21a) to conclude that $\lim_{n\to\infty} ((f_n - f) * g)(x) = 0$. In other words, we have shown that $\lim_{h\to 0} ((T_h f * g))(x) = (f * g)(x)$ for each $x \in \mathbb{R}^d$, meaning that $f * g$ is continuous on $\mathbb{R}^d$.

Exercise 26.   To prove part (a), suppose we are given $f \in L^1(\mathbb{R}^d)$ with $f(x) > 0$ for all $x \in \mathbb{R}^d$. By the triangle inequality, we know that $|\hat{f}(\xi)| \leq \int_{\mathbb{R}^d} |f(x)e^{2\pi i\langle x,\xi\rangle}| dx = \int_{\mathbb{R}^d} f(x)dx := \hat{f}(0)$, where $|f(x)| = f(x)$ follows from our assumption that $f(x) > 0$ for all $x \in \mathbb{R}^d$. To prove the strict inequality $|\hat{f}(\xi)| < \hat{f}(0)$ for all nonzero $\xi \in \mathbb{R}^d$, suppose, to the contrary, that there exists a nonzero $\xi \in \mathbb{R}^d$ such that $|\hat{f}(\xi)| = \hat{f}(0)$. Then

$$\left| \int_{\mathbb{R}^d} f(x)e^{2\pi i\langle x,\xi\rangle} dx \right| = \int_{\mathbb{R}^d} f(x)dx = \int_{\mathbb{R}^d} |f(x)e^{2\pi i\langle x,\xi\rangle}| dx,$$

and we can now invoke Corollary 3.6, which allows us to conclude that

$$\alpha\left(f(x)e^{2\pi i\langle x,\xi\rangle}\right) = \left|f(x)e^{2\pi i\langle x,\xi\rangle}\right| = |f(x)| = f(x),$$

for some complex constant $\alpha := e^{2\pi i\theta}$ on the unit circle, and for almost all $x \in \mathbb{R}^d$ ($\alpha = 1$ is also allowed and poses no problems). In other words, we have $f(x)\left(e^{2\pi i\theta}e^{2\pi i\langle x,\xi\rangle} - 1\right) = 0$ almost everywhere. Now, our assumption that $f(x) > 0$ for all $x \in \mathbb{R}^d$ implies that $e^{2\pi i\theta}e^{2\pi i\langle x,\xi\rangle} = 1$ for almost all x. But this is a contradiction because $e^{2\pi i(\theta+\langle x,\xi\rangle)} = 1$ precisely when $\theta + \langle x,\xi\rangle \in \mathbb{Z}$. That is, the latter condition occurs exactly when x belongs to the discrete union of hyperplanes

$$\{x \in \mathbb{R}^d \mid \langle x,\xi\rangle = -\theta + \mathbb{Z}\},$$

a set of measure 0 (for the d-dimensional meassure in $\mathbb{R}^d$).

Part (b) is almost identical. Again arguing by contradiction, we suppose that there exists a nonzero $\xi \in \mathbb{R}^d$ such that $|\hat{1}_{\mathcal{P}}(\xi)| = \hat{1}_{\mathcal{P}}(0) := \text{vol}\,\mathcal{P}$. We proceed in exactly the same manner, where the only difference is that we replace all the integrals over $\mathbb{R}^d$ by integrals over $\mathcal{P}$. We arrive at the following conclusion: $e^{2\pi i(\theta+\langle x,\xi\rangle)} = 1$ for almost all $x \in \mathcal{P}$.

The latter conclusion is again a contradiction because the solution set to the latter equality is precisely the finite union (using the boundedness of the set $\mathcal{P}$ here) of hyperplanes $\{x \in \mathcal{P} \mid \langle x,\xi\rangle = -\theta + \mathbb{Z}\}$, which has measure 0 as a d-dimensional subset of $\mathbb{R}^d$.

Exercise 28. We need to show that there exist two real numbers r,s such that

$$f := 1_{[-r,r]} * 1_{[-r,r]} + 1_{[-s,s]} * 1_{[-s,s]}$$

enjoys the property

$$\hat{f}(\xi) > 0,$$

for all $\xi \in \mathbb{R}$. Let us pick any two real numbers r,s that are incommensurable, meaning that $\frac{r}{s} \notin \mathbb{Q}$. Using (2.40), we compute $\hat{f}$:

$$\hat{f}(\xi) := \left(\hat{1}_{[-r,r]}(\xi)\right)^2 + \left(\hat{1}_{[-s,s]}(\xi)\right)^2$$

$$= \left(\frac{\sin(2r\pi\xi)}{\pi\xi}\right)^2 + \left(\frac{\sin(2s\pi\xi)}{\pi\xi}\right)^2 \geq 0.$$

To prove strict positivity, suppose, to the contrary, that there exists a nonzero $\xi \in \mathbb{R}$ such that $\hat{f}(\xi) = 0$. Then $(\sin(2r\pi\xi))^2 + (\sin(2s\pi\xi))^2 = 0$, but the vanishing of a sum of two squares (of real numbers) implies that they must both equal 0:

$$\sin(2r\pi\xi) = 0, \quad \text{and} \quad \sin(2s\pi\xi) = 0.$$

Therefore, $2r\pi\xi = m\pi$ and $2s\pi\xi = n\pi$ for some integers m, n. We conclude that $\xi = \frac{m}{2r} = \frac{n}{2s}$, so $\frac{r}{s} = \frac{m}{n} \in \mathbb{Q}$, a contradiction that proves $\hat{f}(\xi) > 0$ for all nonzero real ξ.

Exercise 32. By assumption, $g : \mathbb{R}^d \to \mathbb{C}$ is infinitely smooth, and compactly supported. By Corollary 3.30, $\hat{g}$ is a rapidly decreasing function. Because g has compact support, we also know that $\hat{g}$ is infinitely smooth. So $\hat{g}$ is a Schwartz function (and g is also a Schwartz function—in fact, g is a "bump function", by definition). Therefore we may apply the Poisson summation formula for Schwartz functions (Theorem 3.38) to $\hat{g}$:

$$\sum_{\xi \in \mathbb{Z}^d} \hat{g}(\xi) = \sum_{n \in \mathbb{Z}^d} g(n),$$

which is a finite sum due to the compact support of g.

Exercise 37. If either $a = 0$ or $b = 0$, then the conclusion is clear. Suppose that $a, b > 0$. Using the assumtion $\frac{1}{p} + \frac{1}{q} = 1$, let $t := \frac{1}{p}$, implying that $1 - t = \frac{1}{q}$. The concavity of $\ln(t)$ (which holds by Exercise (36)) now gives us, with $x := a^p, y := b^q$:

(A.10) $\ln(tx + (1-t)y) = \ln(ta^p + (1-t)b^q)$

(A.11) $\geq t\ln(a^p) + (1-t)\ln(b^q)$

(A.12) $= pt\ln a + (1-t)q\ln b$

(A.13) $= \ln a + \ln b.$

Exponentiating both sides of the latter inequality, we obtain Young's inequality:

$$\frac{a^p}{p} + \frac{b^q}{q} \geq ab.$$

Moreover, equality holds in (A.11) $\iff$ equality holds for the ln function, which is a concave function. Since ln is not a linear function, (3.139) tells us that $x = y$, i.e., $a^p = b^q$.

Solutions to Chapter 4

Exercise 1. We are given a symmetric convex body $K \subset \mathbb{R}^2$ of area 4, which contains only the origin. By Theorem 4.8, $\frac{1}{2}K$ must tile $\mathbb{R}^2$ by translations with vectors from $\mathbb{Z}^2$, because $2^2 \det \mathbb{Z}^2 = 4 = \text{vol } K$ (and $\frac{1}{2}K$ is therefore an extremal body). But since $\frac{1}{2}K$ tiles $\mathbb{R}^2$ by translations, so does K itself.

Exercise 2.   Here, $K, L \subset \mathbb{R}^d$ are d-dimensional compact, convex sets. To prove that $K + L$ is convex, pick any $x, y \in K + L$, and we must show that $\lambda_1 x + \lambda_2 y \in K + L$ for all nonnegative λ_1, λ_2 with $\lambda_1 + \lambda_2 = 1$. By assumption $x = k_1 + l_1$ and $y = k_2 + l_2$, with $k_1, k_2 \in K$, $l_1, l_2 \in L$. We have

$$\lambda_1 x + \lambda_2 y = \lambda_1 (k_1 + l_1) + \lambda_2 (k_2 + l_2)$$
$$= (\lambda_1 k_1 + \lambda_2 k_2) + (\lambda_1 l_1 + \lambda_2 l_2) \in K + L,$$

where we used the convexity of K and of L in the very last step above. The same conclusion holds for $K - L$, because the convexity of L implies the convexity of $-L$.

Exercise 3.   We are given d-dimensional compact convex sets $A, B \subset \mathbb{R}^d$. To prove that $A \cap B \subseteq \frac{1}{2}A + \frac{1}{2}B$, we pick any $x \in A \cap B$. Noticing that $x = \frac{1}{2}x + \frac{1}{2}x$, where $\frac{1}{2}x \in \frac{1}{2}A$ and $\frac{1}{2}x \in \frac{1}{2}B$, we are done.

To prove the second containment $\frac{1}{2}A + \frac{1}{2}B \subseteq \operatorname{conv}(A \cup B)$, we pick $y \in \frac{1}{2}A + \frac{1}{2}B$. So we may write $y = \frac{1}{2}a + \frac{1}{2}b$, where $a \in A, b \in B$, which is a convex linear combination of elements from A and B, hence belongs to $\operatorname{conv}(A \cup B)$. We will leave the equality cases for the reader.

Exercise 4.   We are given a d-dimensional convex set $A \subset \mathbb{R}^d$. To prove that $A + A = 2A$, we pick any $x, y \in A$. By the convexity of A, we know that $\frac{1}{2}x + \frac{1}{2}y \in A$, so that $x + y \in 2A$, proving that $A + A \subseteq 2A$. For the reverse inclusion $A + A \supseteq 2A$, we just notice that for any $a \in A$, $2a = a + a \in A + A$.

Exercise 5.   For part (a), we suppose that

(A.14)
$$\frac{1}{2}C - \frac{1}{2}C = C.$$

For any $x \in C$, we need to show that $-x \in C$. Since $x \in \frac{1}{2}C - \frac{1}{2}C$, we know that there must exist $y, z \in C$ such that $x = \frac{1}{2}y - \frac{1}{2}z$. This implies that $-x = \frac{1}{2}z - \frac{1}{2}y \in \frac{1}{2}C - \frac{1}{2}C \subseteq C$. Therefore C is centrally symmetric.

To show part (b), first let us suppose that C is convex and centrally symmetric (cs). Then $\frac{1}{2}C - \frac{1}{2}C = \frac{1}{2}C + \frac{1}{2}C$. Now using convexity, we claim that $\frac{1}{2}C + \frac{1}{2}C = C$. The convexity assumption implies that $\frac{1}{2}C + \frac{1}{2}C \subseteq C$, because for any $x, y \in C$, we have $\frac{1}{2}x + \frac{1}{2}y \in C$. On the other hand, we always have $\frac{1}{2}C + \frac{1}{2}C \supseteq C$, because we can write each $x \in C$ as $x = \frac{1}{2}x + \frac{1}{2}x \in \frac{1}{2}C + \frac{1}{2}C$.

So, altogether we have $\frac{1}{2}C - \frac{1}{2}C = \frac{1}{2}C + \frac{1}{2}C = C$, proving the first direction.

For the other direction of part (b), we assume that

$$(A.15) \qquad\qquad \frac{1}{2}C - \frac{1}{2}C = C,$$

and we need to prove that C is convex and cs. By part (a), we already know that $\frac{1}{2}C - \frac{1}{2}C$ is cs, hence the hypothesis (A.15) shows that C must also be cs.

To prove convexity, let $x, y \in C$. Using the hypothesis (A.15), together with the central symmetry of C, we have $C = \frac{1}{2}C - \frac{1}{2}C = \frac{1}{2}C + \frac{1}{2}C$, so, in particular, $\frac{1}{2}x + \frac{1}{2}y \in C$.

For part (c), a compact counterexample is given by $C := [-2, -1] \cup [1, 2]$, a nonconvex set in $\mathbb{R}$. Here C is centrally symmetric, yet $C - C = [-3, 3] \neq [-4, -2] \cup [2, 4] = 2C$.

Another (noncompact) counterexample is $\mathbb{Z}$, which is not convex, yet clearly centrally symmetric.

Exercise 11. To prove part (a), we are given two convex bodies $A, B \subset \mathbb{R}^d$, so, by definition, we have

$$\text{support}(1_A * 1_B) := \text{clos}\left\{ y \in \mathbb{R}^d \mid \int_{\mathbb{R}^d} 1_A(x)1_B(y - x)dx \neq 0 \right\},$$

and we must prove that $\text{support}(1_A * 1_B) = A + B$, their Minkowski sum. In general, we have

$$(A.16) \qquad 1_A(x)1_B(y - x) > 0 \iff 1_A(x) = 1 \text{ and } 1_B(y - x) = 1$$

$$(A.17) \qquad\qquad\qquad\qquad \iff x \in A \text{ and } y - x \in B$$

$$(A.18) \qquad\qquad\qquad\qquad \iff y \in A + B.$$

If we fix any $y \notin \text{support}(1_A * 1_B)$, then $\int_{\mathbb{R}^d} 1_A(x)1_B(y-x)dx = 0$, which implies that $1_A(x)1_B(y - x) = 0$ for all $x \in \mathbb{R}^d$. But by the equivalences (A.16), we see that $1_A(x)1_B(y - x) = 0 \iff y \notin A + B$, proving that $A + B \subset \text{support}(1_A * 1_B)$.

Conversely, suppose that $y \in \text{support}(1_A * 1_B)$, meaning that there exists a sequence $y_n \in \mathbb{R}^d$ with $\int_{\mathbb{R}^d} 1_A(x)1_B(y_n-x)dx \neq 0$. This implies that for each such y_n, there exists at least one $x \in \mathbb{R}^d$ with $1_A(x)1_B(y_n - x) > 0$. This last inequality, using our equivalences (A.16), implies that the sequence $y_n \in A + B$. Because $A + B$ is a closed set, we finally have $y := \lim_{n \to \infty} y_n \in A + B$.

To prove part (b), we must show that support$(f * g) \subseteq C$, where

$$C := \text{clos}(\text{support}(f) + \text{support}(g)).$$

We will prove the contrapositive: if $x \notin C$, then $x \notin \text{support}(f * g)$. So we suppose $x \notin C$, and we have to prove that $(f * g)(x) = 0$. By our assumption on x, for each $y \in \text{support}(g)$, we have that $x - y \notin \text{support}(f)$. The last assertion means that $f(x - y) = 0$, so we now know that $f(x - y)g(y) = 0$ for all $y \in \mathbb{R}^d$. Finally, we have $(f * g)(x) := \int_{\mathbb{R}^d} f(x - y)g(y)dy = 0$.

Exercise 9. Show that in $\mathbb{R}^d$, an integer simplex Δ is unimodular $\Longleftrightarrow$ vol $\Delta = \frac{1}{d!}$.

Exercise 10. Define $\Delta := \text{conv}\{(0, 0, 0), (1, 1, 0), (1, 0, 1), (0, 1, 1)\}$, an integer 3-simplex. It is clear that Δ is subset of the unit cube $[0, 1]^3$, and therefore Δ has no integer points in its interior. To see that Δ is not a unimodular simplex, it is sufficient to consider its tangent K_0 cone at the origin, and show that this tangent cone is not unimodular. K_0 has primitive integer edge vectors $(1, 1, 0), (1, 0, 1), (0, 1, 1)$, so that the determinant of K_0 is equal to

$$\left| \det \begin{pmatrix} 1 & 1 & 0 \\ 1 & 0 & 1 \\ 0 & 1 & 1 \end{pmatrix} \right| = 2 > 1.$$

Exercise 13. Suppose, to the contrary, that for some polytope $\mathcal{P}$ we have $\hat{1}_{\mathcal{P}}(\xi) = g(\xi)$, a Schwartz function. Taking the Fourier transform of both sides of the latter equality, and using the fact that the Fourier transform takes Schwartz functions to Schwartz functions, we would have $1_{\mathcal{P}}(-x) = \hat{g}(-x)$ is a Schwartz function. But this is a contradiction because the indicator function of a polytope is not even continuous.

Exercise 18. We use the Cauchy–Schwartz inequality:

$$\left\langle \begin{pmatrix} a \\ b \end{pmatrix}, \begin{pmatrix} \sin x \\ \cos x \end{pmatrix} \right\rangle^2 := (a \sin x + b \cos x)^2$$

$$\leq (a^2 + b^2)(\sin^2 x + \cos^2 x)$$

$$= a^2 + b^2.$$

By the equality condition of Cauchy–Schwartz, we see that the maximum is obtained when the two vectors are linearly dependent, which gives $\tan x = \frac{a}{b}$.

Exercise 20. Well, we have $x \in \frac{1}{2}K \cap \left(\frac{1}{2}K + n\right) \Longleftrightarrow x = \frac{1}{2}y$ and $x = \frac{1}{2}z + n$, where $y, z \in K$. The latter conditions hold $\Longleftrightarrow n =$

$\frac{1}{2}y - \frac{1}{2}z \in \frac{1}{2}K - \frac{1}{2}K$. Because of its convexity and central symmetry, we know that the latter condition is equivalent to $n \in K$ by Exercise (5).

Solutions to Chapter 5

Exercise 4. We are given the hyperplanes $H_1 := \{x \in \mathbb{R}^d \mid c_1x_1 + \cdots + c_dx_d = k_1\}$ and $H_2 := \{x \in \mathbb{R}^d \mid c_1x_1 + \cdots + c_dx_d = k_2\}$. First we will pick a point $x \in H_1$, and then we will "walk along its normal vector", until we get to H_2. With this "walk" in mind, we may assume WLOG that $k_2 > k_1$, and that the normal vector is pointing from H_1 towards H_2.

For simplicity, we will let $L := \sqrt{c_1^2 + \cdots + c_d^2}$, and with this definition the unit normal vector to H_1 is $n := \frac{1}{L}(c_1, \ldots, c_d)^T$. We want to find $\delta > 0$ such that $x + \delta n \in H_2$. Unraveling the definition of the latter statement, we must have

$$c_1(x_1 + \delta\tfrac{1}{L}c_1) + \cdots + c_d(x_d + \delta\tfrac{1}{L}c_d) = k_2$$
$$\Longleftrightarrow (c_1x_1 + \cdots + c_dx_d) + \frac{\delta}{L}(c_1^2 + \cdots + c_d^2) = k_2$$
$$\Longleftrightarrow k_1 + \delta\sqrt{c_1^2 + \cdots + c_d^2} = k_2$$
$$\Longleftrightarrow \delta = \frac{k_2 - k_1}{\sqrt{c_1^2 + \cdots + c_d^2}}.$$

Exercise 12. We consider each kth row of M as a vector, call it v_k. By assumption, v_k enjoys the bound

$$\|v_k\| \leq \sqrt{B^2 + \cdots B^2} = B\sqrt{d}.$$

Using Hadamard's inequality (5.8), we have

$$|\det M| \leq \|v_1\| \cdots \|v_d\| \leq \left(B\sqrt{d}\right)^d.$$

Exercise 15. We are given any group G (not necessarily finite), and any element $g \in G$. We note that $gG \subseteq G$ by definition of closure in G: for any $h \in G$, we have $gh \in G$. To show $gG \supseteq G$, we fix any $a \in G$ and we must find some $x \in G$ such that $gx = a$. Since inverses exist in G, we find that $x = g^{-1}a$, and we are done.

Exercise 26. It is easy to see that the inverse matrix for M is

$$M^{-1} := \begin{pmatrix} | & | & \cdots & | \\ \frac{1}{c_1}b_1 & \frac{1}{c_2}b_2 & \cdots & \frac{1}{c_d}b_d \\ | & | & \cdots & | \end{pmatrix}^T.$$

The image of the unit sphere under the matrix M is, by definition,

$$M(S^{d-1}) := \{u \in \mathbb{R}^d \mid u = Mx, x \in S^{d-1}\}$$
$$= \{u \in \mathbb{R}^d \mid M^{-1}u \in S^{d-1}\}$$
$$= \{u \in \mathbb{R}^d \mid \frac{1}{c_1^2}\langle b_1, u\rangle^2 + \cdots + \frac{1}{c_d^2}\langle b_d, u\rangle^2 = 1\},$$

using our description of M^{-1} above.

For part (b), we begin with the definition of volume, and we want to compute the volume of the region $M(B) := \{u \in \mathbb{R}^d \mid u = My, \text{ with } \|y\| \le 1\}$, where B is the unit ball in $\mathbb{R}^d$:

$$\mathrm{vol}(Ellipsoid_M) := \int_{M(B)} du$$
$$= |\det M| \int_B dy$$
$$= |\det M| \, \mathrm{vol}(B),$$

using the change of variable $u = My$, with $y \in B$. We also used the Jacobian, which gives $du = |\det M| dy$.

Finally, we note that the matrix $M^T M$ is a diagonal matrix, with diagonal entries c_k^2, due to the fact that the b_k form an orthonormal basis. Thus we use: $|\det M|^2 = |\det M^T M| = \prod_{k=1}^d c_k^2$, so taking the positive square root, we arrive at $|\det M| = \prod_{k=1}^d c_k$, because all of the c_k are positive by assumption.

Exercise 33. Let $A := \begin{pmatrix} a & b \\ b & d \end{pmatrix}$ be an invertible symmetric matrix. Because A is symmetric, we know both of its eigenvalues λ_1, λ_2 are real. The characteristic polynomial of A, namely $(a - \lambda)(d - \lambda) - b^2$, may also be factored and rewritten as

$$\lambda^2 - (a + d)\lambda + (ad - b^2) = (\lambda - \lambda_1)(\lambda - \lambda_2) = \lambda^2 - (\lambda_1 + \lambda_2)\lambda + \lambda_1\lambda_2.$$

Equating coefficients of the latter identity between polynomials, we therefore have $\lambda_1 + \lambda_2 = \mathrm{Trace}\, A$, and $\lambda_1\lambda_2 = \det A$. From these last two relations, we see that if both eigenvalues are positive, then $\mathrm{Trace}\, A > 0$ and $\det A > 0$.

Conversely, suppose that $\operatorname{Trace} A > 0$ and $\det A > 0$. Then $\lambda_1\lambda_2 > 0$, so either both eigenvalues are positive, or both eigenvalues are negative. But the eigenvalues cannot both be negative, for this would contradict our assumption that $\lambda_1 + \lambda_2 > 0$.

Solutions to Chapter 6

Exercise 2. We are given $Q := \frac{1}{2}K - \frac{1}{2}K$, where $K \subset \mathbb{R}^d$ is compact and convex. We already know that Q is centrally symmetric. Moreover, the convexity of K implies that $\frac{1}{2}K + \frac{1}{2}K = K$. So we have

$$
\begin{aligned}
\tfrac{1}{2}Q - \tfrac{1}{2}Q &= \frac{1}{2}\left(\tfrac{1}{2}K - \tfrac{1}{2}K\right) - \frac{1}{2}\left(\tfrac{1}{2}K - \tfrac{1}{2}K\right) \\
&= \tfrac{1}{4}K - \tfrac{1}{4}K - \tfrac{1}{4}K + \tfrac{1}{4}K \\
&= \tfrac{1}{2}K - \tfrac{1}{2}K \\
&= Q.
\end{aligned}
$$

Exercise 4. We are given $r > 1$, a fixed constant. Dividing the inequality $(x + y)^r \geq x^r + y^r$ by x^r, it suffices to prove that $(1 + t)^r \geq 1 + t^r$, for all positive t. But this follows, for example, from the consideration of the function $f(t) := (1 + t)^r - 1 - t^r$ and the fact that its derivative $f'(t) = r(1 + t)^{r-1} - rt^{r-1}$ is positive on $(0, \infty)$.

Exercise 5. We prove the claim by induction on the dimension d. For $d = 1$, the claim is simply the usual test for convergence of the "p-series" $\sum_{n\geq 1} \frac{1}{n^p}$, and therefore holds. Now we fix any $d \geq 2$, and we assume that $r > d$. We must prove that $\sum_{n\in\mathbb{Z}^d} \frac{1}{\|n\|^r}$ converges. The first step below makes use of the inequality $(x + y)^r \geq x^r + y^r$ for $r > 1$ and $x, y > 0$ (see Exercise (4)). We have

(A.19) $$\|n\|^r := \left(n_1^2 + \cdots + n_d^2\right)^{\frac{r}{2}}$$

(A.20) $$\geq \left(n_1^2\right)^{\frac{r}{2}} + \cdots + \left(n_d^2\right)^{\frac{r}{2}}$$

(A.21) $$= |n_1|^r + |n_2|^r \cdots + |n_d|^r$$

(A.22) $$\geq ((|n_1|^r \cdot |n_2|^r \cdots |n_d|^r))^{\frac{1}{d}}\, d,$$

using the arithmetic-geometric mean inequality in (A.22). When considering the series $\sum_{n\in\mathbb{Z}^d} \frac{1}{\|n\|^r}$, we notice that by induction on the dimension it is sufficient to only prove convergence of the subseries

$$\sum_{\substack{n \in \mathbb{Z}^d \\ n_1 n_2 \cdots n_d \neq 0}} \frac{1}{\|n\|^r}$$

with the property that *none* of the coordinates of $n \in \mathbb{Z}^d$ vanish. From (A.22), we have

$$(A.23) \qquad \sum_{\substack{n \in \mathbb{Z}^d \\ n_1 n_2 \cdots n_d \neq 0}} \frac{1}{\|n\|^r} < \frac{1}{d} \sum_{\substack{n_1 \in \mathbb{Z} \\ n_1 \neq 0}} \frac{1}{|n_1|^{\frac{r}{d}}} \cdots \sum_{\substack{n_d \in \mathbb{Z} \\ n_d \neq 0}} \frac{1}{|n_d|^{\frac{r}{d}}} = \frac{2^d}{d} \zeta^d \left(\frac{r}{d} \right),$$

which converges because $\frac{r}{d} > 1$.

To prove the converse, we fix any $r \leq d$, and we must show that $\sum_{n \in \mathbb{Z}^d - \{0\}} \frac{1}{\|n\|^r}$ diverges. We recall the norm $\|x\|_\infty := \max\{|x_1|, \ldots, |x_d|\}$, for any $x \in \mathbb{R}^d$. By Exercise (1), we had $\|x\| \leq \sqrt{d} \, \|x\|_\infty$, for all $x \in \mathbb{R}^d$. We therefore have

$$(A.24) \qquad \sum_{n \in \mathbb{Z}^d - \{0\}} \frac{1}{\|n\|^r} \geq \frac{1}{d^{\frac{r}{2}}} \sum_{n \in \mathbb{Z}^d - \{0\}} \frac{1}{\|n\|_\infty^r},$$

and the point is that now it is easy to count the number of integer points that have a fixed $\|n\|_\infty$ norm. In fact, to count the number of integer points $n \in \mathbb{Z}^d$ such that $\|n\|_\infty = k$, we realize that this equals the number of integer points that lie on the boundary of the cube $[-k, k]^d$. Thus, we may compute the number of these boundary integer points easily:

$$(2k+1)^d - (2k-1)^d = \sum_{j=0}^{d} \binom{d}{j} (2k)^{d-j} - \sum_{j=0}^{d} \binom{d}{j} (-1)^j (2k)^{d-j}$$

$$= 2 \sum_{m=0}^{d} \binom{d}{2m+1} (2k)^{d-2m-1},$$

where the upper summation limit is never achieved, but takes care of both parity cases of d. We notice that the latter finite sum is a sum of strictly positive terms, and to prove divergence we will only keep the leading term $2d(2k)^{d-1} = d2^d k^{d-1}$. Continuing from (A.24), we have

$$(A.25) \qquad \sum_{n \in \mathbb{Z}^d - \{0\}} \frac{1}{\|n\|^r} \geq \frac{1}{d^{\frac{r}{2}}} \sum_{n \in \mathbb{Z}^d - \{0\}} \frac{1}{\|n\|_\infty^r} > \frac{d2^d}{d^{\frac{r}{2}}} \sum_{k=1}^{\infty} \frac{k^{d-1}}{k^r},$$

which diverges precisely when $r - d + 1 \leq 1$. We conclude that we have divergence when $r \leq d$.

Exercise 6. By the arithmetic-geometric mean inequality, we know that $\frac{1+a_j}{2} \geq \sqrt{a_j}$, for each $1 \leq j \leq d$, and now we multiply all of these together:

$$\frac{1}{2^d}(1+a_1)(1+a_2)\cdots(1+a_d) \geq \sqrt{a_1 a_2 \cdots a_d} = 1.$$

Solutions to Chapter 7

Exercise 1. We are given $\alpha > 0$, and a simplicial cone $\mathcal{K}_v$, with edge vectors $w_1, \ldots, w_d \in \mathbb{R}^d$. By definition, $\det \mathcal{K}_v$ is the determinant of the matrix whose columns are the w_k. Replacing each $w_k(v)$ by $\alpha_k w_k(v)$, we see that the determinant $|\det \mathcal{K}_v|$ gets multiplied by α^d, and so

$$\frac{\alpha^d |\det \mathcal{K}_v|}{\prod_{k=1}^d \langle \alpha w_k(v), z \rangle} = \frac{|\det \mathcal{K}_v|}{\prod_{k=1}^d \langle w_k(v), z \rangle}.$$

Exercise 16. We have to show that if we have the inclusion of cones $\mathcal{K}_1 \subset \mathcal{K}_2$, then $\mathcal{K}_2^* \subset \mathcal{K}_1^*$. So we let $x \in \mathcal{K}_2^* := \{x \in \mathbb{R}^d \mid \langle x, u \rangle < 0 \text{ for all } u \in \mathcal{K}_2\}$, implying that in particular $\langle x, u \rangle < 0$ for all $u \in \mathcal{K}_1$, because $\mathcal{K}_1 \subset \mathcal{K}_2$. But by definition this means that $x \in \mathcal{K}_1^*$ as well.

Exercise 20. Euler's formula gives us

$$V - E + F = 2,$$

and the hypotheses also imply that

(A.26) $5F = 2E$

(A.27) $5F \geq 3V.$

Altogether, we get

$$2 = V - E + F \leq \frac{5}{3}F - \frac{5}{2}F + F = \frac{1}{6}F,$$

so that $F \geq 12$.

Appendix B

The dominated convergence theorem and other goodies

"There are no problems—just pauses between ideas."
– David Morrell, Brotherhood of the Rose

A frequent question is, "when may we take the limit inside the integral?" A general tool that allows us to do so is the dominated convergence theorem. Here we remind the reader of some of the basic results from real analysis, but we skip the proofs and give references for them. For our purposes, we only need these results in Euclidean spaces, although all of these theorems have extensions to arbitrary measure spaces. All functions here are assumed to be measurable functions.

Theorem B.1 (Fatou's lemma). *Fixing any subset $E \subset \mathbb{R}^d$, let $f_n : E \to [0, \infty)$ be a sequence of nonnegative functions. Then we have*

$$\int_E \liminf f_n(x)dx \leq \liminf \int_E f_n(x)dx. \qquad \square$$

The inherent flexibility in **Fatou's lemma** allows it to be useful in many different contexts, because the $\liminf f_n$ always exists, and are even allowed to be equal to $\pm$ infinity. In fact, Fatou's lemma is the main tool in proving Lebesgue's dominated convergence theorem.

Another essential fact for us is **Fubini's theorem**, which allows us to interchange integrals with integrals, and series with integrals, for product spaces. If we write $\mathbb{R}^d = \mathbb{R}^m \times \mathbb{R}^n$, and we denote a point $z \in \mathbb{R}^d$ by $z := (x, y)$, then we may also write $f(z) := f(x, y)$.

Theorem B.2 (Fubini). *Let* $f \in L^1(\mathbb{R}^d)$. *Then*

$$(B.1) \qquad \int_{\mathbb{R}^d} f(z)dz = \int_{\mathbb{R}^n} \left(\int_{\mathbb{R}^m} f(x, y)dx \right) dy,$$

and

$$(B.2) \qquad \int_{\mathbb{R}^d} f(z)dz = \int_{\mathbb{R}^m} \left(\int_{\mathbb{R}^n} f(x, y)dy \right) dx. \qquad \Box$$

There is also a version of Fubini's theorem that uses the counting measure in one of the factors of $\mathbb{R}^m \times \mathbb{R}^n$, giving us

$$(B.3) \qquad \sum_{\xi \in \mathbb{Z}^n} \left(\int_{\mathbb{R}^m} f(x, \xi)dx \right) = \int_{\mathbb{R}^m} \left(\sum_{\xi \in \mathbb{Z}^n} f(x, \xi) \right) dx.$$

See [**219**, p. 220], for a proof of Theorem B.2.

1. The dominated convergence theorem

Theorem B.3 (Dominated convergence theorem). *Suppose that we have a sequence of functions* $f_n(x) : \mathbb{R}^d \to \mathbb{C}$, *for* $n = 1, 2, 3, \ldots$, *and suppose there exists a limit function* $f(x) = \lim_{n \to \infty} f_n(x)$, *valid for all* $x \in \mathbb{R}^d$.

If there exists a function $g \in L^1(\mathbb{R}^d)$ *such that for all* $x \in \mathbb{R}^d$, *we have*

$$|f_n(x)| \leq g(x), \quad n = 1, 2, 3, \ldots,$$

then

(1) $f \in L^1(\mathbb{R}^d)$.

(2) $\lim_{n \to \infty} \int_{\mathbb{R}^d} |f_n(x) - f(x)|dx = 0$.

(3) *And finally, we may interchange limits and integrals:*

$$\lim_{n \to \infty} \int_{\mathbb{R}^d} f_n(x)dx = \int_{\mathbb{R}^d} f(x)dx. \qquad \Box$$

Theorem B.3 is sometimes called the *Lebesgue dominated convergence theorem*, honoring the work of Lebesgue. There is a useful application of Lebesgue's dominated convergence theorem, which allows us to interchange summations with integrals as follows.

Theorem B.4. *Suppose that we have a sequence of functions $f_n(x)$:* $\mathbb{R}^d \to \mathbb{C}$*, such that*

$$\sum_{n=1}^{\infty} \int_{\mathbb{R}^d} |f_n(x)|dx < \infty.$$

Then the series $\sum_{n=1}^{\infty} f_n(x)$ converges for all $x \in \mathbb{R}^d$, and we have

$$\sum_{n=1}^{\infty} \int_{\mathbb{R}^d} f_n(x)dx = \int_{\mathbb{R}^d} \sum_{n=1}^{\infty} f_n(x)dx. \qquad \square$$

See [**217**, p. 26] for a proof of Theorem B.3, and [**217**, p. 29] for a proof of Theorem B.4.

2. Big-O and little-o

Very often we would like to compare, in a quick and dirty way that avoids uncountably many details, how fast two functions grow. We review here two of the most common ways to do this.

Suppose we are given two functions $f, g : \mathbb{R}^d \to \mathbb{C}$. We say that $f(x) = O(g(x))$ (pronounced "Big o"), as $x \to x_0$, if **there exists a positive constant** C such that

(B.4) $$|f(x)| \leq C|g(x)|,$$

for all x that are sufficiently close to x_0. Here we allow x_0 to be any real vector, and we also allow the very common case $x_0 = \pm\infty$. Equivalently, we may say

$$\left|\frac{f(x)}{g(x)}\right| \text{ is eventually bounded above.}$$

Example B.5. We write $e^x = 1 + x + \frac{1}{2}x^2 + O(x^3)$, as $x \to 0$. We could, of course, also write $e^x - (1 + x + \frac{1}{2}x^2) = O(x^3)$, though the former way of writing it is much more common. In this case, we can give a "better" Big-O estimate by adding more terms of the Taylor series: $e^x = 1 + x + \frac{1}{2}x^2 + \frac{1}{6}x^3 + O(x^4)$, as $x \to 0$. $\qquad \square$

Example B.6. Given $f(x) := x\sin\left(\frac{1}{x}\right)$, and $g(x) := x^2 - 12$, we have

$$f(x) = O(g(x)), \text{ as } x \to \infty.$$

In other words, for all sufficiently large x, $|f(x)| \leq Cg(x)$, despite the fact that this statement is false for these particular functions, for some small positive values of x. $\qquad \square$

Claim B.7. *Big-O enjoys transitivity:*

$$\text{If } f = O(g), \text{ and } g = O(h), \text{ then } f = O(h).$$

Proof. For all x sufficiently close to x_0, there exists positive constants C_1, C_2 such that $|f(x)| \leq C_1 |g(x)|$ and $|g(x)| \leq C_2 |h(x)|$, implying that

$$|f(x)| \leq C_1 |g(x)| \leq C_1 C_2 |h(x)|. \qquad \square$$

There is another very useful comparison technique for any two given functions $f, g : \mathbb{R}^d \to \mathbb{C}$. We say that $f(x) = o(g(x))$ (pronounced "little o"), as $x \to x_0$, if **for all positive constants** C, we have

(B.5) $$|f(x)| \leq C|g(x)|,$$

for all x that are sufficiently close to x_0. Again, we allow x_0 to be any real vector, and we also allow the very common case $x_0 = \pm\infty$. Equivalently, we may also write

$$\lim_{x \to x_0} \left| \frac{f(x)}{g(x)} \right| = 0,$$

which intuitively means that g approaches x_0 faster than f does.

Example B.8. Given $f(x) := \sqrt{x}$, and $g(x) := x$, where we restrict the domain of both functions to be $(0, +\infty)$. We claim $f(x) = o(g(x))$, as $x \to 0$.

Proof.

$$\lim_{x \to 0} \left| \frac{f(x)}{g(x)} \right| = \lim_{x \to 0} \left| \frac{\sqrt{x}}{x} \right| = \lim_{x \to 0} \left| \frac{1}{\sqrt{x}} \right| = 0.$$

So g approaches 0 much faster than f. $\qquad \square$

Claim B.9. *Little-o also enjoys transitivity:*

$$\text{If } f = o(g), \text{ and } g = o(h), \text{ then } f = o(h).$$

Proof. The two given limits $\lim_{x \to x_0} \left| \frac{f(x)}{g(x)} \right| = 0$ and $\lim_{x \to x_0} \left| \frac{g(x)}{h(x)} \right| = 0$ together imply that

$$\lim_{x \to x_0} \left| \frac{f(x)}{h(x)} \right| = \lim_{x \to x_0} \left| \frac{f(x)}{g(x)} \right| \left| \frac{g(x)}{h(x)} \right| = 0. \qquad \square$$

3. Various forms of convergence

3.1. Weierstrass M-test.
How can we quickly conclude that certain series converge uniformly? The following criterion, discovered by Karl Weierstrass, comes to the rescue. For the proofs of these basic real analysis results, see the classic book [**217**].

Theorem B.10 (Weierstrass M-test). *Suppose that $f_n(x)$ is a sequence of complex-valued functions defined on a set $E \subset \mathbb{R}$, such that there exists a sequence of numbers $M_n \geq 0$ satisfying the following conditions:*

    (1) $|f_n(x)| \leq M_n$, $\forall n \in \mathbb{Z}$ *and all* $x \in E$.

    (2) $\sum_{n \in \mathbb{Z}} M_n < \infty$.

Then the series $\sum_{n \in \mathbb{Z}} f_n(x)$ converges absolutely and uniformly on E. $\square$

In practice, the Weierstrass M-test gets used together with the following test, which allows us to partially answer the question:

Question B.11. When does a series $\sum_{n \in \mathbb{Z}} f_n(x)$ converge to a continuous function of x?

Theorem B.12 (Uniform limit). *Suppose that $s_n(x) : E \to \mathbb{C}$ is a sequence of continuous functions defined on a set $E \subset \mathbb{R}$, and that s_n converges uniformly to $s(x)$, on E. Then $s(x)$ is continuous on E.* $\square$

3.2. Some things you wanted to know about convergence but were afraid to ask.
It is often useful to pass from L^2 convergence to pointwise convergence, under some additional hypothesis on f. Throughout, we fix a real number $1 \leq p < \infty$. Given a subset $E \subset \mathbb{R}^d$, and a sequence of functions $f_n : E \to \mathbb{C}$, we say that $f_n(x) \to f(x)$ in the p-norm if

$$(\text{B.6}) \qquad \lim_{n \to \infty} \int_E |f_n(x) - f(x)|^p \, dx = 0,$$

for which we will also use here the notation $\lim_{n \to \infty} \|f_n - f\|_{L^p(E)} = 0$. Sometimes, if the constant p is not specified, it is common to simply call (B.6) **convergence in norm**. The two most common subsets are $E := \mathbb{R}^d$, and $E := [0,1]^d$. A natural question arises:

Question B.13. When can we pass from convergence in norm to pointwise convergence?

Given a series $\sum_{n \in \mathbb{Z}^d} f_n(x)$, we consider the sequence of partial sums $S_N(x) := \sum_{|n| < N} f_n(x)$. By definition, we say the series converges

(1) **pointwise on** E if the sequence $\{S_N(x)\}_{N=1}^{\infty}$ converges for each $x \in E$;

(2) **absolutely on** E if the series $\sum_{n \in \mathbb{Z}^d} |f_n(x)|$ converges pointwise, for each $x \in E$;

(3) **uniformly on** E if the sequence of partial sums $S_N(x)$ converge uniformly on E;

(4) **in the** p-**norm** on E if $\lim_{n \to \infty} \|S_n - f\|_{L^p(E)} = 0$.

Lemma B.14. *Consider the partial sums*

$$S_N(x) := \sum_{\substack{|n| < N \\ n \in \mathbb{Z}^d}} f_n(x)$$

for all x in a given subset $E \subset \mathbb{R}^d$. Suppose we have the following two properties:

(1) *There exists a function $f : \mathbb{R}^d \to \mathbb{C}$ such that $S_N(x) \to f(x)$ in the p-norm, on E.*

(2) *$S_N(x)$ converges uniformly to the series $S(x) := \sum_{n \in \mathbb{Z}^d} f_n(x)$ on E.*

Then $S(x) = f(x)$ a.e. on E. $\qquad\square$

Lemma B.15. *Let $f \in L^1([-c, c])$, and suppose we already know that its Fourier series converges pointwise:*

(B.7) $$f(x) = \sum_{n \in \mathbb{Z}} \hat{f}_n e^{\frac{2\pi i n x}{c}}.$$

If the series (B.7) converges absolutely, then f is a continuous function on $[-c, c]$, and $f(-c) = f(c)$.

Proof. The idea is to use the uniform limit, Theorem B.12, together with the fact that the summands $\hat{f}_n e^{\frac{2\pi i n x}{c}}$ are continuous functions of x. So it remains to show that the convergence of the series is uniform:

$$|S_N(x)| := \left| \sum_{|n| < N} \hat{f}_n e^{\frac{2\pi i n x}{c}} \right| \le \sum_{|n| < N} \left| \hat{f}_n e^{\frac{2\pi i n x}{c}} \right| = \sum_{|n| < N} |\hat{f}_n| < \infty,$$

where the penultimate equality holds because $\left| e^{\frac{2\pi i n x}{c}} \right| = 1$, and the last inequality holds by assumption. So by the M-test, with $M_n := |\hat{f}_n|$, we have uniform convergence of the series. Finally, the claim $f(-c) = f(c)$ is trivial, because $f(\pm c) := \sum_{n \in \mathbb{Z}} \hat{f}_n e^{\pm 2\pi i n} = \sum_{n \in \mathbb{Z}} \hat{f}_n$. $\qquad\square$

In the previous lemma, we could have also used the alternate notation of the circle $\mathbb{R}/c\mathbb{Z}$, and rewrite everything in terms of it, which automatically incorporates periodicity. The following **passage from convergence in the $L^2([-c,c])$ norm to pointwise convergence** is often useful.

Lemma B.16. *Let $f \in L^2([-c,c])$ be a continuous function, and write its Fourier series as*

(B.8)
$$f(x) \underset{L^2([-c,c])}{=} \sum_{n\in\mathbb{Z}} \hat{f}_n e^{\frac{2\pi i n x}{c}},$$

which, by definition, means that this series converges in the $L^2([-c,c])$-norm.

If the series (B.8) converges absolutely, then it also converges pointwise and uniformly to $f(x)$, for all $x \in [-c,c]$.

Proof. Repeating the computation of the previous proof, we have

$$|S_N(x)| := \left| \sum_{||n|<N} \hat{f}_n e^{\frac{2\pi i n x}{c}} \right| \leq \sum_{|n|<N} \left| \hat{f}_n e^{\frac{2\pi i n x}{c}} \right| \leq \sum_{|n|<N} |\hat{f}_n| < \infty.$$

Therefore by the M-test again, $S_N(x)$ converges uniformly to the series

$$S(x) := \sum_{n\in\mathbb{Z}} \hat{f}_n e^{\frac{2\pi i n x}{c}}$$

for all $x \in [-c,c]$. We also know, by Lemma B.15, that $S(x)$ is continuous on $[-c,c]$. We still need to prove that the series converges to f, but now we at least know that both hypotheses of Lemma B.14 are satisfied (with $p=2$ and $E := [-c,c]$), and therefore $S(x) = f(x)$ a.e. on E.

To prove that $S(x) = f(x)$ for all $x \in [-c,c]$, we observe that the summands $\hat{f}_n e^{\frac{2\pi i n x}{c}}$ are continuous functions of x, and hence by the uniform limit theorem (Theorem B.12), the series $S(x)$ is itself a continuous function of x. Since f is also continuous on $[-c,c]$, and $S(x) = f(x)$ almost everywhere, they must agree everywhere. $\qquad\square$

3.3. Bump functions and inner products. Perhaps the easiest bump function to define is the function [**245**, page 209]

$$\varphi(x) := \begin{cases} c\, e^{-\frac{1}{1-\|x\|^2}} & \text{if } \|x\| < 1, \\ 0 & \text{if } \|x\| \geq 1, \end{cases}$$

where the constant c is chosen so that $\int_{\mathbb{R}^d} \varphi(x)dx = 1$. By definition, φ is compactly supported on the unit ball. It turns out that φ is infinitely smooth. As usual, using φ we can build a family of integrable functions:

$$\varphi_\varepsilon(x) := \varepsilon^{-d}\varphi(x\varepsilon^{-1}), \text{ for all } 0 < \varepsilon \le 1.$$

Thus, the family $\{\varphi_\varepsilon\}$ is an approximate identity.

More generally, a **bump function** is defined to be any infinitely smooth function $\varphi : \mathbb{R}^d \to \mathbb{C}$ that is compactly supported. By Lemma 3.37, we know that any such bump function φ lies in the Schwartz class $S(\mathbb{R}^d)$. Clearly finite linear combinations of bump functions are again bump functions, making the space of bump functions a vector subspace of the space of Schwartz functions.

Often, a slightly more general sort of space than a Hilbert space is required. Suppose there exists a function called $\langle \cdot, \cdot \rangle$, defined from $V \times V \to \mathbb{R}$, that enjoys the following properties:

(1) (Strict positivity). $\langle x, x \rangle > 0$, for all nonzero $x \in V$.

(2) (Symmetry). $\langle x, y \rangle = \langle y, x \rangle$, for all $x, y \in V$.

(3) (Linearity). For any fixed $a \in V$, the function $x \to \langle x, a \rangle$ is linear, which means that

$$\langle x + y, a \rangle = \langle x, a \rangle + \langle y, a \rangle,$$

for all $x, y \in V$, and $\langle cx, a \rangle = c\langle x, a \rangle$, for all scalars $c \in \mathbb{R}$.

Then $\langle \cdot, \cdot \rangle$ is called an **inner product on** V, and V is an **inner product space** (over $\mathbb{R}$). Inner products also interact well with continuity in the following precise sense [79, p. 74]:

Lemma B.17. *If $x_n \to x$ in V, and $y_n \to y$ in V, then $\langle x_n, y_n \rangle \to \langle x, y \rangle$.*

We say that an inner product space V is **complete**, relative to the distance function

$$d(x_n, x_m) := \langle x_n - x_m, x_n - x_m \rangle^{\frac{1}{2}}$$

if every Cauchy sequence $\{x_n\}_{n=1}^\infty$ in V converges to a point of V. Finally, we mention a basic fact about linear functions acting on complete inner product space.

Theorem B.18 (Riesz representation theorem). *Let V be a complete inner product space (finite or infinite dimensional), and suppose that $f : V \to \mathbb{R}$ is a continuous linear functional on V. Then there exists a unique $w \in V$ such that*

$$f(x) = \langle x, w \rangle$$

for all $x \in V$.

Credits for photographs and pictures

(1) Figure of Joseph Fourier:
   `https://en.wikipedia.org/wiki/Joseph_Fourier`
   By Julien-Léopold Boilly Restored by: Bammesk. Source:
   `https://www.gettyimages.com.au/license/169251384https://wellcomecollection.org/works/b4qh352u`,
   Public Domain:
   `https://commons.wikimedia.org/w/index.php?curid=114366437`

(2) Figure of Simeon Denis Poisson:
   `https://en.wikipedia.org/wiki/Simeon_Denis_Poisson`
   By François-Séraphin Delpech,
   `http://web4.si.edu/sil/scientific-identity/display_results.cfm?alpha_sort=W`
   Public Domain:
   `https://commons.wikimedia.org/w/index.php?curid=536305`

(3) Figure of John Conway:
   Creative Commons 2.0 license

https://en.wikipedia.org/wiki/John_Horton_Conway

By Thane Plambeck,

https://www.flickr.com/photos/thane/20366806/,
CC BY 2.0

https://commons.wikimedia.org/w/index.php?curid=
13076802

(4) Figure of Hermann Minkowski:

https://en.wikipedia.org/wiki/Hermann_Minkowski

By Hermann Minkowski—scan from original book, Public Domain:

https://commons.wikimedia.org/w/index.php?curid=
59559231

(5) Figure of Hans Blichfeldt:

https://mathshistory.st-andrews.ac.uk/
Biographies/Blichfeldt/

Source:

https://mathshistory.st-andrews.ac.uk/
Biographies/Blichfeldt/
https://commons.wikimedia.org/wiki/File:
Dodecahedron_climbing_wall.jpg

By Petey21, Own work, Public Domain,

https:
//commons.wikimedia.org/w/index.php?curid=7512079

(6) Figure 7.2, of the C_{60} molecule, is from the source:

https://phys.org/news/2015-07-scientists-advance-
tunable-carbon-capture-materials.html

Used by permission under a Creative Commons license.

Bibliography

[1] A. V. Akopyan and R. N. Karasev, *Bounding minimal solid angles of polytopes*, Preprint, arXiv:1505.05263, (2015).

[2] A. D. Alexandrov, *Convex polyhedra*, Springer Monographs in Mathematics, Springer-Verlag, Berlin, 2005. Translated from the 1950 Russian edition by N. S. Dairbekov, S. S. Kutateladze and A. B. Sossinsky; With comments and bibliography by V. A. Zalgaller and appendices by L. A. Shor and Yu. A. Volkov. MR2127379

[3] Tom M. Apostol, *Introduction to analytic number theory*, Undergraduate Texts in Mathematics, Springer-Verlag, New York-Heidelberg, 1976. MR434929

[4] David Austin, *Fedorov's five parallelohedra*, Notices of the American Math. Society, Feature column, 2013. http://www.ams.org/publicoutreach/feature-column/fc-2013-11

[5] Gennadiy Averkov, *Equality case in van der Corput's inequality and collisions in multiple lattice tilings*, Discrete Comput. Geom. **65** (2021), no. 1, 212–226, DOI 10.1007/s00454-019-00089-8. MR4194441

[6] L. Babai, *On Lovász' lattice reduction and the nearest lattice point problem*, Combinatorica **6** (1986), no. 1, 1–13, DOI 10.1007/BF02579403. MR856638

[7] Robert Baillie, David Borwein, and Jonathan M. Borwein, *Surprising sinc sums and integrals*, Amer. Math. Monthly **115** (2008), no. 10, 888–901, DOI 10.1080/00029890.2008.11920606. MR2468551

[8] Velleda Baldoni, Nicole Berline, and Michèle Vergne, *Local Euler-Maclaurin expansion of Barvinok valuations and Ehrhart coefficients of a rational polytope*, Integer points in polyhedra—geometry, number theory, representation theory, algebra, optimization, statistics, Contemp. Math., vol. 452, Amer. Math. Soc., Providence, RI, 2008, pp. 15–33, DOI 10.1090/conm/452/08769. MR2405762

[9] Keith Ball, *A lower bound for the optimal density of lattice packings*, Internat. Math. Res. Notices **10** (1992), 217–221, DOI 10.1155/S1073792892000242. MR1191572

[10] W. Banaszczyk, *New bounds in some transference theorems in the geometry of numbers*, Math. Ann. **296** (1993), no. 4, 625–635, DOI 10.1007/BF01445125. MR1233487

[11] Imre Bárány, *Random points and lattice points in convex bodies*, Bull. Amer. Math. Soc. (N.S.) **45** (2008), no. 3, 339–365, DOI 10.1090/S0273-0979-08-01210-X. MR2402946

[12] Arseniy Akopyan, Imre Bárány, and Sinai Robins, *Algebraic vertices of non-convex polyhedra*, Adv. Math. **308** (2017), 627–644, DOI 10.1016/j.aim.2016.12.026. MR3600068

[13] David Alonso-Gutiérrez, C. Hugo Jiménez, and Rafael Villa, *Brunn-Minkowski and Zhang inequalities for convolution bodies*, Adv. Math. **238** (2013), 50–69, DOI 10.1016/j.aim.2013.01.013. MR3033630

[14] A. I. Barvinok, *Exponential integrals and sums over convex polyhedra* (Russian), Funktsional. Anal. i Prilozhen. **26** (1992), no. 2, 64–66, DOI 10.1007/BF01075276; English transl., Funct. Anal. Appl. **26** (1992), no. 2, 127–129. MR1173086

[15] Alexander I. Barvinok, *A polynomial time algorithm for counting integral points in polyhedra when the dimension is fixed*, Math. Oper. Res. **19** (1994), no. 4, 769–779, DOI 10.1287/moor.19.4.769. MR1304623

[16] Alexander Barvinok, *Combinatorics, Geometry, and Complexity of integer points*, Online lecture notes: http://www.math.lsa.umich.edu/~barvinok/latticenotes669.pdf

[17] Alexander Barvinok, *A course in convexity*, Graduate Studies in Mathematics, vol. 54, American Mathematical Society, Providence, RI, 2002, DOI 10.1090/gsm/054. MR1940576

[18] Alexander Barvinok, *Integer points in polyhedra*, Zurich Lectures in Advanced Mathematics, European Mathematical Society (EMS), Zürich, 2008, DOI 10.4171/052. MR2455889

[19] Alexander Barvinok and James E. Pommersheim, *An algorithmic theory of lattice points in polyhedra*, New perspectives in algebraic combinatorics (Berkeley, CA, 1996), Math. Sci. Res. Inst. Publ., vol. 38, Cambridge Univ. Press, Cambridge, 1999, pp. 91–147. MR1731815

[20] Victor V. Batyrev, *Dual polyhedra and mirror symmetry for Calabi-Yau hypersurfaces in toric varieties*, J. Algebraic Geom. **3** (1994), no. 3, 493–535. MR1269718

[21] Victor Batyrev and Johannes Hofscheier, *A generalization of a theorem of White*, Mosc. J. Comb. Number Theory **10** (2021), no. 4, 281–296, DOI 10.2140/moscow.2021.10.281. MR4366115

[22] Matthias Beck and Raman Sanyal, *Combinatorial reciprocity theorems*, Graduate Studies in Mathematics, vol. 195, American Mathematical Society, Providence, RI, 2018. An invitation to enumerative geometric combinatorics, DOI 10.1090/gsm/195. MR3839322

[23] Nicole Berline and Michèle Vergne, *Local Euler-Maclaurin formula for polytopes* (English, with English and Russian summaries), Mosc. Math. J. **7** (2007), no. 3, 355–386, 573, DOI 10.17323/1609-4514-2007-7-3-355-386. MR2343137

[24] József Beck, *Probabilistic Diophantine approximation*, Springer Monographs in Mathematics, Springer, Cham, 2014. Randomness in lattice point counting, DOI 10.1007/978-3-319-10741-7. MR3308897

[25] Matthias Beck and Sinai Robins, *Computing the continuous discretely*, 2nd ed., Undergraduate Texts in Mathematics, Springer, New York, 2015. Integer-point enumeration in polyhedra; With illustrations by David Austin, DOI 10.1007/978-1-4939-2969-6. MR3410115

[26] Matthias Beck and Sinai Robins, *Explicit and efficient formulas for the lattice point count in rational polygons using Dedekind-Rademacher sums*, Discrete Comput. Geom. **27** (2002), no. 4, 443–459, DOI 10.1007/s00454-001-0082-3. MR1902672

[27] Matthias Beck, Ricardo Diaz, and Sinai Robins, *The Frobenius problem, rational polytopes, and Fourier-Dedekind sums*, J. Number Theory **96** (2002), no. 1, 1–21. MR1931190

[28] Matthias Beck, Sinai Robins, and Steven V. Sam, *Positivity theorems for solid-angle polynomials*, Beiträge Algebra Geom. **51** (2010), no. 2, 493–507. MR2663951

[29] U. Betke, M. Henk, and J. M. Wills, *Successive-minima-type inequalities*, Discrete Comput. Geom. **9** (1993), no. 2, 165–175, DOI 10.1007/BF02189316. MR1194034

[30] Christian Bey, Martin Henk, and Jörg M. Wills, *Notes on the roots of Ehrhart polynomials*, Discrete Comput. Geom. **38** (2007), no. 1, 81–98, DOI 10.1007/s00454-007-1330-y. MR2322117

[31] R. P. Bambah and A. C. Woods, *Minkowski's conjecture for $n = 5$; a theorem of Skubenko*, J. Number Theory **12** (1980), no. 1, 27–48, DOI 10.1016/0022-314X(80)90070-0. MR566866

[32] W. Banaszczyk, *New bounds in some transference theorems in the geometry of numbers*, Math. Ann. **296** (1993), no. 4, 625–635, DOI 10.1007/BF01445125. MR1233487

[33] W. Banaszczyk, *Inequalities for convex bodies and polar reciprocal lattices in $\mathbf{R}^n$*, Discrete Comput. Geom. **13** (1995), no. 2, 217–231, DOI 10.1007/BF02574039. MR1314964

[34] Gabriele Bianchi, *The covariogram and Fourier-Laplace transform in* $\mathbb{C}^n$, Proc. Lond. Math. Soc. (3) **113** (2016), no. 1, 1–23, DOI 10.1112/plms/pdw020. MR3544772

[35] James Bisgard, *Analysis and linear algebra: the singular value decomposition and applications*, Student Mathematical Library, vol. 94, American Mathematical Society, Providence, RI, [2021] ©2021. MR4256003

[36] H. F. Blichfeldt, *A new principle in the geometry of numbers, with some applications*, Trans. Amer. Math. Soc. **15** (1914), no. 3, 227–235, DOI 10.2307/1988585. MR1500976

[37] H. F. Blichfeldt, *The minimum value of quadratic forms, and the closest packing of spheres*, Math. Ann. **101** (1929), no. 1, 605–608, DOI 10.1007/BF01454863. MR1512555

[38] R. P. Boas Jr., *Summation formulas and band-limited signals*, Tohoku Math. J. (2) **24** (1972), 121–125, DOI 10.2748/tmj/1178241524. MR330915

[39] Sebastian Böcker and Zsuzsanna Lipták, *The money changing problem revisited: computing the Frobenius number in time* $O(ka_1)$, Computing and combinatorics, Lecture Notes in Comput. Sci., vol. 3595, Springer, Berlin, 2005, pp. 965–974, DOI 10.1007/11533719_97. MR2191039

[40] Ruel V. Churchill, *Recent Publications: Lectures on Fourier Integrals*, Amer. Math. Monthly **67** (1960), no. 8, 819, DOI 10.2307/2308692. MR1530928

[41] Jürgen Bokowski, Hugo Hadwiger, and Jörg M. Wills, *Eine Ungleichung zwischen Volumen, Oberfläche und Gitterpunktanzahl konvexer Körper im* n-*dimensionalen euklidischen Raum* (German), Math. Z. **127** (1972), 363–364, DOI 10.1007/BF01111393. MR315595

[42] Enrico Bombieri, *Sulla dimostrazione di C. L. Siegel del teorema fondamentale di Minkowski nella geometria dei numeri* (Italian, with English summary), Boll. Un. Mat. Ital. (3) **17** (1962), 283–288. MR147456

[43] Bence Borda, *Lattice points in algebraic cross-polytopes and simplices*, Discrete Comput. Geom. **60** (2018), no. 1, 145–169, DOI 10.1007/s00454-017-9946-z. MR3807352

[44] Maciej Borodzik, Danny Nguyen, and Sinai Robins, *Tiling the integer lattice with translated sublattices*, Mosc. J. Comb. Number Theory **6** (2016), no. 4, 3–26. MR3607789

[45] P. L. Butzer, P. J. S. G. Ferreira, G. Schmeisser, and R. L. Stens, *The summation formulae of Euler-Maclaurin, Abel-Plana, Poisson, and their interconnections with the approximate sampling formula of signal analysis*, Results Math. **59** (2011), no. 3-4, 359–400, DOI 10.1007/s00025-010-0083-8. MR2793463

[46] L. Brandolini, L. Colzani, S. Robins, and G. Travaglini, *Pick's theorem and convergence of multiple Fourier series*, Amer. Math. Monthly **128** (2021), no. 1, 41–49, DOI 10.1080/00029890.2021.1839241. MR4200451

[47] Luca Brandolini, Leonardo Colzani, Sinai Robins, and Giancarlo Travaglini, *An Euler-Maclaurin formula for polygonal sums*, Trans. Amer. Math. Soc. **375** (2022), no. 1, 151–172, DOI 10.1090/tran/8462. MR4358665

[48] Michel Brion, *Points entiers dans les polyèdres convexes* (French), Ann. Sci. École Norm. Sup. (4) **21** (1988), no. 4, 653–663. MR982338

[49] Michel Brion and Michèle Vergne, *Residue formulae, vector partition functions and lattice points in rational polytopes*, J. Amer. Math. Soc. **10** (1997), no. 4, 797–833, DOI 10.1090/S0894-0347-97-00242-7. MR1446364

[50] Leon Brown, Bertram M. Schreiber, and B. Alan Taylor, *Spectral synthesis and the Pompeiu problem* (English, with French summary), Ann. Inst. Fourier (Grenoble) **23** (1973), no. 3, 125–154. MR352492

[51] Richard A. Brualdi and Peter M. Gibson, *Convex polyhedra of doubly stochastic matrices. I. Applications of the permanent function*, J. Combinatorial Theory Ser. A **22** (1977), no. 2, 194–230, DOI 10.1016/0097-3165(77)90051-6. MR437562

[52] M. D. Buhmann, *Radial functions on compact support*, Proc. Edinburgh Math. Soc. (2) **41** (1998), no. 1, 33–46, DOI 10.1017/S0013091500019416. MR1604361

[53] Kristin A. Camenga, *Vector spaces spanned by the angle sums of polytopes*, Beiträge Algebra Geom. **47** (2006), no. 2, 447–462. MR2307914

[54] L. Carlitz, *The reciprocity theorem for Dedekind-Rademacher sums*, Acta Arith. **29** (1976), no. 3, 309–313, DOI 10.4064/aa-29-3-309-313. MR401618

[55] J. W. S. Cassels, *An introduction to the geometry of numbers*, Classics in Mathematics, Springer-Verlag, Berlin, 1997. Corrected reprint of the 1971 edition. MR1434478

[56] William Y. C. Chen and Peter L. Guo, *Equivalence classes of full-dimensional 0/1-polytopes with many vertices*, Discrete Comput. Geom. **52** (2014), no. 4, 630–662, DOI 10.1007/s00454-014-9630-5. MR3279542

[57] Henry Cohn, Abhinav Kumar, Stephen D. Miller, Danylo Radchenko, and Maryna Viazovska, *The sphere packing problem in dimension 24*, Ann. of Math. (2) **185** (2017), no. 3, 1017–1033, DOI 10.4007/annals.2017.185.3.8. MR3664817

[58] Henry Cohn and Noam Elkies, *New upper bounds on sphere packings. I*, Ann. of Math. (2) **157** (2003), no. 2, 689–714, DOI 10.4007/annals.2003.157.689. MR1973059

[59] J. H. Conway and N. J. A. Sloane, *Sphere packings, lattices and groups*, 3rd ed., Grundlehren der mathematischen Wissenschaften [Fundamental Principles of Mathematical Sciences], vol. 290, Springer-Verlag, New York, 1999. With additional contributions by E. Bannai, R. E. Borcherds, J. Leech, S. P. Norton, A. M. Odlyzko, R. A. Parker, L. Queen and B. B. Venkov, DOI 10.1007/978-1-4757-6568-7. MR1662447

[60] John H. Conway, *The sensual (quadratic) form*, Carus Mathematical Monographs, vol. 26, Mathematical Association of America, Washington, DC, 1997. With the assistance of Francis Y. C. Fung. MR1478672

[61] Antonio Córdoba, *La formule sommatoire de Poisson* (French, with English summary), C. R. Acad. Sci. Paris Sér. I Math. **306** (1988), no. 8, 373–376. MR934622

[62] Dan Cristofaro-Gardiner, Teresa Xueshan Li, and Richard Stanley, *New examples of period collapse*, Perprint, arXiv:1509.01887v1, (2015).

[63] V. I. Danilov, *The geometry of toric varieties* (Russian), Uspekhi Mat. Nauk **33** (1978), no. 2(200), 85–134, 247. MR495499

[64] N. G. de Bruijn, *Filling boxes with bricks*, Amer. Math. Monthly **76** (1969), 37–40, DOI 10.2307/2316785. MR234841

[65] Sergei Tabachnikov, *Dragon curves revisited*, Math. Intelligencer **36** (2014), no. 1, 13–17, DOI 10.1007/s00283-013-9428-y. MR3166985

[66] Jesús A. De Loera, Raymond Hemmecke, and Matthias Köppe, *Algebraic and geometric ideas in the theory of discrete optimization*, MOS-SIAM Series on Optimization, vol. 14, Society for Industrial and Applied Mathematics (SIAM), Philadelphia, PA; Mathematical Optimization Society, Philadelphia, PA, 2013. MR3024570

[67] Jesús A. De Loera, Jörg Rambau, and Francisco Santos, *Triangulations*, Algorithms and Computation in Mathematics, vol. 25, Springer-Verlag, Berlin, 2010. Structures for algorithms and applications, DOI 10.1007/978-3-642-12971-1. MR2743368

[68] David Desario and Sinai Robins, *Generalized solid-angle theory for real polytopes*, Q. J. Math. **62** (2011), no. 4, 1003–1015, DOI 10.1093/qmath/hap030. MR2853227

[69] Persi Diaconis and Anil Gangolli, *Rectangular arrays with fixed margins*, Discrete probability and algorithms (Minneapolis, MN, 1993), IMA Vol. Math. Appl., vol. 72, Springer, New York, 1995, pp. 15–41, DOI 10.1007/978-1-4612-0801-3_3. MR1380519

[70] Ricardo Diaz and Sinai Robins, *The Ehrhart polynomial of a lattice polytope*, Ann. of Math. (2) **145** (1997), no. 3, 503–518, DOI 10.2307/2951842. MR1454701

[71] Ricardo Diaz, Quang-Nhat Le, and Sinai Robins, *Fourier transforms of polytopes, solid angle sums, and discrete volumes*, Preprint, https://drive.google.com/file/d/0B223XJaVpyE_MU16UER2VnFQRHc/view

[72] Mathieu Dutour Sikirić, Alexey Garber, Achill Schürmann, and Clara Waldmann, *The complete classification of five-dimensional Dirichlet-Voronoi polyhedra of translational lattices*, Acta Crystallogr. Sect. A **72** (2016), no. 6, 673–683, DOI 10.1107/s2053273316011682. MR3573502

[73] H. Dym and H. P. McKean, *Fourier series and integrals*, Probability and Mathematical Statistics, No. 14, Academic Press, New York-London, 1972. MR442564

[74] F. J. Dyson, *On the product of four non-homogeneous linear forms*, Ann. of Math. (2) **49** (1948), 82–109, DOI 10.2307/1969116. MR25515

[75] Eugène Ehrhart, *Sur les polyèdres rationnels homothétiques à n dimensions* (French), C. R. Acad. Sci. Paris **254** (1962), 616–618. MR130860

[76] E. Ehrhart, *Sur un problème de géométrie diophantienne linéaire. I. Polyèdres et réseaux* (French), J. Reine Angew. Math. **226** (1967), 1–29, DOI 10.1515/crll.1967.226.1. MR213320

[77] E. Ehrhart, *Sur un problème de géométrie diophantienne linéaire. II. Systèmes diophantiens linéaires* (French), J. Reine Angew. Math. **227** (1967), 25–49, DOI 10.1515/crll.1967.227.25. MR217010

[78] E. Ehrhart, *Polynômes arithmétiques et méthode des polyèdres en combinatoire*, International Series of Numerical Mathematics, Vol. 35, Birkhäuser Verlag, Basel-Stuttgart, 1977. MR432556

[79] Manfred Einsiedler and Thomas Ward, *Functional analysis, spectral theory, and applications*, Graduate Texts in Mathematics, vol. 276, Springer, Cham, 2017. MR3729416

[80] Konrad Engel, *An identity theorem for the Fourier-Laplace transform of polytopes on nonzero complex multiples of rationally parameterizable hypersurfaces*, Discrete Comput. Geom. **69** (2023), no. 1, 209–231, DOI 10.1007/s00454-022-00467-9. MR4527540

[81] Alireza Entezari, Ramsay Dyer, and Torsten Möller, *From sphere packing to the theory of optimal lattice sampling*, Mathematical foundations of scientific visualization, computer graphics, and massive data exploration, Math. Vis., Springer, Berlin, 2009, pp. 227–255, DOI 10.1007/b106657_12. MR2560516

[82] Charles L. Epstein, *Introduction to the mathematics of medical imaging*, 2nd ed., Society for Industrial and Applied Mathematics (SIAM), Philadelphia, PA, 2008, DOI 10.1137/1.9780898717792. MR2378706

[83] David V. Feldman and Daniel A. Klain, *Angles as probabilities*, Amer. Math. Monthly **116** (2009), no. 8, 732–735, DOI 10.4169/193009709X460868. MR2572108

[84] David Feldman, James Propp, and Sinai Robins, *Tiling lattices with sublattices, I*, Discrete Comput. Geom. **46** (2011), no. 1, 184–186, DOI 10.1007/s00454-010-9272-1. MR2794364

[85] Benjamin Fischer and Jamie Pommersheim, *An algebraic construction of sum-integral interpolators*, Pacific J. Math. **318** (2022), no. 2, 305–338, DOI 10.2140/pjm.2022.318.305. MR4474365

[86] Gerald B. Folland, *Fourier analysis and its applications*, The Wadsworth & Brooks/Cole Mathematics Series, Wadsworth & Brooks/Cole Advanced Books & Software, Pacific Grove, CA, 1992. MR1145236

[87] Jerome Franel, *Les suites de Farey et le problème des nombres premiers*, Gött. Nachr. (1924), 198–201.

[88] Bent Fuglede, *Commuting self-adjoint partial differential operators and a group theoretic problem*, J. Functional Analysis **16** (1974), 101–121, DOI 10.1016/0022-1236(74)90072-x. MR470754

[89] Lenny Fukshansky and Stephan Ramon Garcia, *Geometric Number Theory*, Cambridge University Press, to appear in 2023.

[90] Lenny Fukshansky and Sinai Robins, *Bounds for solid angles of lattices of rank three*, J. Combin. Theory Ser. A **118** (2011), no. 2, 690–701, DOI 10.1016/j.jcta.2010.06.001. MR2739513

[91] William Fulton, *Introduction to toric varieties*, Annals of Mathematics Studies, vol. 131, Princeton University Press, Princeton, NJ, 1993. The William H. Roever Lectures in Geometry, DOI 10.1515/9781400882526. MR1234037

[92] Stavros Garoufalidis and James Pommersheim, *Sum-integral interpolators and the Euler-Maclaurin formula for polytopes*, Trans. Amer. Math. Soc. **364** (2012), no. 6, 2933–2958, DOI 10.1090/S0002-9947-2012-05381-5. MR2888234

[93] Sigrid Grepstad and Nir Lev, *Multi-tiling and Riesz bases*, Adv. Math. **252** (2014), 1–6, DOI 10.1016/j.aim.2013.10.019. MR3144222

[94] Ewgenij Gawrilow and Michael Joswig, *polymake: a framework for analyzing convex polytopes*, Polytopes—combinatorics and computation (Oberwolfach, 1997), DMV Sem., vol. 29, Birkhäuser, Basel, 2000, pp. 43–73. MR1785292

[95] Nick Gravin, Mihail N. Kolountzakis, Sinai Robins, and Dmitry Shiryaev, *Structure results for multiple tilings in 3D*, Discrete Comput. Geom. **50** (2013), no. 4, 1033–1050, DOI 10.1007/s00454-013-9548-3. MR3138144

[96] Gene H. Golub and Charles F. Van Loan, *Matrix computations*, 4th ed., Johns Hopkins Studies in the Mathematical Sciences, Johns Hopkins University Press, Baltimore, MD, 2013. MR3024913

[97] Daniel Gourion and Alberto Seeger, *Deterministic and stochastic methods for computing volumetric moduli of convex cones*, Comput. Appl. Math. **29** (2010), no. 2, 215–246, DOI 10.1590/S1807-03022010000200007. MR2672258

[98] Peter M. Gruber, *Convex and discrete geometry*, Grundlehren der mathematischen Wissenschaften [Fundamental Principles of Mathematical Sciences], vol. 336, Springer, Berlin, 2007. MR2335496

[99] P. M. Gruber and C. G. Lekkerkerker, *Geometry of numbers*, 2nd ed., North-Holland Mathematical Library, vol. 37, North-Holland Publishing Co., Amsterdam, 1987. MR893813

[100] Nick Gravin, Sinai Robins, and Dmitry Shiryaev, *Translational tilings by a polytope, with multiplicity*, Combinatorica **32** (2012), no. 6, 629–649, DOI 10.1007/s00493-012-2860-3. MR3063154

[101] Branko Grünbaum, *Convex polytopes*, 2nd ed., Graduate Texts in Mathematics, vol. 221, Springer-Verlag, New York, 2003. Prepared and with a preface by Volker Kaibel, Victor Klee and Günter M. Ziegler, DOI 10.1007/978-1-4613-0019-9. MR1976856

[102] Branko Grünbaum, *Are your polyhedra the same as my polyhedra?*, Discrete and computational geometry, Algorithms Combin., vol. 25, Springer, Berlin, 2003, pp. 461–488, DOI 10.1007/978-3-642-55566-4_21. MR2038487

[103] Paul E. Gunnells and Robert Sczech, *Evaluation of Dedekind sums, Eisenstein cocycles, and special values of L-functions*, Duke Math. J. **118** (2003), no. 2, 229–260, DOI 10.1215/S0012-7094-03-11822-0. MR1980994

[104] Mei Han, Kirati Sriamorn, Qi Yang, and Chuanming Zong, *Characterization of the three-dimensional multiple translative tiles*. part B, Adv. Math. **410** (2022), no. part B, Paper No. 108755, 27, DOI 10.1016/j.aim.2022.108755. MR4500641

[105] Thomas C. Hales, *A proof of the Kepler conjecture*, Ann. of Math. (2) **162** (2005), no. 3, 1065–1185, DOI 10.4007/annals.2005.162.1065. MR2179728

[106] G. H. Hardy, *Divergent Series*, Oxford, at the Clarendon Press, 1949. MR30620

[107] G. H. Hardy, *Notes on special systems of orthogonal functions. IV. The orthogonal functions of Whittaker's cardinal series*, Proc. Cambridge Philos. Soc. **37** (1941), 331–348, DOI 10.1017/S0305004100017977. MR5145

[108] G. H. Hardy, *A Theorem Concerning Fourier Transforms*, J. London Math. Soc. **8** (1933), no. 3, 227–231, DOI 10.1112/jlms/s1-8.3.227. MR1574130

[109] G. H. Hardy and J. E. Littlewood, *Some problems of Diophantine approximation: The lattice-points of a right-angled triangle. (Second memoir.)* (German), Abh. Math. Sem. Univ. Hamburg **1** (1922), no. 1, 211–248, DOI 10.1007/BF02940594. MR3069402

[110] G. H. Hardy and E. M. Wright, *An introduction to the theory of numbers*, 6th ed., Oxford University Press, Oxford, 2008. Revised by D. R. Heath-Brown and J. H. Silverman; With a foreword by Andrew Wiles. MR2445243

[111] Martin Henk, *Inequalities between successive minima and intrinsic volumes of a convex body*, Monatsh. Math. **110** (1990), no. 3-4, 279–282, DOI 10.1007/BF01301681. MR1084317

[112] Martin Henk, *Successive minima and lattice points*, Rend. Circ. Mat. Palermo (2) Suppl. **70** (2002), 377–384. IV International Conference in "Stochastic Geometry, Convex Bodies, Empirical Measures & Applications to Engineering Science", Vol. I (Tropea, 2001). MR1962579

[113] Martin Henk, Achill Schürmann, and Jörg M. Wills, *Ehrhart polynomials and successive minima*, Mathematika **52** (2005), no. 1-2, 1–16 (2006), DOI 10.1112/S0025579300000292. MR2261838

[114] Martin Henk and Jörg M. Wills, *A Blichfeldt-type inequality for the surface area*, Monatsh. Math. **154** (2008), no. 2, 135–144, DOI 10.1007/s00605-008-0530-8. MR2419059

[115] Martin Henk, Matthias Henze, and Jörg M. Wills, *Blichfeldt-type inequalities and central symmetry*, Adv. Geom. **11** (2011), no. 4, 731–744, DOI 10.1515/ADVGEOM.2011.032. MR2852929

[116] Martin Henk, *An introduction to geometry of numbers*, lecture notes, preprint.

[117] Douglas Hensley, *Lattice vertex polytopes with interior lattice points*, Pacific J. Math. **105** (1983), no. 1, 183–191. MR688412

[118] I. N. Herstein, *Topics in algebra*, 2nd ed., Xerox College Publishing, Lexington, Mass.-Toronto, Ont., 1975. MR356988

[119] John R. Higgins, *Sampling Theory in Fourier and Signal Analysis*, Clarendon Press, Oxford, (1996), 1–222.

[120] Edmund Hlawka, Johannes Schoissengeier, and Rudolf Taschner, *Geometric and analytic number theory*, Universitext, Springer-Verlag, Berlin, 1991. Translated from the 1986 German edition by Charles Thomas, DOI 10.1007/978-3-642-75306-0. MR1123023

[121] Edmund Hlawka, *Zur Geometrie der Zahlen* (German), Math. Z. **49** (1943), 285–312, DOI 10.1007/BF01174201. MR9782

[122] Alex Iosevich, Nets Katz, and Terence Tao, *The Fuglede spectral conjecture holds for convex planar domains*, Math. Res. Lett. **10** (2003), no. 5-6, 559–569, DOI 10.4310/MRL.2003.v10.n5.a1. MR2024715

[123] Vojtěch Jarník, *Zwei Bemerkungen zur Geometrie der Zahlen* (Czech, with German summary), Věstník Královské České Společnosti Nauk. Třída Matemat.-Přírodověd. **1941** (1941), 12. MR15429

[124] Katharina Jochemko, *A brief introduction to valuations on lattice polytopes*, Algebraic and geometric combinatorics on lattice polytopes, World Sci. Publ., Hackensack, NJ, 2019, pp. 38–55. MR3971684

[125] Ravi Kannan, *Lattice translates of a polytope and the Frobenius problem*, Combinatorica **12** (1992), no. 2, 161–177, DOI 10.1007/BF01204720. MR1179254

[126] Jean-Michel Kantor and Askold Khovanskii, *Une application du théorème de Riemann-Roch combinatoire au polynôme d'Ehrhart des polytopes entiers de $\mathbf{R}^d$* (French, with English and French summaries), C. R. Acad. Sci. Paris Sér. I Math. **317** (1993), no. 5, 501–507. MR1239038

[127] Roman Karasev, Jan Kynčl, Pavel Paták, Zuzana Patáková, and Martin Tancer, *Bounds for Pach's selection theorem and for the minimum solid angle in a simplex*, Discrete Comput. Geom. **54** (2015), no. 3, 610–636, DOI 10.1007/s00454-015-9720-z. MR3392968

[128] Yael Karshon, Shlomo Sternberg, and Jonathan Weitsman, *The Euler-Maclaurin formula for simple integral polytopes*, Proc. Natl. Acad. Sci. USA **100** (2003), no. 2, 426–433, DOI 10.1073/pnas.0237168100. MR1950644

[129] Yael Karshon, Shlomo Sternberg, and Jonathan Weitsman, *Exact Euler-Maclaurin formulas for simple lattice polytopes*, Adv. in Appl. Math. **39** (2007), no. 1, 1–50, DOI 10.1016/j.aam.2006.04.003. MR2319562

[130] Leetika Kathuria and Madhu Raka, *On conjectures of Minkowski and Woods for $n = 10$*, Proc. Indian Acad. Sci. Math. Sci. **132** (2022), no. 2, Paper No. 45, 27, DOI 10.1007/s12044-022-00679-2. MR4455085

[131] Yitzhak Katznelson, *An introduction to harmonic analysis*, 3rd ed., Cambridge Mathematical Library, Cambridge University Press, Cambridge, 2004, DOI 10.1017/CBO9781139165372. MR2039503

[132] Eric Katz and Alan Stapledon, *Local h-polynomials, invariants of subdivisions, and mixed Ehrhart theory*, Adv. Math. **286** (2016), 181–239, DOI 10.1016/j.aim.2015.09.010. MR3415684

[133] Donald E. Knuth, *Notes on generalized Dedekind sums*, Acta Arith. **33** (1977), no. 4, 297–325, DOI 10.4064/aa-33-4-297-325. MR485660

[134] Daniel A. Klain, *The Minkowski problem for polytopes*, Adv. Math. **185** (2004), no. 2, 270–288, DOI 10.1016/j.aim.2003.07.001. MR2060470

[135] Caroline J. Klivans, *The mathematics of chip-firing*, Discrete Mathematics and its Applications (Boca Raton), CRC Press, Boca Raton, FL, 2019. MR3889995

[136] T. Kobayashi, *The null variety of the Fourier transform of the characteristic function of a bounded domain*, Semin. Rep. Unitary Represent. **6** (1986), 1–18.

[137] Toshiyuki Kobayashi, *Asymptotic behaviour of the null variety for a convex domain in a non-positively curved space form*, J. Fac. Sci. Univ. Tokyo Sect. IA Math. **36** (1989), no. 3, 389–478. MR1039482

[138] Alexander Koldobsky, *Fourier analysis in convex geometry*, Mathematical Surveys and Monographs, vol. 116, American Mathematical Society, Providence, RI, 2005, DOI 10.1090/surv/116. MR2132704

[139] M. N. Kolountzakis, *On the structure of multiple translational tilings by polygonal regions*, Discrete Comput. Geom. **23** (2000), no. 4, 537–553, DOI 10.1007/s004540010014. MR1753701

[140] Mihail N. Kolountzakis, *The study of translational tiling with Fourier analysis*, Fourier analysis and convexity, Appl. Numer. Harmon. Anal., Birkhäuser Boston, Boston, MA, 2004, pp. 131–187. MR2087242

[141] A. Korkine and G. Zolotareff, *Sur les formes quadratiques positives quaternaires* (French), Math. Ann. **5** (1872), no. 4, 581–583, DOI 10.1007/BF01442912. MR1509795

[142] A. Korkinge and G. Zolotareff, *Sur les formes quadratiques positives* (French), Math. Ann. **11** (1877), no. 2, 242–292, DOI 10.1007/BF01442667. MR1509914

[143] T. W. Körner, *Fourier analysis*, Cambridge University Press, Cambridge, 1988, DOI 10.1017/CBO9781107049949. MR924154

[144] Greg Kuperberg, *Notions of denseness*, Geom. Topol. **4** (2000), 277–292, DOI 10.2140/gt.2000.4.277. MR1788269

[145] Roger L. Kraft, *What's the difference between Cantor sets?*, Amer. Math. Monthly **101** (1994), no. 7, 640–650, DOI 10.2307/2974692. MR1289273

[146] Jeffrey C. Lagarias and Günter M. Ziegler, *Bounds for lattice polytopes containing a fixed number of interior points in a sublattice*, Canad. J. Math. **43** (1991), no. 5, 1022–1035, DOI 10.4153/CJM-1991-058-4. MR1138580

[147] Jeffrey C. Lagarias and Chuanming Zong, *Mysteries in packing regular tetrahedra*, Notices Amer. Math. Soc. **59** (2012), no. 11, 1540–1549, DOI 10.1090/noti918. MR3027108

[148] Joseph-Louis Lagrange, *Recherches d'arithmétique*, Nouveaux Mémoires de L'Académie royal des Sciences et Belles-Lettres de Berlin (1773), 265–312.

[149] Jean B. Lasserre, *Integration on a convex polytope*, Proc. Amer. Math. Soc. **126** (1998), no. 8, 2433–2441, DOI 10.1090/S0002-9939-98-04454-2. MR1459132

[150] Jean B. Lasserre, *Volume of slices and sections of the simplex in closed form*, Optim. Lett. **9** (2015), no. 7, 1263–1269, DOI 10.1007/s11590-015-0898-z. MR3396537

[151] Jean B. Lasserre and Eduardo S. Zeron, *On counting integral points in a convex rational polytope*, Math. Oper. Res. **28** (2003), no. 4, 853–870, DOI 10.1287/moor.28.4.853.20518. MR2015915

[152] Jim Lawrence, *Rational-function-valued valuations on polyhedra*, Discrete and computational geometry (New Brunswick, NJ, 1989/1990), DIMACS Ser. Discrete Math. Theoret. Comput. Sci., vol. 6, Amer. Math. Soc., Providence, RI, 1991, pp. 199–208, DOI 10.1090/dimacs/006/12. MR1143297

[153] Jim Lawrence, *Polytope volume computation*, Math. Comp. **57** (1991), no. 195, 259–271, DOI 10.2307/2938672. MR1079024

[154] Quang-Nhat Le, *A discrete Stokes formula and the solid-angle sum of polytopes*, undergraduate dissertation, (2009).

[155] Quang-Nhat Le and Sinai Robins, *Macdonald's solid-angle sum for real dilations of rational polygons*, preprint.

[156] Nir Lev and Bochen Liu, *Multi-tiling and equidecomposability of polytopes by lattice translates*, Bull. Lond. Math. Soc. **51** (2019), no. 6, 1079–1098, DOI 10.1112/blms.12297. MR4041013

[157] Nir Lev and Máté Matolcsi, *The Fuglede conjecture for convex domains is true in all dimensions*, Acta Math. **228** (2022), no. 2, 385–420, DOI 10.4310/acta.2022.v228.n2.a3. MR4448683

[158] M. J. Lighthill, *Introduction to Fourier analysis and generalised functions*, Cambridge University Press, New York, 1960. MR0115085

[159] Eva Linke, *Rational Ehrhart quasi-polynomials*, J. Combin. Theory Ser. A **118** (2011), no. 7, 1966–1978, DOI 10.1016/j.jcta.2011.03.007. MR2802181

[160] Jacques-Louis Lions, *Support de produits de composition. II* (French), C. R. Acad. Sci. Paris **232** (1951), 1622–1624. MR43255

[161] Bochen Liu, *Periodic structure of translational multi-tilings in the plane*, Amer. J. Math. **143** (2021), no. 6, 1841–1862, DOI 10.1353/ajm.2021.0047. MR4349134

[162] I. G. Macdonald, *The volume of a lattice polyhedron*, Proc. Cambridge Philos. Soc. **59** (1963), 719–726. MR154188

[163] I. G. Macdonald, *Polynomials associated with finite cell-complexes*, J. London Math. Soc. (2) **4** (1971), 181–192, DOI 10.1112/jlms/s2-4.1.181. MR298542

[164] Fabricio Caluza Machado and Sinai Robins, *The null set of a polytope, and the Pompeiu property for polytopes*, J. Anal. Math. **150** (2023), no. 2, 673–683, DOI 10.1007/s11854-023-0290-3. MR4645053

[165] Fabricio Caluza Machado and Sinai Robins, *Coefficients of the solid angle and Ehrhart quasi-polynomials*, preprint, 2019.

[166] Romanos-Diogenes Malikiosis, *A discrete analogue for Minkowski's second theorem on successive minima*, Adv. Geom. **12** (2012), no. 2, 365–380, DOI 10.1515/advgeom-2012-0002. MR2911155

[167] Jacques Martinet, *Perfect lattices in Euclidean spaces*, Grundlehren der mathematischen Wissenschaften [Fundamental Principles of Mathematical Sciences], vol. 327, Springer-Verlag, Berlin, 2003, DOI 10.1007/978-3-662-05167-2. MR1957723

[168] Michel Faleiros Martins and Sinai Robins, *The covariogram and extensions of the Bombieri-Siegel formula*, Preprint, arXiv:2204.08606, (2023).

[169] Tyrrell B. McAllister and Kevin M. Woods, *The minimum period of the Ehrhart quasi-polynomial of a rational polytope*, J. Combin. Theory Ser. A **109** (2005), no. 2, 345–352, DOI 10.1016/j.jcta.2004.08.006. MR2121031

[170] Curtis T. McMullen, *Minkowski's conjecture, well-rounded lattices and topological dimension*, J. Amer. Math. Soc. **18** (2005), no. 3, 711–734, DOI 10.1090/S0894-0347-05-00483-2. MR2138142

[171] P. McMullen, *Lattice invariant valuations on rational polytopes*, Arch. Math. (Basel) **31** (1978/79), no. 5, 509–516, DOI 10.1007/BF01226481. MR526617

[172] P. McMullen, *Non-linear angle-sum relations for polyhedral cones and polytopes*, Math. Proc. Cambridge Philos. Soc. **78** (1975), no. 2, 247–261, DOI 10.1017/S0305004100051665. MR394436

[173] Peter McMullen, *Angle-sum relations for polyhedral sets*, Mathematika **33** (1986), no. 2, 173–188 (1987), DOI 10.1112/S0025579300011165. MR882490

[174] P. McMullen, *Valuations and Euler-type relations on certain classes of convex polytopes*, Proc. London Math. Soc. (3) **35** (1977), no. 1, 113–135, DOI 10.1112/plms/s3-35.1.113. MR448239

[175] P. McMullen, *Polytopes with centrally symmetric faces*, Israel J. Math. **8** (1970), 194–196, DOI 10.1007/BF02771315. MR262924

[176] James Mercer, *Functions of positive and negative type and their connection with the theory of integral equations*, Philosophical Transactions of the Royal Society A, 209 (441–458): (1909), 415–446.

[177] John Milnor and Dale Husemoller, *Symmetric bilinear forms*, Ergebnisse der Mathematik und ihrer Grenzgebiete [Results in Mathematics and Related Areas], Band 73, Springer-Verlag, New York-Heidelberg, 1973. MR506372

[178] Hermann Minkowski, *Geometrie der Zahlen* (German), Bibliotheca Mathematica Teubneriana, Band 40, Johnson Reprint Corp., New York-London, 1968. MR249269

[179] Hermann Minkowski, *Allgemeine Lehrsatze iiber konvexen Polyeder*, Nachr. K. Akad. Wiss. Gottingen, Math.-Phys. Kl. ii (1897), 198–219.

[180] Jan Draisma, Tyrrell B. McAllister, and Benjamin Nill, *Lattice-width directions and Minkowski's 3^d-theorem*, SIAM J. Discrete Math. **26** (2012), no. 3, 1104–1107, DOI 10.1137/120877635. MR3022127

[181] Robert Morelli, *Pick's theorem and the Todd class of a toric variety*, Adv. Math. **100** (1993), no. 2, 183–231, DOI 10.1006/aima.1993.1033. MR1234309

[182] L. J. Mordell, *On some arithmetical results in the geometry of numbers*, Compositio Math. **1** (1935), 248–253. MR1556892

[183] Morris Newman, *Integral matrices*, Pure and Applied Mathematics, Vol. 45, Academic Press, New York-London, 1972. MR340283

[184] Marina Nechayeva and Burton Randol, *Asymptotics of weighted lattice point counts inside dilating polygons*, Additive number theory, Springer, New York, 2010, pp. 287–301, DOI 10.1007/978-0-387-68361-4_20. MR2744763

[185] Benjamin Nill and Andreas Paffenholz, *On the equality case in Ehrhart's volume conjecture*, Adv. Geom. **14** (2014), no. 4, 579–586, DOI 10.1515/advgeom-2014-0001. MR3276123

[186] M. Nosarzewska, *Évaluation de la différence entre l'aire d'une région plane convexe et le nombre des points aux coordonnées entières couverts par elle* (French), Colloq. Math. **1** (1948), 305–311, DOI 10.4064/cm-1-4-305-311. MR30551

[187] C. D. Olds, Anneli Lax, and Giuliana P. Davidoff, *The geometry of numbers*, Anneli Lax New Mathematical Library, vol. 41, Mathematical Association of America, Washington, DC, 2000. Appendix I by Peter D. Lax. MR1817689

[188] Daniel J. O'Loughlin, *The Scarcity of Regular Polygons on the Integer Lattice*, Math. Mag. **75** (2002), no. 1, 47–51. MR1573582

[189] Brad G. Osgood, *Lectures on the Fourier transform and its applications*, Pure and Applied Undergraduate Texts, vol. 33, American Mathematical Society, Providence, RI, 2019. MR3887604

[190] Sam Payne, *Ehrhart series and lattice triangulations*, Discrete Comput. Geom. **40** (2008), no. 3, 365–376, DOI 10.1007/s00454-007-9002-5. MR2443289

[191] Daniel P. Petersen and David Middleton, *Sampling and reconstruction of wave-number-limited functions in N-dimensional Euclidean spaces*, Information and Control **5** (1962), 279–323. MR151331

[192] M. A. Perles and G. C. Shephard, *Angle sums of convex polytopes*, Math. Scand. **21** (1967), 199–218 (1969), DOI 10.7146/math.scand.a-10860. MR243425

[193] Mark A. Pinsky, *Introduction to Fourier analysis and wavelets*, Brooks/Cole Series in Advanced Mathematics, Brooks/Cole, Pacific Grove, CA, 2002. MR2100936

[194] Oleg Pikhurko, *Lattice points in lattice polytopes*, Mathematika **48** (2001), no. 1-2, 15–24 (2003), DOI 10.1112/S0025579300014339. MR1996360

[195] A. N. Podkorytov and Mai Van Minh, *The Fourier formula for discontinuous functions of several variables*, J. Math. Sci. (N.Y.) **124** (2004), no. 3, 5018–5025, DOI 10.1023/B:JOTH.0000046213.25374.15. Problems in mathematical analysis. No. 29. MR2160264

[196] James E. Pommersheim, *Toric varieties, lattice points and Dedekind sums*, Math. Ann. **295** (1993), no. 1, 1–24, DOI 10.1007/BF01444874. MR1198839

[197] James Pommersheim and Hugh Thomas, *Cycles representing the Todd class of a toric variety*, J. Amer. Math. Soc. **17** (2004), no. 4, 983–994, DOI 10.1090/S0894-0347-04-00460-6. MR2083474

[198] Bjorn Poonen and Fernando Rodriguez-Villegas, *Lattice polygons and the number 12*, Amer. Math. Monthly **107** (2000), no. 3, 238–250, DOI 10.2307/2589316. MR1742122

[199] Alexander Postnikov, *Permutohedra, associahedra, and beyond*, Int. Math. Res. Not. IMRN **6** (2009), 1026–1106, DOI 10.1093/imrn/rnn153. MR2487491

[200] Gervásio Protásio dos Santo Neto, *The theory and computation of solid angles*, Master's thesis, IME, Universidade de São Paulo, (2021), 1–85.

[201] Srinivasa Ramanujan, *Some definite integrals*, Messenger of Mathematics **44** (1915), 10–18.

[202] J. L. Ramírez-Alfonsín, *Complexity of the Frobenius problem*, Combinatorica **16** (1996), no. 1, 143–147, DOI 10.1007/BF01300131. MR1394516

[203] Burton Randol, *On the Fourier transform of the indicator function of a planar set*, Trans. Amer. Math. Soc. **139** (1969), 271–278, DOI 10.2307/1995319. MR251449

[204] Burton Randol, *On the asymptotic behavior of the Fourier transform of the indicator function of a convex set*, Trans. Amer. Math. Soc. **139** (1969), 279–285, DOI 10.2307/1995320. MR251450

[205] Burton Randol, *On the number of integral lattice-points in dilations of algebraic polyhedra*, Internat. Math. Res. Notices **6** (1997), 259–270, DOI 10.1155/S1073792897000196. MR1440303

[206] Oded Regev, *On lattices, learning with errors, random linear codes, and cryptography*, J. ACM **56** (2009), no. 6, Art. 34, 40, DOI 10.1145/1568318.1568324. MR2572935

[207] Robert Remak, *Vereinfachung eines Blichfeldtschen Beweises aus der Geometrie der Zahlen* (German), Math. Z. **26** (1927), no. 1, 694–699, DOI 10.1007/BF01475484. MR1544885

[208] Robert Remak, *Verallgemeinerung eines Minkowskischen Satzes* (German), Math. Z. **18** (1923), no. 1, 173–200, DOI 10.1007/BF01192403. MR1544627

[209] Bruce Reznick, *Lattice point simplices*, Discrete Math. **60** (1986), 219–242, DOI 10.1016/0012-365X(86)90015-4. MR852110

[210] Jason M. Ribando, *Measuring solid angles beyond dimension three*, Discrete Comput. Geom. **36** (2006), no. 3, 479–487, DOI 10.1007/s00454-006-1253-4. MR2255515

[211] Sinai Robins, *The integer point transform as a complete invariant*, Commun. Math. **31** (2023), no. 2, 157–172. MR4622170

[212] Sinai Robins, *A friendly invitation to Fourier analysis on polytopes*, 33° Colóquio Brasileiro de Matemática, Instituto Nacional de Matemática Pura e Aplicada (IMPA), Rio de Janeiro, 2021. MR4472815

[213] C. A. Rogers, *Packing and covering*, Cambridge Tracts in Mathematics and Mathematical Physics, No. 54, Cambridge University Press, New York, 1964. MR172183

[214] C. A. Rogers and G. C. Shephard, *Convex bodies associated with a given convex body*, J. London Math. Soc. **33** (1958), 270–281, DOI 10.1112/jlms/s1-33.3.270. MR101508

[215] Tiago Royer, *Reconstruction of rational polytopes from the real-parameter Ehrhart function of its translates*, Preprint, arXiv:1712.01973, (2017).

[216] Tiago Royer, *Reconstruction of symmetric convex bodies from Ehrhart-like data*, Preprint, arXiv:1712.03937, (2017).

[217] Walter Rudin, *Real and complex analysis*, 3rd ed., McGraw-Hill Book Co., New York, 1987. MR924157

[218] Walter Rudin, *Fourier analysis on groups*, Wiley Classics Library, John Wiley & Sons, Inc., New York, 1990. Reprint of the 1962 original; A Wiley-Interscience Publication, DOI 10.1002/9781118165621. MR1038803

[219] Paul J. Sally Jr., *Fundamentals of mathematical analysis*, Pure and Applied Undergraduate Texts, vol. 20, American Mathematical Society, Providence, RI, 2013. MR3014419

[220] Alexander Schiemann, *Ein Beispiel positiv definiter quadratischer Formen der Dimension 4 mit gleichen Darstellungszahlen* (German), Arch. Math. (Basel) **54** (1990), no. 4, 372–375, DOI 10.1007/BF01189584. MR1042130

[221] Alexander Schiemann, *Ternäre positiv definite quadratische Formen mit gleichen Darstellungszahlen* (German), Bonner Mathematische Schriften [Bonn Mathematical Publications], vol. 268, Universität Bonn, Mathematisches Institut, Bonn, 1994. Dissertation, Universität Bonn, Bonn, 1993. MR1294141

[222] Ludwig Schläfli, *Gesammelte mathematische Abhandlungen. Band I* (German), Verlag Birkhäuser, Basel, 1950. MR34587

[223] Saul Schleimer and Henry Segerman, *Puzzling the 120-cell*, Notices Amer. Math. Soc. **62** (2015), no. 11, 1309–1316, DOI 10.1090/noti1297. MR3443711

[224] Hans-Jürgen Schmeisser and Winfried Sickel, *Sampling theory and function spaces*, Applied mathematics reviews, Vol. 1, World Sci. Publ., River Edge, NJ, 2000, pp. 205–284, DOI 10.1142/9789812792686_0008. MR1782733

[225] Rolf Schneider, *Convex bodies: the Brunn-Minkowski theory*, Second expanded edition, Encyclopedia of Mathematics and its Applications, vol. 151, Cambridge University Press, Cambridge, 2014. MR3155183

[226] Rolf Schneider and Wolfgang Weil, *Stochastic and integral geometry*, Probability and its Applications (New York), Springer-Verlag, Berlin, 2008, DOI 10.1007/978-3-540-78859-1. MR2455326

[227] Alexander Schrijver, *Combinatorial optimization. Polyhedra and efficiency. Vol. C*, Algorithms and Combinatorics, vol. 24, Springer-Verlag, Berlin, 2003. Disjoint paths, hypergraphs; Chapters 70–83. MR1956926

[228] Marjorie Senechal and R. V. Galiulin, *An introduction to the theory of figures: the geometry of E. S. Fedorov*, Structural Topology **10** (1984), 5–22. Dual French/English text. MR768703

[229] Jeffrey Shallit, *The Frobenius problem and its generalizations*, Developments in language theory, Lecture Notes in Comput. Sci., vol. 5257, Springer, Berlin, 2008, pp. 72–83, DOI 10.1007/978-3-540-85780-8_5. MR2490946

[230] Claude E. Shannon, *Communication in the presence of noise*, Proc. I.R.E. **37** (1949), 10–21. MR28549

[231] G. C. Shephard, *Polytopes with centrally symmetric faces*, Canadian J. Math. **19** (1967), 1206–1213, DOI 10.4153/CJM-1967-109-3. MR221381

[232] G. C. Shephard, *An elementary proof of Gram's theorem for convex polytopes*, Canadian J. Math. **19** (1967), 1214–1217, DOI 10.4153/CJM-1967-110-7. MR225228

[233] Carl Ludwig Siegel, *Lectures on the geometry of numbers*, Springer-Verlag, Berlin, 1989. Notes by B. Friedman; Rewritten by Komaravolu Chandrasekharan with the assistance of Rudolf Suter; With a preface by Chandrasekharan, DOI 10.1007/978-3-662-08287-4. MR1020761

[234] Carl Ludwig Siegel, *A mean value theorem in geometry of numbers*, Ann. of Math. (2) **46** (1945), 340–347, DOI 10.2307/1969027. MR12093

[235] M. M. Skriganov, *Ergodic theory on homogeneous spaces and the enumeration of lattice points in polyhedra* (Russian), Dokl. Akad. Nauk **355** (1997), no. 5, 609–611. MR1600382

[236] M. M. Skriganov, *Ergodic theory on* $SL(n)$, *Diophantine approximations and anomalies in the lattice point problem*, Invent. Math. **132** (1998), no. 1, 1–72, DOI 10.1007/s002220050217. MR1618631

[237] B. F. Skubenko, *A proof of Minkowski's conjecture on the product of n linear inhomogeneous forms in n variables for n ≤ 5* (Russian), Zap. Naučn. Sem. Leningrad. Otdel. Mat. Inst. Steklov. (LOMI) **33** (1973), 6–36. Investigations in number theory, 2. MR366815

[238] Duncan M. Y. Sommerville, *The relation connecting the angle-sums and volume of a polytope in space of n dimensions*, Proc. Roy. Soc. London, Ser. A **115** (1927), 103–119.

[239] Richard P. Stanley, *Combinatorial reciprocity theorems*, Advances in Math. **14** (1974), 194–253, DOI 10.1016/0001-8708(74)90030-9. MR411982

[240] Richard P. Stanley, *Enumerative combinatorics. Volume 1*, 2nd ed., Cambridge Studies in Advanced Mathematics, vol. 49, Cambridge University Press, Cambridge, 2012. MR2868112

[241] Richard P. Stanley, *Decompositions of rational convex polytopes*, Ann. Discrete Math. **6** (1980), 333–342. MR593545

[242] Richard P. Stanley, *Combinatorics and commutative algebra*, 2nd ed., Progress in Mathematics, vol. 41, Birkhäuser Boston, Inc., Boston, MA, 1996. MR1453579

[243] Alan Stapledon, *Additive number theory and inequalities in Ehrhart theory*, Int. Math. Res. Not. IMRN **5** (2016), 1497–1540, DOI 10.1093/imrn/rnv186. MR3509934

[244] Elias M. Stein and Guido Weiss, *Introduction to Fourier analysis on Euclidean spaces*, Princeton Mathematical Series, No. 32, Princeton University Press, Princeton, NJ, 1971. MR304972

[245] Elias M. Stein and Rami Shakarchi, *Fourier analysis*, Princeton Lectures in Analysis, vol. 1, Princeton University Press, Princeton, NJ, 2003. An introduction. MR1970295

[246] Bernd Sturmfels, *On vector partition functions*, J. Combin. Theory Ser. A **72** (1995), no. 2, 302–309, DOI 10.1016/0097-3165(95)90067-5. MR1357776

[247] Axel Thue, *Über die dichteste Zuzammenstellung von kongruenten Kreisen in der Ebene*, Norske Vid. Selsk. Skr. 1 (1910), 1–9.

[248] E. C. Titchmarsh, *The Zeros of Certain Integral Functions*, Proc. London Math. Soc. (2) **25** (1926), 283–302, DOI 10.1112/plms/s2-25.1.283. MR1575285

[249] E. C. Titchmarsh, *Introduction to the theory of Fourier integrals*, 3rd ed., Chelsea Publishing Co., New York, 1986. MR942661

[250] László Fejes Tóth, *Some packing and covering theorems*, Acta Sci. Math. (Szeged) **12** (1950), 62–67. MR38086

[251] Giancarlo Travaglini, *Number theory, Fourier analysis and geometric discrepancy*, London Mathematical Society Student Texts, vol. 81, Cambridge University Press, Cambridge, 2014, DOI 10.1017/CBO9781107358379. MR3307692

[252] Audrey Terras, *Harmonic analysis on symmetric spaces and applications. I*, Springer-Verlag, New York, 1985, DOI 10.1007/978-1-4612-5128-6. MR791406

[253] Audrey Terras, *Fourier analysis on finite groups and applications*, London Mathematical Society Student Texts, vol. 43, Cambridge University Press, Cambridge, 1999, DOI 10.1017/CBO9780511626265. MR1695775

[254] Michael Unser, *Sampling - 50 years after Shannon*, Proceedings of the IEEE, **88**, issue 4, (2000), 569–587.

[255] *Publication list: J. G. van der Corput*, Acta Arith. **36** (1980), no. 1, 91–99. MR576585

[256] Akshay Venkatesh, *A note on sphere packings in high dimension*, Int. Math. Res. Not. IMRN **7** (2013), 1628–1642, DOI 10.1093/imrn/rns096. MR3044452

[257] Sven Verdoolaege, *Software package barvinok*, (2004), electronically available at http://freshmeat.net/projects/barvinok/.

[258] Stan Wagon, *Fourteen proofs of a result about tiling a rectangle*, Amer. Math. Monthly **94** (1987), no. 7, 601–617, DOI 10.2307/2322213. MR935845

[259] G. K. White, *A refinement of van der Corput's theorem on convex bodies*, Amer. J. Math. **85** (1963), 320–326, DOI 10.2307/2373218. MR154187

[260] J. M. Wills, *Über konvexe Gitterpolygone* (German), Comment. Math. Helv. **48** (1973), 188–194, DOI 10.1007/BF02566121. MR335441

[261] Kevin Woods, *The unreasonable ubiquitousness of quasi-polynomials*, Electron. J. Combin. **21** (2014), no. 1, Paper 1.44, 23, DOI 10.37236/3750. MR3177539

[262] Qi Yang and Chuanming Zong, *Multiple lattice tilings in Euclidean spaces*, Canad. Math. Bull. **62** (2019), no. 4, 923–929, DOI 10.4153/s0008439518000103. MR4028498

[263] Stephen T. Yau and Letian Zhang, *An upper estimate of integral points in real simplices with an application to singularity theory*, Math. Res. Lett. **13** (2006), no. 5-6, 911–921, DOI 10.4310/MRL.2006.v13.n6.a6. MR2280784

[264] Wenxing Ye and Alireza Entezari, *A geometric construction of multivariate sinc functions*, IEEE Trans. Image Process. **21** (2012), no. 6, 2969–2979, DOI 10.1109/TIP.2011.2162421. MR2925353

[265] Günter M. Ziegler, *Lectures on polytopes*, Graduate Texts in Mathematics, vol. 152, Springer-Verlag, New York, 1995, DOI 10.1007/978-1-4613-8431-1. MR1311028

[266] Chuanming Zong, *Classification of the sublattices of a lattice*, Bull. Aust. Math. Soc. **103** (2021), no. 1, 50–61, DOI 10.1017/S0004972720000325. MR4205758

[267] Chuanming Zong, *The cube: a window to convex and discrete geometry*, Cambridge Tracts in Mathematics, vol. 168, Cambridge University Press, Cambridge, 2006, DOI 10.1017/CBO9780511543173. MR2221660

[268] Chuanming Zong, *Sphere packings*, Universitext, Springer-Verlag, New York, 1999. MR1707318

[269] Chuanming Zong, *Packing, covering and tiling in two-dimensional spaces*, Expo. Math. **32** (2014), no. 4, 297–364, DOI 10.1016/j.exmath.2013.12.002. MR3279483

[270] A. Zygmund, *Trigonometric series. Vol. I, II*, 3rd ed., Cambridge Mathematical Library, Cambridge University Press, Cambridge, 2002. With a foreword by Robert A. Fefferman. MR1963498

Index

SELECTED PUBLISHED TITLES IN THIS SERIES